Barometer Makers and Retailers

1660 — 1900

Also by the author and published by Baros Books:

Antique Barometers: an Illustrated Survey

Barometers: Aneroid and Barographs

Barometers: Stick or Cistern Tube

Barometers: Wheel or Banjo

Visiting Cards and Cases

Also published by Baros Books:

Care and Restoration of Barometers by Philip R. Collins

Barometer Makers and Retailers

1660 — 1900

Edwin Banfield

Baros Books

First published 1991. Reprinted 2000

Baros Books
5 Victoria Road
Trowbridge
Wiltshire
BA14 7LH

A catalogue record of this book is available from the British Library

ISBN 0-948382-06-6

Cover illustration: Negretti & Zambra's shop at Sydenham (*The British Library*)

Typesetting by Ex Libris Press, 1 The Shambles, Bradford-on-Avon, Wiltshire.
Illustrations screened by Norton Photo Litho, New Pitt Cottages, Paulton, Bristol.
Printed and bound in Great Britain by The Cromwell Press, Trowbridge, Wiltshire.

Contents

Preface

> Mathematical Instruments are the means by which those noble Sciences, Geometry and Philosophy, are rendered useful in the Affairs of Life. By their Assistance an abstracted and unprofitable Speculation, is made beneficial in a thousand instances: In a Word, they enable us to connect Theory with Practice, and so turn what was only bare Contemplation, into the most substantial Uses. (George Adams, instrument-maker to George III)

The barometer was invented by Evangelista Torricelli in Italy in 1643, and was introduced to England by Robert Boyle. He was a student in Italy during the period of the 'Torricellian experiment' and studied the writings of Galileo. On his return to England in 1644 he established a private laboratory in Oxford and proved that the phenomenon of the experiment was, indeed, caused by the varying pressure of air. He developed the experiment into a practical barometer by being the first to use a graduated scale to record the height of the mercury in the tube.

At first, the barometer was developed as an instrument mainly for the measurement of heights, and only gradually, from around 1660, did meteorologists realise that variations in air pressure corresponded with changes in the weather, and that the barometer could be a useful aid to weather forecasting.

The earliest barometers were made by instrument-makers and clockmakers to the order and design of scientists for experimental work, and it was not until around 1670 that they were made for domestic use. In the eighteenth century scientific instruments were divided into three main categories: mathematical instruments which were used to take measurements, optical instruments used for studying small and distant objects and philosophical instruments used to create and demonstrate various physical operations and effects.

The barometer was included in the category of philosophical instruments, although a large number of mathematical and optical instrument-makers also made them. A maker described as a mathematical, optical and philosophical instrument-maker indicated that he made or retailed the full range of scientific instruments which, of course, included barometers. All the makers and retailers that comprise this book made or retailed barometers, so no name is specifically designated as 'barometer maker'.

The wheel-type barometer was the most popular domestic instrument during the first half of the nineteenth century, and the vast majority of these were made by

Italian immigrants who settled in London from around 1780. Other Italians settled in the larger towns and cities as glassblowers, carvers, gilders, opticians and barometer makers. Even in small towns, barometers were sold engraved with Italian names such as 'Giobbio, Trowbridge' and 'Cattanio, Malton'. Whether these Italians were all barometer makers, or just shopkeepers and retailers who had their names engraved on them, is in doubt. There is a theory that the retailers were, in fact, Englishmen who arranged for Italian names to be engraved on their barometers because they were more popular than barometers bearing English names. It is also thought that some Italian makers, who were wholesalers, engraved their own names on the barometers but added the town or address of the retailer. This was certainly the practice of some clockmakers and it could account for the very large number of Italians who, on the face of it, appear to have been living in small towns up and down the country. Some Italians were described as pedlars or hawkers and travelled from place to place.

The spelling of Italian names on barometers presents a particular problem. The letters J, K, W and Y do not exist in the Italian alphabet, while H, which is always silent, only occurs in a very few words. The X is rarely used and only in words of Latin and Greek origin. Christian names were generally changed to the English equivalent: for example, Antonio (Anthony), Guiseppi (Joseph), Giovanni (John), Luigi (Louis or Lewis) and Vittore (Victor). The spelling of surnames is also sometimes changed with K used in place of CH as in Ronchetti (Ronketti). Y or E is occasionally substituted for I as in Corti (Corty or Corte).

Rather than clutter this volume with likely name variations and separate cross-references (Ronketti, for example, was variously Ronkite, Roncheti, Ronchetti, Roncketi and Ronkitte), I have grouped likely variations together under one entry. The reader is therefore advised to 'look around' an entry to trace a particular maker if spelling discrepancy is likely.

It is, in many cases, difficult to establish who actually made a particular barometer. Some makers made the complete instrument; others made some parts and bought in the rest, while some bought all the parts, including the case, and then assembled them. The remainder, who should be described as retailers, bought barometers from wholesalers and had their name engraved on the dial or level plate. Some makers advertised barometers for sale 'wholesale or retail'.

If the standard or quality of the engraving of the name is below that of the other engraving on the barometer, then it is very likely that the name is the retailer's; the contrast is often more marked on wheel barometers where the retailer's name is engraved on the level plate in capital letters, while the rest of the engraving is in Roman upper and lower case italics and joined copperplate script. When the name is engraved in the latter style, with extravagant flourishes, it is often very difficult to decipher the individual letters and errors are often made in spelling Italian names, particularly in auction catalogues. A number of nineteenth-century wheel barometers have no name and only 'Warranted Correct' on the level plate; this lettering appears to have been used when retailers purchased a single or a small number of barometers from a maker.

This book contains the names of the great majority of barometer makers, but only some of the vast number of retailers such as clock and watch makers, ophthalmic opticians and chemists who were in business all over the country during the period. The book's prime purpose is to assist in the dating of barometers from the name of the maker or retailer which is usually engraved on the dial, the register plates or the spirit level plate. The list includes details of working dates, the maker's business address where known and other activities or achievements of the maker. I have noted where barometers made or handled were unusual in style, but for general information on typical styles of the period or of the individual maker, the reader is referred to my other books on barometers given in the bibliography.

The list of makers and retailers has been compiled from the barometers I have seen or handled over many years, old directories, trade cards and information obtained from the books listed in the bibliography. I have examined more than a thousand catalogues of fine art auctioneers and very many collectors and dealers have very kindly supplied me with lists and dates of barometers.

In particular I should like to thank Mark Shanks of Park Street Antiques, Berkhamsted for making available his record of barometers which he has maintained since starting in business; also Richard Cookson of the Barometer Shop, Bristol who allowed me to examine his workshop records. I have also had help from Dr Gloria Clifton of Project SIMON, a programme of research into the scientific-instrument making trade, based at Imperial College, London, under the direction of Professor G. L. E. Turner of the History of Science and Technology Group. I should also like to thank my daughter Sue Ashton for editing the manuscript.

Abbreviations

b	Born
c	Circa (about or around)
d	Died
e	Estimated dates based on extant barometers
fl.	Floruit (period when most active)
IM	Instrument-maker
IS	Instrument seller
M	Maker
Math.	Mathematical
Naut.	Nautical
Opt.	Optical
Phil.	Philosophical
S	Seller
w	Working dates from various sources. The recorded working dates often do not cover the full period of the working life of the maker or retailer. Where it is obvious from signed extant barometers that they were made before, or after, the working date recorded, then estimated working dates are added after the working dates.

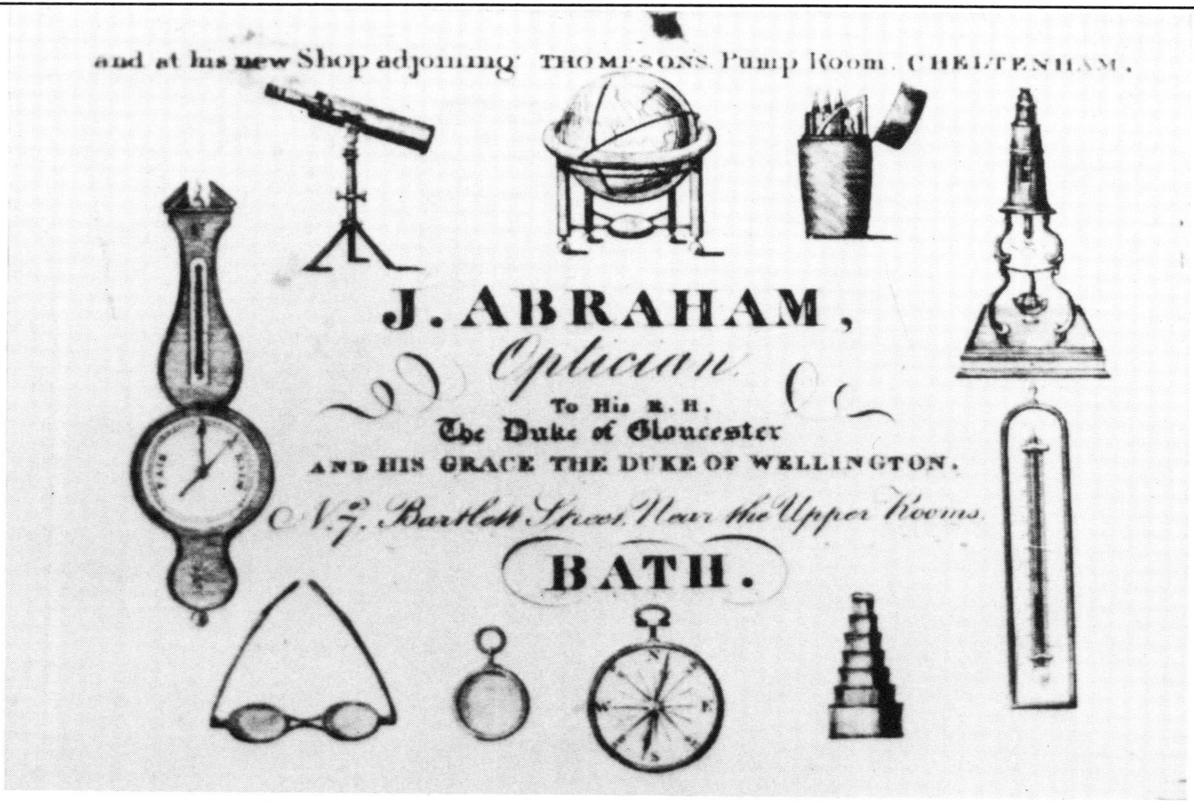

and at his new Shop adjoining THOMPSONS Pump Room, CHELTENHAM.

J. ABRAHAM,

Optician.

To His R. H.

The Duke of Gloucester

AND HIS GRACE THE DUKE OF WELLINGTON.

No. 7, Bartlett Street, Near the Upper Rooms,

BATH.

Fig. 1 Trade card of J. Abraham *(Municipal Library, Bath)*

Makers and Retailers

A

ABAFSI, O. e1815-35. Watch M. Fakenham

ABATTE, J. e1810-30. Grantham

ABATTE, J. e1810-30. Peterborough

ABBOTT, Joseph. w1805-11. Math. IM. 2 Woods Place, Bowling Green Lane, Clerkenwell, London

ABEL Bros. w1877. e1875-95. Clock & watch M. Farringdon

ABEL, E. w1864. Clock & watch M. Farringdon

ABEL, Thomas. fl.1838-41. Thermo. M & glazier. 55 Ray St, Clerkenwell, London

ABRAHAM, A. & Co. w1838-43. Math. opt. & phil. IM. Glasgow
8 Exchange Square (1838-40) 82 Queen St (1841-43)
A partnership between Abraham Abraham of the Liverpool firm Abraham Abraham & Co. and Simeon Phineas Cohen. It was opened as a retail branch of the Liverpool firm and sold and repaired all types of instruments. In 1843 Cohen took over the business and in 1844 traded in his own name until 1853 when he was made bankrupt owing Abraham £1,960.

ABRAHAM, Abraham & Co. w1817-75. Opt. math. & phil. IM. Liverpool
8 Lord St (1817-20) 10 Lord St (1821-22) 7 Lord St (1823-28) 9 Lord St (1829-34) 76 Lord St (1835-36) 84 Lord St (1837-39) 20 Lord St West (1840-75) 15 London Road East (1870-75)
Instruments also signed 'ABRAHAM'. Important makers who exhibited at the Great Exhibition at the Crystal Palace in 1851. Issued in 1855 a 'Descriptive and Illustrated Catalogue of Optical, Mathematical and Philosophical Instruments manufactured'.

ABRAHAM & DANCER w1841-45. Opt. math. & phil. IM. 13 Cross St, King St, Manchester
A partnership between Abraham Abraham and John Benjamin Dancer which only lasted four years with Dancer subsequently continuing alone, concentrating on microscopes. A barometer is recorded with a Bow Street address.

ABRAHAM, E. e1820-40. Opt. IM. Exeter

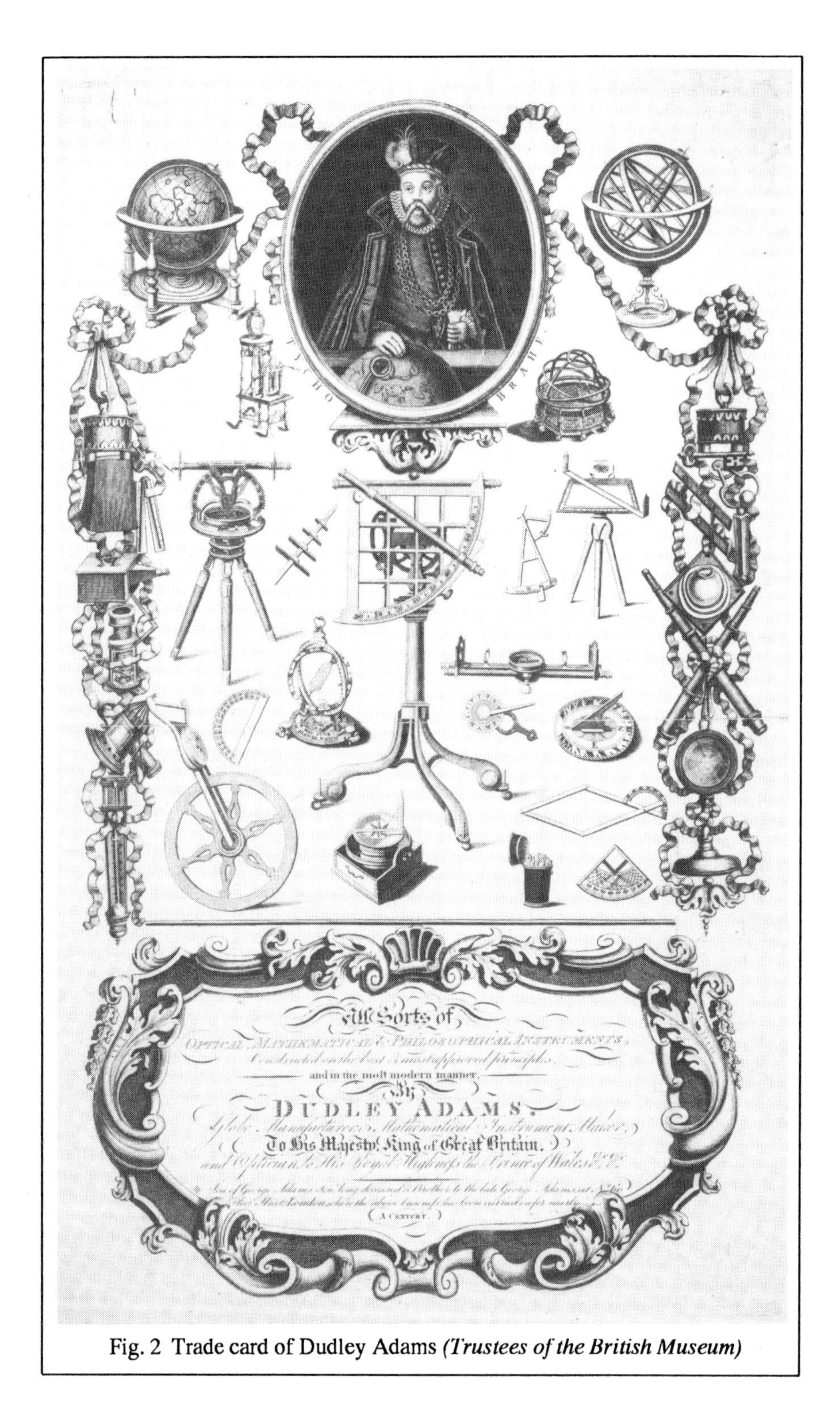

Fig. 2 Trade card of Dudley Adams *(Trustees of the British Museum)*

ABRAHAM, Jacob. fl.1805-41. Opt. & math. IM. Bath and Cheltenham
1 St Andrew's Terrace, Bath (1809) 7 Bartlett St, Bath (1819-41) Adjoining Mr Thompson's Pump Room, Cheltenham (1830-41)
An important maker whose trade card shows that he made stick and wheel barometers. Instrument-maker to the Duke of Gloucester and the Duke of Wellington. (See Fig. 1.)

ABRAHAM, Josiah. w1796-1879. Clock & watch M. Liskeard

ACCUM & GARDEN w1804-17. Chemical & phil. IM. Compton St, Soho, London
A partnership between Frederick Accum and Alexander Garden. Accum was an instrument-maker and lecturer.

ADAM e1820-40. Dundee

ADAMOS, W. e1830-50. Monmouth

ADAMS, Dudley. b1762-d1826. Opt. math. & phil. IM. London
53 Charing Cross (1793-95) 6 Jewry Lane (1800-22) 60 Fleet St (1796-1821)
The son of George Adams (senior). He was apprenticed to his elder brother George Adams (junior) in 1777, and was in business on his own at 53 Charing Cross by 1793. His brother George died in 1795 and Dudley took over the running of the family business at 60 Fleet St. His decorative trade card of around 1800 shows that he made 'All sorts of Optical, Mathematical and Philosophical Instruments, constructed on the best and most approved principles and in the modern manner'. He was instrument-maker to George III and optician to the Prince of Wales. He described himself as 'Son of George Adams senior long deceased and brother of the late George Adams at No. 60 Fleet Street, London, where the above business has been carried on for nearly a century'. A son, George Adams, was apprenticed to him but he did not take his freedom. (See Fig. 2.)

ADAMS, George (senior). b1704-d1773. Math. IM. London
Tycho Brahe's Head in Fleet St (1735-57) 60 Fleet St (1757-73)
An outstanding instrument-maker who advertised 'Curious barometers, diagonal, wheel, standard or portable, with or without thermometers'. Adams was apprenticed to James Parker in 1724 and then to Thomas Heath in 1726 who was a notable instrument-maker. Adams was one of the first to use mass-production methods and explained his responsibilities in his workshop with regard to his instruments as: 'That their exactness may be particularly attended to, I always inspect and direct the several pieces myself, see them all combined in my own house, and finish the most curious parts thereof with my own hands.' Between 1746 and 1748 Adams was instrument-maker to His Majesty's Office of Ordnance; he was later instrument-maker to the Prince of Wales which continued when he became King in 1760. Adams had two sons, George and Dudley; they both became instrument-makers and successively traded from 60 Fleet St when their father died in 1773.

ADAMS, George (junior). b1750-d1795. Opt. & math. IM. London
60 Fleet St (1773-95)
Apprenticed to his father George Adams (senior) in 1765, he took over the family business when his father died in 1773. He also succeeded to the title of instrument-maker to George III and later became optician to the Prince of Wales. The quality of

his instruments was at least as good as those of his father, and he wrote various essays and dissertations on instruments, including one on barometers, thermometers and other meteorological instruments in 1790. In these he claimed that his father was the first to apply a floating gauge to a barometer which had been previously ascribed to Jesse Ramsden.

ADAMSON, Humphrey. w1668-82. Clock & watch M & IM. London
Near the Turnstiles in Holborn. At the House of Jonas Moore, in the Tower
He made and sold mathematical and scientific instruments designed by Sir Samuel Morland; these included a calculating machine and a barometer which Charles II admired.

ADAMSON, John. e1805-25. Clock & watch M. London
Barometers also signed 'ADAMSON & Co.' e1825-45. This was probably a partnership between father and son.

ADIE, Alexander. b1775-d1858. Math. opt. & phil. IM. Edinburgh
15 Nicholas St (1822-28) 58 Princes St (1828-35)
Adie was the nephew of John Miller, one of the leading eighteenth-century instrument-makers in Scotland, and was apprenticed to him in 1789. In 1804 his uncle took him into partnership under the name of Miller & Adie and the business continued until 1822, although Miller died in 1815. Adie concentrated on meteorological instruments, and in 1818 he obtained a British Patent No. 4323 for an improved air barometer, known as the sympiesometer. For this invention, and other research, he was elected a Fellow of the Royal Society of Edinburgh in 1819. He was optician to William IV and Queen Victoria. In 1835 he took his son John into partnership under the name of Adie & Son. Two other sons, Richard and Patrick, were also instrument-makers and extended the business to Liverpool and London.

ADIE, Patrick. b1821-d1886. Opt. & phil. IM. London
1A Conduit St, Regent St (1846) 14 Conduit St (1847) 395 Strand (1848-68) 15 Pall Mall (1869-1900+) 29 Regent St (1869-74) Broadway Works, Westminster St (1874-1900+)
A son of Alexander Adie, he specialised in marine barometers and worked with John Welsh of Kew Observatory to develop the 'Kew Pattern' barometer. He also made improvements to the Fortin barometer and was responsible for no less than twenty-one patents covering barometers and other instruments.

ADIE, Richard. b1810-d1881. Opt. math. & phil. IM. Liverpool
26 Bold St (1835-38) 55 Bold St (1839-81)
Richard worked for his father, Alexander Adie, before starting in business in Liverpool at the age of twenty-five. He specialised in barometers, and between 1837 and 1868 published twenty-seven papers on philosophical instruments. On the death of his brother John Adie in 1857, Richard spent half of his time in Edinburgh looking after the family business of Adie & Son until he died in 1881.

ADIE & Son. w1835-81. Math. opt. & phil. IM. Edinburgh
58 Princes St (1835-43) 50 Princes St (1844-76) 37 Hanover St (1876-81)
A partnership between Alexander Adie and his son John. It achieved renown, holding the warrant as opticians to William IV and Queen Victoria. Father and son were the only two instrument-makers to be elected Fellows of the Royal Society of Edinburgh.

Of the father it was said: 'His attention to business, with his skill as a mechanic, his quick inventive powers, and his sound judgement, led him to his being much employed by all kinds of inventors.' Of John it was said: 'Mr Adie's enrolment among us is a sufficient proof that he successfully followed his calling. He was greatly esteemed as a man conversant with the highest branches of his profession, and who has left behind him in that respect scarcely an equal, certainly no superior, in Edinburgh, or perhaps even in London itself.' Alexander died in 1858 and John, who suffered 'fits of Despondency' shot himself in 1857. Richard Adie, a son of Alexander, who had a similar business in Liverpool, managed the business on a part-time basis from 1858 until he died in 1881.

ADIE & WEDDERBURN w1881-1913. Math. opt. & phil. IM. Edinburgh
37 Hanover St (1881-82) 17 Hanover St (1882-1902)
On the death of Richard Adie in 1881, Thomas Wedderburn, who was previously foreman, assumed control of the Adie & Son business and changed the name to Adie & Wedderburn. He died in 1886 and the business was purchased by Alexander James Menzies. He died a year later and an optician, Thomas Mein, took control.

ADKINS, John. w1865-78. Opt. & naut. IM. London
19 Upper East St, Smithfield (1865-70) 3 Upper East St, Smithfield (1871-78)

AGGIO, Paul. e1820-45. Colchester

AGNEW, Thomas. b1794-d1871. Carver, gilder & print seller. Manchester
18 Exchange St (1835) 14 Exchange St (1841)
He originally worked for Vittore Zanetti who made him a partner in 1817 under the name of Zanetti & Agnew. This was followed by a partnership with Zanetti's son from 1825 to 1834 in the name of Agnew & Zanetti. He was subsequently on his own in Exchange Street trading in barometers, thermometers, mirrors, prints, pictures and artists materials and was the founder of Thomas Agnew & Sons the present London art dealers.

AGNEW & ZANETTI w1825-34. Optician, carver, gilder & print seller. Manchester
94 Market St (1825-26) 10 Exchange St (1826-32) 18 Exchange St (1834)
A partnership between Thomas Agnew and Joseph Zanetti, the son of Vittore Zanetti. They split up after nine years and ran individual businesses in Manchester.

AGOSTI, G. e1830-60. Marine barometers. Falmouth

AGOSTI, I. 1830-60. Falmouth

AIANO, Charles. e1790-1820. London
Barometers also signed 'AIANO & Co. FECIT LONDON'. A maker of stick, wheel and double barometers; he probably moved to Canterbury around 1825.

AIANO, Charles. w1828-41. Clock M & optician. 91 Northgate, Canterbury
A maker of stick, wheel and double barometers; he probably moved from London to Canterbury around 1825.

AINSWORTH, Henry. w1855-74. Clock & watch M. Romford

AIRD & THOMPSON. fl.1877. Clock & watch M. Glasgow
Made barometers with clocks set above the circular dial.

AIRS, William. w1863-78. Math. & phil. IM. London
32 Upper Rosoman St (1863-77) 95 Rosoman St (1878)

AITCHISON e1870-1900+. Opt. IM. London and Leeds
Instruments also signed 'AITCHISON & Co. OPT. TO H.M. GOVERNMENT'.

ALBERTI, Angelo. w1822-28. Optician. Sheffield
35 Church St. Fargate
Some barometers signed 'A. ALBERTO', and some wheel barometers are shield-shaped above the main dial.

ALBINO, Donello. w1840-56. Clock & watch M. Cheltenham

ALBINO, John. fl.1839-86. Looking glass M. London
47 St John St, West Smithfield (1839-49) 63 Hatton Garden (1850-68) 54 Stamford St (1869-80)

ALBINO, Joseph. w1870-79. Clock & watch M. Cheltenham

ALBINO, J. & W. e1820-40. 177 High St, Cheltenham

ALBINO, Vittore. w1850. Clock & watch M. Bourton, Glos

ALBINO, W. w1868. Clock & watch M. Stratford-on-Avon

ALBINO, William. w1870. Clock & watch M. Stroud

ALDRED & Son. e1880-1900+. Barograph M. Weymouth

ALDRED, S. H. & Son. w1830-75. Clock & watch M. Great Yarmouth

ALEXANDER, Alexander. e1812-60. Opt. IM. 6 High St, Exeter
Made marine barometers. Optician to Queen Victoria.

ALEXANDER, J. e1835-55. Norwich

ALFIERI, P. e1805-25. Halifax

ALFIERI, P. e1820-50. Manchester

ALFORD, G. e1840-60. Tavistock

ALIETTI, C. e1810-30. Oxford

ALIETTI, Christopher. w1842. Clock & watch M & jeweller. Highworth

ALLAN, Alexander. w1806-35. Phil IM. Edinburgh
Baron Grant's Close (1806-10) 9 Lothian St (1811-35)

Noted as maker of Thomas Thomson's direct-reading saccharometer, known as Allan's saccharometer. Peter Stevenson took over the business.

ALLEN, John. w1841-57. Math & phil. IM. London
35 St Swithin's Lane (1841-46) 5 Three Kings Court, Lombard St (1847-57)

ALLEN, William. fl.1838. Math. & phil. IM. 29 Seaward St, Goswell St, London

ALLEN, William. w1849-76. Clock & watch M. Market Harborough

ALLIS, John Hagger. w1850-70. Clock & watch M. Bristol

ALMENT, John. c1740-87. Opt. & math. IM. Dublin
Next door to the sign of the White Hart, Mary's Abbey (1767-88)
Worked as foreman for John Margas before starting in business on his own in 1767. Advertised that he made cases of drawing instruments, theodolites, sundials, electrical machines, weather glasses and 'various other instruments too tedious to insert'. He also advertised, in 1768, 'the improved barometer, which has had the approbation of the Dublin Society and made only by John Alment'.

ALTRIA, Caesar. w1846-68. Optician & glassblower. Aberdeen

ALUTTI, C. e1820-40. Cirencester

AMADIO, Francis (senior). fl.1800-44. Opt. math. & phil. IM. London
10 St John St Rd (1820-28) 118 St John St Rd (1828-44)
A prolific maker of high-quality barometers who appears to have been in partnership with his son Francis Amadio (junior) for many years, as some barometers signed F. Amadio & Son can be dated between 1800 and 1810 and are similar to those signed F. Amadio; these all have the address of 118 St John St Rd.

AMADIO, Francis (junior). fl.1840-65. Opt. & phil. IM. London
63 Moorgate (1840-41) 35 Moorgate (1842-51) 5 Cowpers Court (1852-65) 5 Birchin Lane (1852-65)
The son of Francis Amadio (senior). He was in partnership with his father for about thirty-five years before starting on his own.

AMADIO, F. & J. w1862-64 Opt. & phil. IM. 7 Throgmorton St, London

AMADIO, F. & Son. e1805-40. Opt. math. & phil. IM. 118 St John St Rd, London
A partnership between Francis Amadio and his son of the same name. It appears to have started soon after the father commenced in business as some barometers signed F. Amadio & Son appear to have been made very early in the nineteenth century.

AMADIO, J. w1843-62. Opt. IM. London
6 Shorter's Court, Throgmorton St (1843-53) 7 Throgmorton St (1854-62)
Probably related to the Francis Amadio family. He made wheel barometers with moulded edges and profusely inlaid with cut mother-of-pearl foliate decoration, mounted with a bow-fronted thermometer.

AMBROGI, G. e1820-40. Chelmsford

AMBROSINI e1820-40. Portsea

AMBROSINI, Francis. w1875-81. London

AMBROSINI, G. e1820-40. Chelmsford

AMBROSINI & MANZINI e1805-25. Portsea

AMBROSINI & Son. w1851. Brighton

A & NCOSL w1879-1900+. General retailers. Westminster, London
This is an abbreviation for Army & Navy Cooperative Society Limited. The company retailed a large number of watch-sized or pocket aneroid barometers; some were purchased by the army and navy which were then inscribed on the reverse side and given as prizes for achievements. For example: 'Army & Navy Rifle Meeting Portsmouth 1879. Won by T. R. Swinburne'.

ANDERSON e1750-70. Elgin, Scotland

ANDERSON, Frederick B. w1823-51. Clock & watch M. Gravesend

ANDERSON, Hugh. w1839-66. Clock & watch M. Gravesend.

ANDERSON, James. w1890-92. Phil. IM. 37 Skinner St, Clerkenwell, London

ANDERSON, T. e1800. Gravesend

ANDREWS e1820-40. Sheffield

ANDREWS, Henry J. e1800-30. Royston

ANDREWS, Nathan. Apprenticed 1724-d1782 (murdered). Clock & watch M. Yatebank, Lancs. and, later, Sheffield

ANDREWS, William. w1840. e1830-60. Clock & watch M. Royston
Son of William Henry Andrews.

ANDREWS, William Henry. e1790-1830. Clock & watch M. Royston
Father of William Andrews.

ANGELINETTA & BREGAZZI w1859-76. Looking glass M. 25 St John's Lane, London

ANGELINETTA, Lorenzo. w1879. 76 Paul St, Finsbury, London

ANGELINETTI, P. e1830-50. Worcester

ANGELL, William George. w1891-1900+. Earl's Buildings, Featherstone St, London

ANONE, Francis. w1802-8. e1800-20. London
2 Holborn. 26 High Holborn (1802-8) 82 High Holborn. 87 Holborn. 242 High

Holborn. 8 Ely Court, Holborn
An Italian immigrant who made and sold high-quality barometers, thermometers, telescopes and prints.

ANONE, John. e1810-30. Chelmsford

ANTHONY, John Bray. w1844-73. Clock & watch M. St Ives, Cornwall

APPS, Alfred. w1864-1900+. Opt. math. & phil. IM. 433 West Strand, Near Charing Cross Railway Station, London.

APRILE, F. e1815-35. Braintree

APRILE, J. & N. e1845-65. Sudbury

APRILE, Joseph. w1839. e1825-45. Clock & watch M. Sudbury

APRILE, Napoleon. e1865-85. Sudbury

ARCHBUTT, John & William Edward. w1867-92. Math. & phil. IM. London
201 Westminster Bridge Rd (1867-92) 8 Bridge St, Westminster (1876-89)

ARCHBUTT, William Edward. w1893-1900+. Opt. math. & phil. IM. 201 Westminster Bridge Rd, Lambeth, London

ARCHETTO, Louis. w1869-75. Clock & watch M. London

ARIVA & Co. e1850-70. Glasgow

ARMSTRONG, Joseph B. w1860. Clock & watch M. Optician. Douglas, Isle of Man

ARMSTRONG, Thomas & Brother. e1875-1900+. Math. & phil. IM. Manchester and Liverpool
78 Deansgate, Manchester. 88-90 Deansgate, Manchester
Also traded under the name of T. ARMSTRONG, T. & W. ARMSTRONG and ARMSTRONG Bros. Produced a large quantity of aneroid barometers.

ARMSTRONG, W. & Co. e1865-85. Chichester

ARNABOLDI, A. w1869-77. Clock & watch M. Buckingham

ARNABOLDI, Lewis. e1825-45. 7 Watton Place, Blackfriars Rd, London

ARNABOLDI, Lewis. fl.1835. Steep Hill, Lincoln

ARNOLD, James. fl.1830. Opt. math. & phil. IM. 5 Union Crescent, Whitechapel, London

ARNOLDI, Donato. e1820-50. Gloucester

ARNOLDI, D. & SAGOLINI e1810-30. Gloucester

Barometers also signed ARNOLDI & Co.

ARONSBERG, A. w1896-1923. 12 Victoria St, Manchester

ARONSBERG & Co. e1880-1900+. 39 Castle St, Liverpool

ARONSBERG, Maurice. e1858-75. Liverpool
Brother of William Aronsberg.

ARONSBERG, William. w1864-96. Manchester
3 Lever St (1864-68) 12 Victoria St (1868-96)
Brother of Maurice Aronsberg. Barometers also signed W. ARONSBERG & Co.

ARTALLI, D. e1815-35. Bath

ARZONI, G. e1840-60. Canterbury

ARZONI, J. e1830-50. Canterbury

ASAM, Giasani. e1810-30. Wolverhampton

ASCOLI, A. w1866. Manningtree

ASH, M. e1730-50. Birmingham

ASH, Moses. fl.1856-60. Opt. IM. Birmingham
36 1/2 Tower St. 75 Dale End

ASHBY, C. B. w1852-57. 3 Green Terrace, New River Head, London

ASHTON & MANDER w1871-1900+. Math. opt. & phil. IM. London
25 Old Compton St (1871-97) 61 Old Compton St (1898-1900+)

ASPREY e1870-1900+. Bond St, London

ATERZZA e1810-30. Nottingham

ATKIN, S. w1861. e1845-65. Clock & watch M. Alford, Lincoln

ATKINS & Co. e1810-40. Fenchurch St, London

ATKINS, Francis. b1730-d1809. Clock & watch M. Clement's Lane, London
An important clockmaker who also made very fine wheel barometers but not of the banjo design. In 1780 he became Master of the Clockmaker's Company.

ATTWELL, William Henry. w1828-74. Clock & watch M. Romford

AUGUSTUS, John Anthony. e1815-35. Math. IM. Church St, Falmouth

AUSTEN, John. e1815-35. Watch M. 81 High St, St John's Wood, London

AUSTIN, W. e1830-50. Ryde, Isle of Wight

AYSCOUGH, James. c1732-63. Opt. IM. London
At the Great Golden Spectacles and Quadrant, 33 Ludgate St, Near St Paul's
A noted optician who occupied 'The Original Shop for superfine Crown-Glass Spectacles'. He was the son of a Wiltshire clergyman and apprenticed to James Mann (junior) before setting up his own business in 1732 in Ludgate St. In 1743 he went into partnership with Mann but they split up in 1749. He specialised in spectacles, lenses and microscopes but a trade card shows that he sold 'barometers, diagonal, standard, or portable'. He was succeeded by his apprentice, Joseph Linnell, who continued to use the name of Ayscough until 1767. (See Fig. 3.)

B

BADDELY, J. c1800. Math. IM. Albrighton

BAILEY, R. e1865-85. 14 & 15 Bennetts Hill, Birmingham

BAILEY, Samuel. w1852-58. Clock & watch M. Newcastle upon Tyne

BAILEY, T. e1790-1810. Stanion, Northamptonshire

BAINES, A. R. e1860-80. Harrogate

BAIRD, T. e1880-1900. Aneroid barometers. Glasgow

BAIRD & TATLOCK w1881-1900+. Laboratory furnishers and chemical, math. & phil. IM. Glasgow, Edinburgh and London
100 Sauchiehall St, Glasgow (1881-88) 40 Renfrew St, Glasgow (1889-97) 40 & 50 Renfrew St, Glasgow (1898-1900) 10 Drummond St, Edinburgh (1897) 2 Teviot Place, Edinburgh (1898-1900) 14 Cross St, Hatton Garden, London (1889-1900+)
A partnership between Hugh Harper Baird and John Tatlock. Instruments were manufactured for the Admiralty, the War Office, the India Office and the Crown Agents for the Colonies.

BAKER & CAPNER w1872-74. Phil. IM. 20 Northampton Square, London

BAKER, Charles. w1851-1900+. Opt. & phil. IM. 244 High Holborn, London

BAKER, Francis & Son. w1866-1900+. Phil. IM. London
23 Great Sutton St, Clerkenwell (1868-81) 12 Clerkenwell Rd (1881-1900+)

BAKER, Henry. w1848-59. Opt. & phil. IM. 90 Hatton Garden, London

BAKER, William. w1821-57. Watch M, silversmith & cutler. Cornmarket, Shrewsbury
On his death in 1857 the *Shrewsbury Journal* reported: 'He was one of the oldest and most respected tradesmen in the town and his death will be regretted by a large circle of friends.'

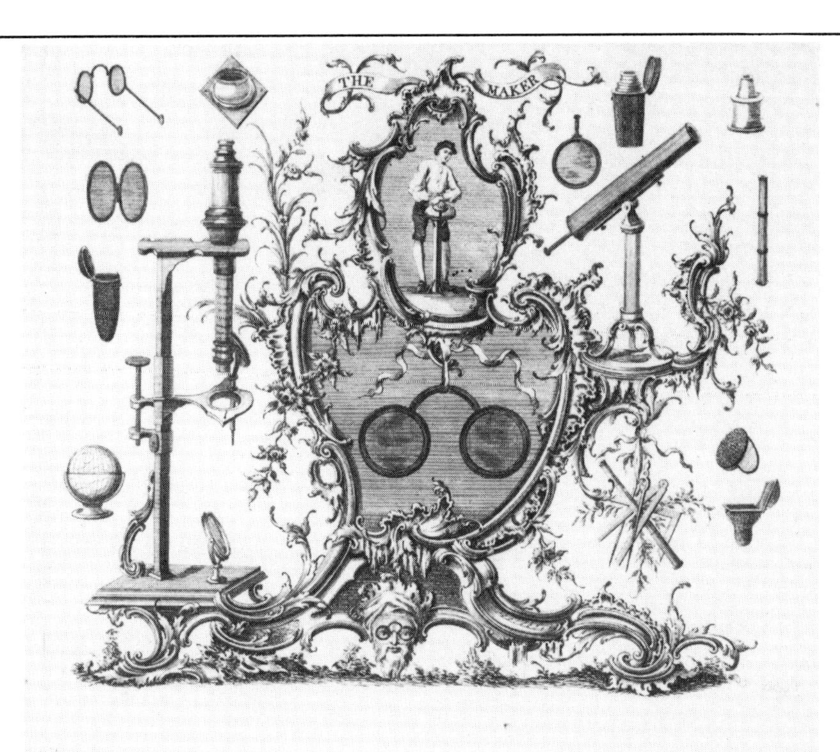

JAMES AYSCOUGH,

OPTICIAN,

At the Great GOLDEN SPECTACLES, in *Ludgate-Street*, near St. PAUL'S, *LONDON*,

(*Removed from Sir* ISAAC NEWTON'S HEAD *in the ſame Street*)

AKES and SELLS, (Wholeſale and Retail) SPECTACLES and READING-GLASSES, either of *Brazil*-Pebbles, White, Green, or Blue Glaſs, ground after the trueſt Method, ſet in neat and commodious Frames.

CONCAVES for SHORT-SIGHTED PERSONS.

REFLECTING and REFRACTING TELESCOPES of various Lengths, (ſome of which are peculiarly adapted to uſe at Sea;) Double and Single MICROSCOPES, with the lateſt Improvements; PRISMS; CAMERA OBSCURA'S; Concave and Convex SPECULUMS; MAGICK LANTHORNS; OPERA GLASSES; BAROMETERS and THERMOMETERS; SPEAKING and HEARING-TRUMPETS; with all other Sorts of Optical, as well as Mathematical and Philoſophical Inſtruments.

Together with Variety of MAPS, and GLOBES of all Sizes.

Fig. 3 Trade card of James Ayscough *(Science Museum, London)*

BAKER, William David. w1855-78. Clock & watch M. Horsham

BALARINI, P. e1810-30. York

BALE, Thomas. w1850-70. Clock & watch M. Bristol

BALEE e1845-65. Hotton

BALERNA, Lewis. w1834-53. Clock & watch M & silversmith. Halifax
8 Northgate St (1841) 44 Northgate St (1842-47) 71 Northgate St (1853)
Brother of Richard Balerna.

BALERNA, Richard. w1837. e1825-45. Clock & watch M. Halifax
Brother of Lewis Balerna.

BALERNO, Domenico. w1846-53. Barometer & mirror M. 14 Yeaman Shore, Dundee
It is said that he hawked his goods about the street, and usually had a barometer under his arm.

BALLARD, Frederick & William. w1847-66. Clock & watch M. Cranbrook
Also BALLARD & Co. (w1845) and Henry BALLARD (w1847-58).

BALLARD, James. w1826-55. Clock M. Lamberhurst

BALLARD, T. w1805. e1800-30. 13 Charles St, Hatton Garden, London

BALLARINI, P. b1801-d1858. Kings Staith, York

BALLO, E. w1848. Titchfield

BALSARY, G. e1815-35. London
Also G. BALSARY & Co. e1835-55.

BAMFORTH, M. e1810-30. Leeds

BANCE, Matthew. w1793-97. Clock & watch M. Hungerford

BANCKS, Robert. fl.1796-1820. Math, opt. & phil. IM. London
440 Strand. 441 Strand
His trade card shows that he made and sold 'all sorts of instruments on the most improved principles and lowest terms, wholesale and retail'. Bancks was optician to the Prince of Wales who later became George IV. Some barometers are signed BANKS and some printed literature has the name spelt BANKS. A few barometers have the address as 440-1 Strand, which suggests that both premises were occupied at the same time for a period.

BANCKS & Son. fl.1820-34. Math. opt. & phil. IM. 119 New Bond St, London
A partnership between Robert Bancks and his son. Appointed instrument-makers and opticians to George IV.

BANDOCK, C. e1835-55. London

BANELLI, Joseph & Co. e1820-40. Reading

BANKES, James. w1848-64. Gold balance M. Moor St, Ormskirk

BANKS e1815-35. Chippenham

BANNER, F. E. e1800-50. Optician. Banbury

BANNISTER, Henry. w1791-1820. Clock & watch M. Lichfield
Maker of angle barometers.

BARANZINO, S. e1820-40. 281 High Holborn, London

BARAZONI, Anthony. w1840. Optician. 23 Lodge Walk, Aberdeen

BARBON & Co. also BARBON e1810-30. Fullwood Rents, Holborn, London

BARBON, P. also BARBON e1780-1830. 281 Holborn, London

BARBON, Peter. w1809-12. Opt. IM. Edinburgh
4 Lothian St (1809) 18 Nicholson St (1810) 77 Princes St (1811-12)

BARBON, S. & Co. e1800-50. Edinburgh

BARCLAY, William. fl.1731-d1758. Opt. IM. Edinburgh

BARELLA & Co. e1835-55. Newcastle upon Tyne

BARELLI, D. e1800-20. Bristol

BARELLI, Domco. e1820-40. London

BARELLI, Frans. e1810-30. Reading

BARELLI, J. e1780-1800. London

BARELLI, Jno & Co. e1810-30. Bath

BARELLI, Joseph H. & Co. e1800-45. Reading

BARINI, P. also BARINE e1800-30. York

BARKER e1840-60. Tunstall

BARKER, F. & Son. w1866-1900+. Math. naut. & phil. IM. London
23 Great Sutton St, Clerkenwell (1868-81) 12 Clerkenwell Rd (1881-1900)
Wholesale makers who specialised in pocket and surveying aneroid barometers.

BARKER, John & Co. e1890-1900+. 71 Kensington High St, London

BARKER, W. e1835-55. Shrewsbury

BARKER, William. w1748-86. Clock M & gunsmith. Wigan
Known to have made a wheel barometer to set in the door of a longcase clock.

BARNARD & BOLTON e1845-65. Norwich

BARNARDA, P. also BARNARDA, P. & Co. fl.1803-14. Looking glass M. 22 West St, West Smithfield, London

BARNASCHINA, A. e1825-45. 68 Leather Lane, Holborn, London

BARNASCHINA, Anthony. w1826-28. Opt. IM. New Rd, Gravesend

BARNASCHINA, B. e1820-40. Boston

BARNASCHINA, Charles. e1815-35. Newcastle upon Tyne

BARNASCHINA, L. e1835-55. Gravesend

BARNASCHONE e1815-35. Devizes

BARNASCHONE, Charles. e1810-30. Boston

BARNASCONE, Andrew. fl.1822. e1820-40. High St, Boston

BARNASCONE, G. B. e1810-30. 13 St Michael's Square, Southampton

BARNASCONE, J. & Co. also BARNASCONE & Co. e1810-40. London

BARNASCONE, M. e1825-50. Leeds
Also spelt BARNASCONI and BERNASCONI. Also BARNASCONI & Co.

BARNASCONI e1840-60. Abergavenny

BARNASCONI, F. e1820-40. Bath

BARNASCONI, Francis. w1827-58. Optician. Newcastle
34 The Side (1827-34) 16 Groat Market (1838) 28 Groat Market (1841) 29 Groat Market (1844) 20 High Bridge (1847-53) 35 High Bridge (1855-8)

BARNASCONI, L. also BARNASCONE e1820-45. Trowbridge

BARNASCONI, Lewis, also BARNASCONE fl.1833-41. Retailer. Sheffield
42 Burgess St (1833-37) 23 Waingate (1834-41) 19 Waingate (1841)

BARNASCONI & Son. fl.1841-53. Optician. Newcastle
A partnership between Francis Barnasconi and his son which seems to have been carried on at the same time, and at the same addresses, as the father was in business on his own.

BARNETT, Thomas. b1768-d1810. Opt. math. & phil. IM. London
21 East St, Lambeth (1789) 61 Great Tower St. 4 Mores Yard, Old Fish St, near Doctors Common
Apprenticed in 1782. His trade card shows that he was 'Instrument-maker to His Majesty's Board of Customs and Excise'; also that he made and sold 'wholesale and retail, at the lowest prices, Barometers for indicating the Approach of a Storm at Sea, and other Barometers, either Diagonal, Wheel, Standard, or Portable'.

BARNUCCA, F. e1800

BARNUKA, N. e1795-1820. Bury

BARNY e1800-20. London
Some barometers have French inscriptions which suggests that he was an exporter.

BARRAGI, Louis. w1865-66. 90 Hatton Garden, London

BARRANDS e1800-20. London

BARRAUD, Hilton P. w1851-69. Clock & watch M. 41 Cornhill, London
Marine barometers bear his signature.

BARRET, Dom. e1780-1800
A maker of angle barometers.

BARRETA, Dominick. e1790-1810. 67 Holborn, London

BARRETT, Edward. w1848-55. Clock & watch M. Blandford

BARRETT, Richard Montague. w1847-79. Opt. & naut. IM. London
4 Jamaica Terrace, Limehouse (1848-74) 80 West India Dock Rd (1875-79)

BARROW e1870-90. Malvern
Aneroid barometers.

BARROW, Benjamin Francis. w1851-81. Clock & watch M. London

BARRY, George & Charles. w1843. Opt. math. & phil. IM. 4 Luke St, Finsbury, London

BARTLETT, J. w1894. Instrument-maker. London
In 1894 he patented a barograph which recorded the air pressure on a vertical circular chart instead of on the usual round drum.

BARTRUM, C. O. w1892. Phil. IM. London
In 1892 he patented a two-liquid open-scale barometer on the same principle as the Descartes two-liquid barometer.

BASERGA, A. e1810-30. Preston

BASERGA, F. & Co. e1810-30. Ipswich

BASS, George. w1841-69. Clock & watch M. Northampton

BASS, George & Son. w1869-77. Clock & watch M. Northampton

BASSNETT, James. fl.1829-55. Clock M, opt. naut. & phil. IM. Liverpool
1 Roberts St (1829-51) 58 Roberts St (1855)
First appeared in the Liverpool directory in 1829 as 'Basnett, clockmaker'. He doubled the 's' in 1841, and in 1855 he took his son into partnership. Produced marine barometers.

BASSNETT, James & Son. w1855. Opt. naut & phil. IM. Liverpool
58 Roberts St (1855-57) 8 Roberts St
A partnership between James Bassnett and a son, probably Thomas. The son could have been in business until 1887 because in that year a firm styled Thomas Bassnett & Company was formed.

BASSNETT, T. e1850-70. Paris and Liverpool

BASSNETT, Thomas & Co. w1887-88. Naut. math. & opt. IM. 10 Bath St, Liverpool
This was the Liverpool branch of the Glasgow firm M. Walker & Son and it is probable that it was formed by taking over the business of Thomas Bassnett.

BASTARD, John. b1688-d1770. Clock M & cabinet M. Blandford
The brother of William Bastard and Thomas Bastard (who died in 1731). When their father, Thomas Bastard, died in 1720 the three brothers worked together in Blandford as architects, builders, joiners, cabinet-makers, clockmakers, barometer makers, monumental masons and undertakers. The barometers were of the wheel type with rectangular dial and a chapter ring for the weather indications.

BASTARD, William. b1689-d1766. Clock M & cabinet M. Blandford
The brother of John Bastard, William made similar wheel barometers with a square dial, also a chapter ring.

BATCH, J. e1840-60. Chichester

BATE, Robert Brettell. w1807-49. Opt. math. & phil. IM. London
17 Poultry, Cheapside. 20 Poultry, Cheapside. 21 Poultry, Cheapside (1840-50)
'Instrument-maker to Her Majesty's Honourable Boards of Excise and Customs'. He was celebrated for his nautical instruments including marine barometers.

BATE, T. e1850-70. Bristol

BATES, John. w1830-54. e1820-54. Clock & watch M. Kettering

BATES, Thomas. w1828-35. Clock & watch M. Market Harborough

BATTISTA, B. D. e1850-70. Downham

BATTISTESSA & Co. w1830-43. Looking glass M. London
13 Baldwins Gardens (1830-33) 106 Hatton Garden (1840-43)

BATTISTESSA & Co. w1838-42. Carvers & gilders. 8 & 9 Carlton St, Edinburgh

BATTISTESSA, MOLTENI & GUANZIROLI fl.1834. Looking glass M. 13 Baldwins Gardens, London

BAUMBACH, Otto. e1900. Instrument M. 10 Lime Grove, Oxford Rd, Manchester
A maker of scientific apparatus and glassblower by appointment to the University of Manchester. Made double barometers which he called contra-barometers.

BAURLE, L. & F. w1874. Chatham

BAXTER, William. w1800-5. Clock & watch M. 8 Little Turnstile, Holborn, London

BAYLEY, W. e1840-60. London

BAZELEY, Dove. e1850-70. Cheltenham

BEALE, John. e1812. Math. opt. & phil. IM. 76 Maid Lane near the Borough, London

BEALL, Joseph. w1830-39. Clock & watch M. St Ives, Hunts
The business was carried on by his widow Mary BEALL on his death in 1839.

BEARD e1855-75. Cheltenham

BEARETTI, Peter. w1833-34. 26 Great Bath St, Clerkenwell, London

BEAUMONT e1860-80. Grosvenor Square, London

BEAVEN, James. e1835-55. Trowbridge
Barometer signed BEAVES recorded.

BECK, Richard & Joseph. w1867-1900+. Opt. & phil. IM. London
31 Cornhill (1867-80) 68 Cornhill (1881-1900+) Factory at Lister Works, Kentish Town, Holloway
Originally named SMITH & BECK and then SMITH, BECK & BECK. Renowned for their microscopes and photographic lenses. Sometimes recorded as 'R. & J. BECK Ltd' from 1894.

BECKER, Charles. w1854-63. Math. & phil. IM. London
29 Newman St, Oxford St (1855) 39 Newman St, Oxford St (1856-58) 30 Strand (1859-63)

BECKER, F. E. & Co. w1884-1900+. Chemical glass & apparatus M. 33, 35 & 37 Hatton Wall, Hatton Garden, London

BEILBY, e1795-1815. Bristol

BEL, August & Co. w1877-81. 34 Maiden Lane, London

BELL & DAMS w1868-76. Clock & watch M. Uttoxeter

BELL, Henry. w1856-81. Naut. & opt. IM. Glasgow
48 Maxwell St (1856-57) 50 Maxwell St (1858-59) 701/2 Great Clyde St (1863-81)

BELL, James. w1836-38. Phil. IM. 54 South Bridge, Edinburgh

BELL & Son. e1870-90. Cheltenham

della BELLA e1840-60. Preston

BELLAMY, A. e1790-1810. Wycombe

BELLATTI, C. also spelt BELATI e1810-30. Burton

BELLATTI, C. & Son. e1830-50. Newark

BELLATTI, Louis. w1828. e1825-45. Clock & opt. IM & jeweller. High St, Grantham.
He produced angle barometers.

BELLATTI, Louis Lawrence. w1849-68. Clock & watch M. 34 Sheep Hill, Lincoln

BELLENGER e1825-45. London

BELLONI, Frederick, also spelt BELZONI. w1830-55. Clock & watch M. Shaftesbury

BELOTTI & GUGERI w1822-36. Looking glass M. London
15 Upper Union Court, Holborn (1829) 16 Charles St, Hatton Garden (1830-36)
Belotti also spelt BELLOTTI. Barometers also signed GUGERI & BELOTTI.

BELOTTI, Thomas. e1835-55. St Ives

BELOZZI, John B. w1830. Clock & watch M. Weymouth

BENBOW, John. b1699-d1806. Clock & watch M. Northwood, Salop
Epitaph in the *Salopian Journal* 12 March 1806: 'Died at the age of 107. He was of the same family as Admiral Benbow; was universally esteemed for his integrity and ingenuity, and what is very surprising, he executed the most intricate branches of his profession till within a few years of his death, and retained his mental faculties unimpaired to his latest moments. He lived in three centuries and was remarkable for sobriety, early rising and retiring soon to rest; the liquor to which he was most partial was treacle beer. About three years ago his tailor brought him a new coat, which he examined, and perceiving a velvet collar had been forgotten, was so irritated that he walked to Whitchurch, the distance of seven miles, to buy one, and returned home in a few hours, to the great astonishment of his family.'

BENBOW, Thomas. w1778-c1800. Clock & watch M. Newport, Salop

BENDON, George & Co. w1878-1902. Clock & watch M & opt. math. & phil. IM. London
36 & 37 Ely Place and 1 Charterhouse St
Specialised in aneroid barometers.

BENES, Ernest. e1835-55. Ilford

BENETFINK & Co. e1865-85. Cheapside, London

BENHAM e1840-60. Bristol

BENHAM, John. e1825-45. Clock M. Cullompton

BENJIE e1870-90. Cowes, Isle of Wight

BENNETT, Anthony. w1841. Clock & watch M. Kettering

BENNETT, J. e1835-55. Kettering

BENNETT, John. c1743-68. Math. phil. & opt. IM. London
At the Globe in Crown Court, between St Ann's Soho & Golden Square
'Instrument-maker to Their Royal Highnesses the Duke of Gloucester and Duke of Cumberland'. His trade card advertised 'Barometers and Thermometers of all kinds, Wholesale or Retail, Warranted Standard'. Some of his cistern tubes were widened to a bulb at the top with a diameter of approximately two inches. This was designed to dilute the effect of any air that might, in time, percolate into the vacuum. He was succeeded by James Search. (See Fig. 4.)

BENNETT, John. w1850-72. Math. IM. London
65 Cheapside (1850-72) 62 Cornhill (1861-64) 64 Cheapside (1861-72)

BENNETT, Sir John. w1873-89. Math. IM. 64 & 65 Cheapside, London

BENNETT, Sir John Ltd w1890-1900+. Math. IM. 65 Cheapside, London

BENNETT, Thomas. w1810-67. Math. opt. & phil. IM. Cork
Patrick St (1810-17) 2 Patrick St (1820) 65 Patrick St (1824) 45 Patrick St (1826-28) 124 Patrick St (1844-67) 15 Scott's Square, Queenstown (1863)
A respected and inventive instrument-maker who made improvements to instruments and manufacturing tools. He made and repaired stick, marine and aneroid barometers. Succeeded by Reynolds & Wiggins.

BENNETT, Thomas. c1830. Phil. & math. IM. 162 Goswell St, London

BENNETT, William Cox. w1866. Clock & watch M. Blackheath

BENTHAM e1840-60. Bristol

BENTLEI e1820-40. Thirsk

BENTLEY, Thomas. w1776. Clock & watch M. Darlington

BENZIE, Simpson. w1867-78. Clock, watch & barograph M. West Cowes, Isle of Wight

BERGE, John. born c1742-d1808. Opt. math. & phil. IM. London
Johnson Court, Fleet St (1791) 3 Crane Court, Fleet St (1797-1803) 26 Lower Eaton St, Pimlico (1805-7)

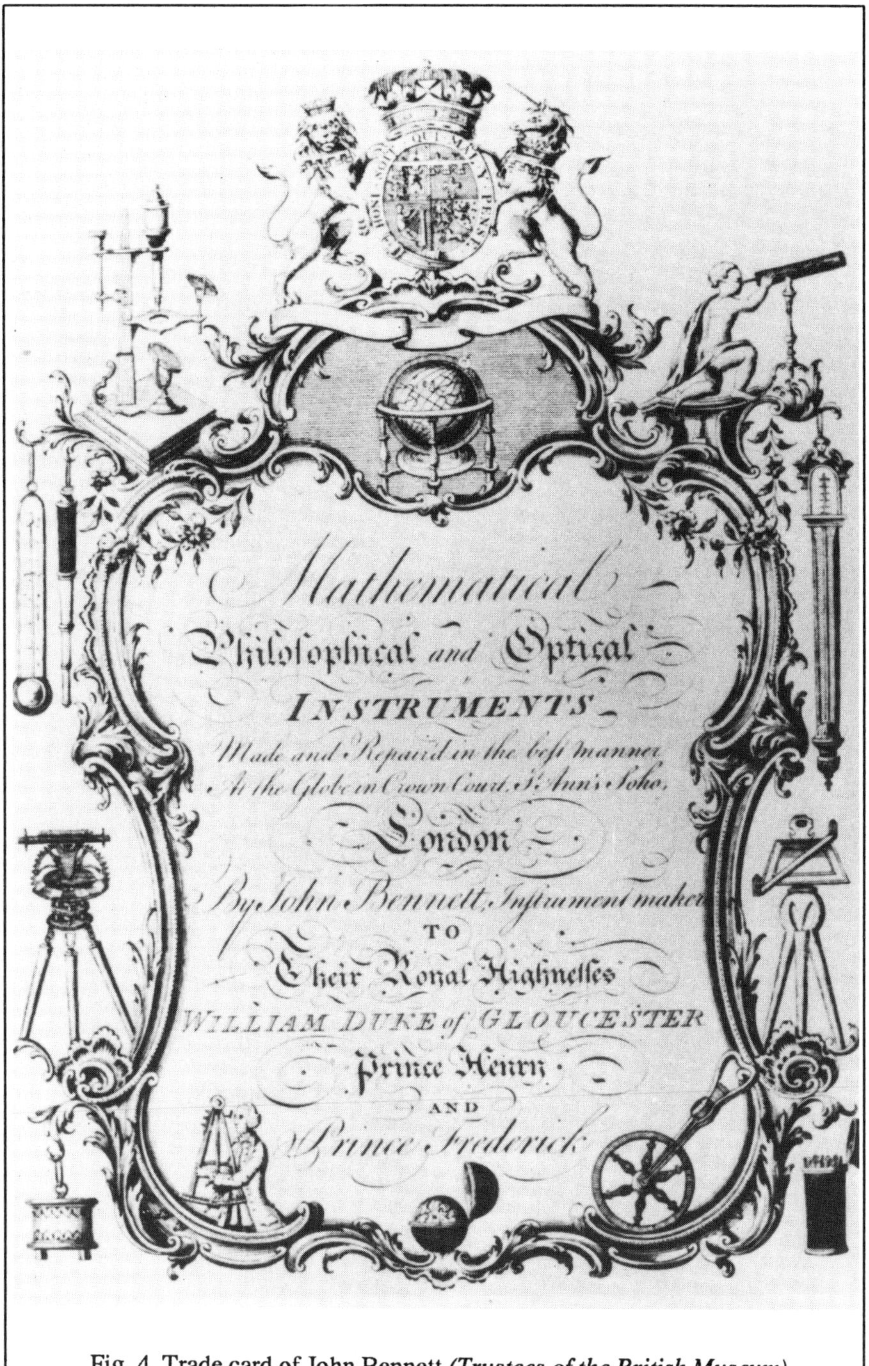

Fig. 4 Trade card of John Bennett *(Trustees of the British Museum)*

Apprenticed to Peter Dollond in 1756 and admitted to the Spectaclemakers' Company in 1773. He worked for Peter Dollond and Jesse Ramsden before starting on his own in 1791.

BERGE, Matthew. w1800-d1819. Opt. math. & phil. IM. 199 Piccadilly, London
He took over the business of Jesse Ramsden in Piccadilly when Ramsden died in 1800. Berge made stick and marine barometers and some are signed 'Berge, London late Ramsden'. He was, no doubt, trading on the very high reputation that Ramsden had built up over the years.

BERGNA, John Baptist. w1825-61. St Nicholas Churchyard, Newcastle

BERI & DELARA w1860. e1840-60. Clock & watch M. Leek
Barometers also signed 'G. BERI' and 'BERI & DALER'.

BERNARD, R. c1860. Writer and divider. 14 Lebanon St, Walworth, London

BERNARDI, N. e1820-40. London

BERNASCHONE, B. e1840-60. Merthyr Tydfil
Also spelt 'BERNASCONE'.

BERNASCHONE & MONTHI e1800-20. Leicester
Also spelt 'BERNASCONE' and 'MONTI'.

BERNASCONE, Innocent. w1830. Clock & watch M. High Wycombe

BERNASCONE, L. e1825-45. Sheffield

BERNASCONI e1810-30. Brecknock

BERNASCONI, A. e1820-40. Boston

BERNASCONI, A. e1820-50. Newcastle

BERNASCONI, M. e1840-60. Leeds

BERQUEZ, Francis. w1815-30. Clock & watch M. London
He made large wheel barometers with a clock above the dial.

BERRINGER, Henry. e1810-30. Clock & watch M. London

BERRINGTON, John. w1815-18. Optician. Leicester

BERRY, Anthony. e1840-60. Hereford

BERRY, D. w1847. Clock & watch M. Huntingdon

BERRY, I. e1810-20. Great Windmill St, Haymarket, London

BERRY, J. e1810-20. 16 Berwick St, Soho, London

BERRY, J. e1820-40. 12 Litle Chapple St, Soho, London

BERRY, J. e1830-50. 12 Panton St, Haymarket, London

BERRY, J. e1830-50. 78 Wardour St, Soho, London

BERRY, J. e1835-55. 50 Brewer St, Golden Square, London

BERRY, James. w1835-56. w1866-78. Naut. & opt. IM. Aberdeen
52 Castle St (1835-52) 52 Marischal St (1852) 88 Union St (1853-56) 59½ Marischal St (1866-78)
He had a mechanical genius and was interested in nautical subjects and astronomy, on which he lectured throughout Scotland. He took a son, George, into partnership in 1857 but, when George left the partnership to start up on his own, James continued the business in his sole name.

BERRY, James & Son. w1857-65. Naut. & opt. IM. Aberdeen
88 Union St (1857-60) 29 Union St (1861) 29 St Nicholas St (1862-65) 59½ Marischal St (1865)
A partnership between James Berry and a son George. George later left to start up in business on his own.

BERRY, John. w1738-62. Clock & watch M. The Dial near the Cross, Manchester

BERRY & MACKAY w1879-1900+. Naut. & opt. IM. Aberden
59½ Marischal St (1879-80) 65 Marischal St (1881-1900+)
A partnership between James Berry and Alexander Spence Mackay.

BERRY, S. e1840-60. Huntingdon

BERTOLA, A. also spelt BERTOLLA e1835-55. Oxford

BERTOLA, T. & Co. e1830-50. Edinburgh

BESOZZI, B. e1810-30. Weymouth

BESOZZI, B. also BESOZZI, B. & Co. e1810-30. Shaftesbury

BESOZZI, G. & Co. e1810-30. Shaftesbury

BETTALLY, Christopher. w1787-93. Phil. IM. London
1 Charlotte St, Pimlico. 292 Oxford St, opposite Stratford Place
Barometers signed 'BETALI London' are extant. One of the first Italians to arrive in England, he made distinctive barometers with the circular dial at the base of the instrument. His trade card indicates that he was the 'Constructor of all sorts of Barometers, Thermometers, Hygrometers and all sorts of Phisical Instruments of Glass'. He also had a shop in Paris. (See Fig. 5.)

BEVAN, Edward. w1865-78. Clock & watch M. Birkenhead
Maker of marine barometers.

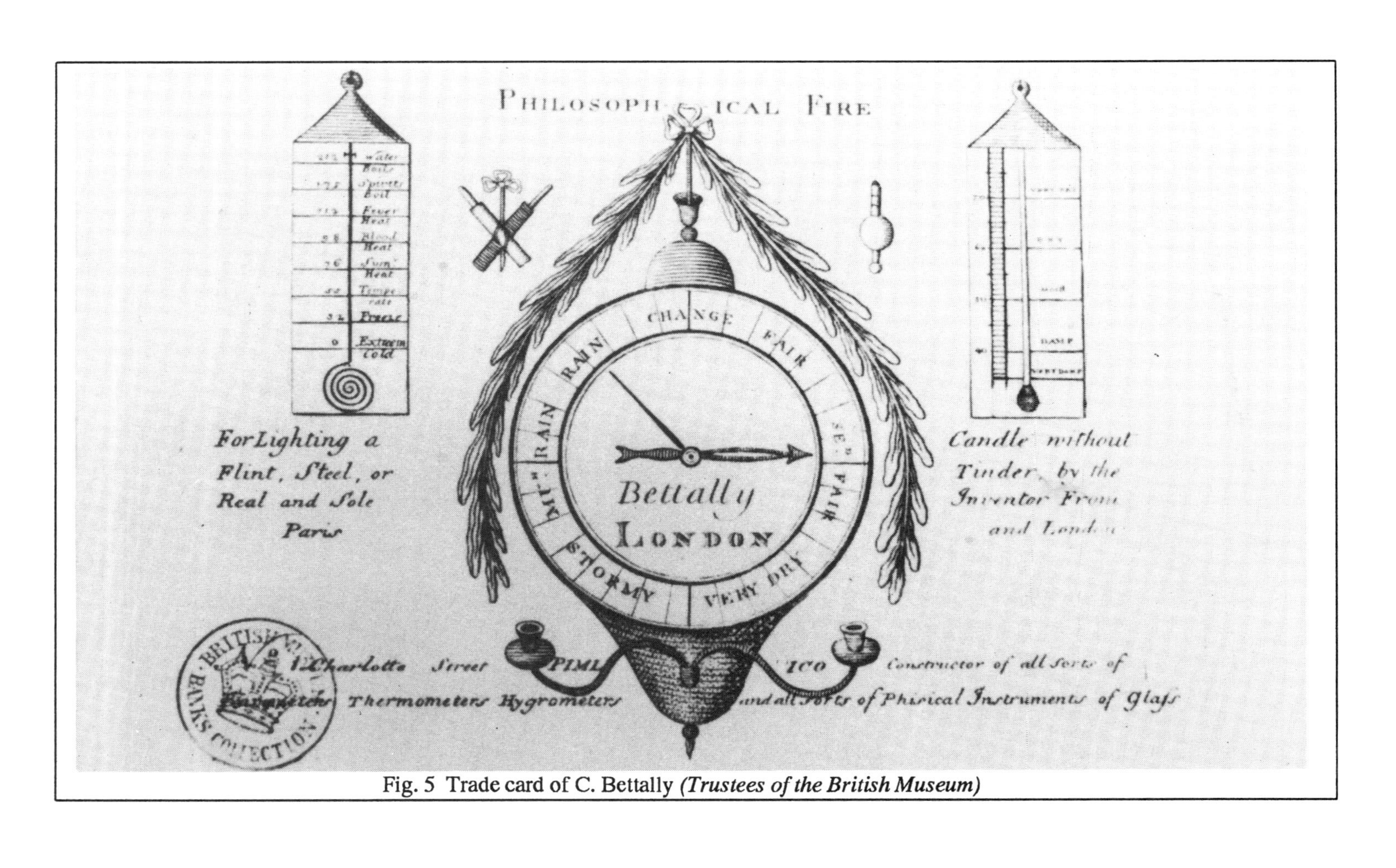

Fig. 5 Trade card of C. Bettally *(Trustees of the British Museum)*

BEVAN & WEARE w1857. e1840-60. Clock & watch M. Birkenhead

BIAGINI e1800-20. London

BIANCHI e1820-40. Manchester

BIANCHI, A. & Co. e1835-55. Wolverhampton

BIANCHI, B. e1810-30. 63 St Mary's St, Portsmouth

BIANCHI, B. w1855-77. e1845-77. Clock & watch M. Tunbridge Wells

BIANCHI & BARNASCONE e1810-30. Blackburn

BIANCHI, F. & Co. e1810-30. Leicester

BIANCHI, G. e1800-20. Edinburgh

BIANCHI, George. w1805-16. Ipswich
St Clement's St (1805-8) Westgate St (1809-16)

BIANCHI, J. also BIANCHI, G. w1847-64. Clock & watch M. Windsor

BIANCHI, N. e1835-55. Braintree

BIANCHI, P. e1800-20. Blandford

BIANCHI, P. e1835-55. Lane End, Bucks

BIANCHI, V. e1810-30. Belfast

BIANCHI, V. e1820-40. Dublin

BIDSTRUP, J. w1793. Opt. math. & phil. IM. 36 St Martin's St, Leicester Square, London

BIGGS, Bryan. w1875-87. e1860-87. Clock & watch M. Cardiff

BIGNELL, Charles. e1810-30. Clock & watch M. London

BINDA, John. w1846-52. Optician. 25 Duncan St, Cork
Exhibited at the National Exhibition held in Cork in 1852.

BIOLA, B. e1810-30. Cambridge

BIOLETTI b1779-1869. Wincanton

BIOLO, B. e1820-40. Norwich

BIRCH & MASTERS w1836-47. e1825-47. Clock & watch M. Tenterden
A partnership between William Birch who was working on his own between 1823

and 1839, and John Masters (b1818-d1887).

BIRD, John. b1709-d1776. Math. & opt. IM. London
At the Sea Quadrant, Court Gardens, Strand
The work of John Bird had a profound influence on the middle decades of the eighteenth century. He lived in Durham until he moved to London in 1740 and worked for George Graham and Jonathan Sisson. It is not known exactly when he acquired his own shop in the Strand, but by 1744 he had made a barometer for the Meteorological Station of Roger Pickering who wrote: 'It was made by Mr. Bird of the Strand, whose accuracy in graduation deserves, I think, notice and encouragement.' Bird was a well-known maker of barometers, thermometers and astronomical instruments and was renowned for his accurate scales. In 1767 he published his method of dividing astronomical instruments, and he improved the vernier by developing a tangent screw, which was a slow-motion precision screw for fine adjustment. (See Fig. 6.)

BIRD, John. w1839-44. Clock & watch M. London

BIRD, Thomas. fl.1856-60. 39 Charles St, Hatton Garden, London

BIRKLE Bros. w1851-55. Clock & watch M. Croydon

BIRKLE Bros & Co. w1857-81. Clock & watch M. 28 Commercial Rd East, London

BIRLEY, George & Co. e1870-1900. Worcester
Produced angle barometers.

BISHOP, James. w1794. e1794-1830. Clock & watch M. Edinburgh

BISHOP, John. w1830. e1820-50. Clock & watch M & silversmith. Cheap St, Sherborne

BISHOP, William. w1842-59. Clock & watch M. Fore St, Trowbridge
Also William BISHOP & Son. w1859-75.

BITHRAY, A. e1846-60. Royal Exchange, London
Probably the son of Stephen Bithray.

BITHRAY, Stephen. fl.1827-46. Opt. IM. London
Northgate, 29 Royal Exchange (1827) 6 Spread-eagle Court, Finchley (1843)
Succeeded James Smith, and some barometers are signed 'S. Bithray late J. Smith'.

BLACHFORD & IMRAY w1837-45. Naut. IM. 116 Minories, London

BLACK, A. & Co. w1893-1900+. Naut. IM. Glasgow
126 Broomielaw and 2 York St (1893-1900+)

BLACKBOURN, Cuthbert. w1848. 7 Alfred St, City Rd, London

BLACKHAM, Arthur. e1875-1900. Leamington Spa

BLACKHAM, Henry. e1875-1900. Opt. IM. Wolverhampton

Fig. 6 John Bird (1709-76)

Fig. 7 John Dollond (1706-61)

BLACKIE, George. b1813-d1885. Watch & marine chronometer M. London

BLAIR, J. e1800-20. 45 Prince St, Bristol

BLAKELEY, Benjamin. w1844-45. Math. & phil. IM. 11 High St, Lambeth, London

BLAKENEY, John W. & Co. w1861-73. Naut. IM. Glasgow
94 & 96 Jamaica St and 25 Turner's Court (1861-63) 25 Turner's Court (1864-73)
In partnership with Paul Cameron as CAMERON & BLAKENEY (1853-60).

BLAKEWAY, Charles. w1774-95. Clock & watch M. Albrighton

BLAND & LONG w1853-57. Opt. & phil. IM. 153 Fleet St, London

BLAND, William Russell & Co. w1859-64. Opt. & phil. IM. 153 Fleet St, London

BLATT, I. also BLATT, J. e1820-40. Brighton

BLEULER, John. b1757-d1829. Opt. math & phil. IM. 27 Ludgate St, London
He was apprenticed to Henry Shuttleworth in 1771 and appears to have worked for him until 1791 when he took over the business of a Mr Whitfield at the above address. He appears to have made barometers until his death.

BLOOM e1875-1900+. Sunderland
Aneroid barometers extant.

BLOUNT e1800-25. London

BLUNT, Charles. fl.1811-40. Math. IM. 38 or 58 Tavistock St, London

BLUNT, Thomas. c1760-d1822. Opt. & math. IM. London
22 Cornhill. 136 Minories (1814-20)
Apprenticed to Edward Nairne in 1760 and became his partner in 1774, trading under the name of Nairne & Blunt. The partnership lasted until 1793 but Blunt had been joined by his son in the business by that date. It appears that whilst in partnership both Nairne and Blunt continued their own individual businesses using their sole names. Blunt became mathematical instrument-maker to George III, probably because he designed some of the components for the 'New Barometer' by the Portuguese scientist J. H. de Magellan, used for measuring heights. A feature of Blunt's stick barometers is the egg-shaped cistern cover that he used almost exclusively. (See Fig. 8.)

BLUNT, T. & T. w1805-22. London

BOANI e1810-30. Birmingham

BOCK, Hilmar. w1893. 11 Sun St, Finsbury, London

BODOLI e1835-55. Andover

BOESE, B. w1868-76. Clock & watch M. Kidderminster

Fig. 8 Trade card of Thomas Blunt *(Trustees of the British Museum)*

BOFFI, Leopold. w1835-39. Clock & watch M. Battle and Hastings

BOFFI, P. e1810-30. Hastings
Also BOFFI, A. P. e1835-55.

BOGGAIA, D. w1839. $29^{1/2}$ Great Warner St, London

BOLL, John. w1666. London
He made a three-tube diagonal barometer in 1666.

BOLONGARO, Dominic. w1817-48. Carver, gilder & print seller. Manchester
2 Old Millgate (1817-30) 14 Market St (1832-33) 32 Market St (1834-48)
Came to Manchester from Tavernerio, near Lake Como, Italy around 1787 with Charles Joshua Ronchetti and Lewis Casartelli. He worked for Vincent Zanetti with a view to becoming a partner, but when this did not materialise he started a business on his own.

BOLONGARO & Son. w1848-83. Carver, gilder & print seller. Manchester
32 Market St (1848-54) 30-2 Market St (1855-83)
A partnership between Dominic Bolongaro and his son Peter.

BOLONI, P. e1825-45. 7 Union Court, Holborn, London

BOLTON, John. b1761-d1821. Clock & watch M. Chester-le-Street and Durham

BOMBELLI, Baldisaro. w1828-34. Math. IM. 6 King St, Whitehaven

BON, John. w1840-46. Chronometer, watch & naut. IM. Dundee
17 Dock St (1840) 25 Dock St (1845) 26 Dock St East (1846)
The business was continued by Mrs John Bon at 24 Dock St East in 1850.

BONACINI, C. w1862-64. 37 Charles St, Hatton Garden, London

BONACINI, Constante. w1880-88. 21 Cross St, Hatton Garden, London

BOND, e1835-55. Okehampton

BOND, Henry. w1850-70. Clock & watch M. Cirencester

BOND, John. e1805-25. Coton
Made wheel barometers with a clock above the dial.

BONETTO, Peter. w1857. Clock & watch M. London

BONFIGLIO, B. w1875. Clock & watch M. Cardiff

BORBRIDGE, Charles. e1825-45. Math. IM. 1 King St, Whitehaven

BORDER, George. w1828-68. Clock & watch M. Sleaford

BORDESSA & EATON w1854-65. Looking glass & spectacle M. London

54 Exmouth St, Clerkenwell (1855) 87 Hatton Garden (1859) 14 Cross St, Hatton Garden (1861)

BORDESSA, Pietro or Peter. w1834-60. Jeweller & toy S. 33 Bridge St Row, Chester

BORDOLI, B. e1830-50. Andover

BORDOLI, Bernard. e1810-30. Marlborough

BORDOLI & CASSAROTI e1810-30. Stamford

BORDOLI, P. e1830-50. 22 Charles St, Hatton Garden, London

BORELLI, Anthony. w1852-64. Looking glass M. London
14 Leather Lane (1852-54) 7 Great Warner St (1855-64)

BORELLI, Charles. w1851-78. Clock & watch M. Farnham, Surrey

BORELLI, D. e1830-50. Farnham, Surrey

BORELLI, Gaetano. w1877. e1860-80. Clock & watch M. Reading

BORELLI, J. e1835-55. Basingstoke

BORINI, P. e1810-30. Carver & gilder. Snowhill, Birmingham

BORINI, P. e1810-45. Bull St, Birmingham

BORINI, Peter & Co. w1808. e1805-25. 14 Edgbaston St, Birmingham

BORLINA, Edward. b1806-51. Clock & watch M. London

BOSETTI, Francis. w1851. 5 Wardrobe Place, London

BOSETTI & VANELLO e1800-20. London

BOSSI, L. e1810-30. Hastings

BOSSI, Paul. e1820-40. Rayleigh

BOTTA, C. e1830-50. Poole
Maker of marine barometers.

BOTTA, Louis or Luigi. e1835-55. Evesham and Worcester

BOTTERELL, James Hosking. w1873. e1845-73. Watch M. Liskeard

BOTTO, Luigi. e1810-45. Evesham

BOTTOMLEY, Robert Forster. w1876-89. Math. naut. & opt. IM. London
11 Billiter St (1878-88) 120 Fenchurch St (1889)

BOUCHETTE, Henry Joseph. w1880. 31 Glasshouse Yard, Aldersgate, London

BOUFFLER, R. e1835-55. 1 Beauchamp St, Brooks Market, London

BOUFFLER, R. e1835-55. 17 Leather Lane, Holborn, London

BOUFFLER, Robert. w1839. 7 Bell Court, Gray's Inn Lane, London

BOURN, P. w1839. 40 Bull St, Birmingham

BOURNE & TAYLOR e1860-80. London

BOUSFIELD, E. R. (Mrs). w1860. Math. IM. 4 Penton Place, Kennington Rd, London

BOUSFIELD, Henry. w1857-59. Math. opt. & phil. IM. London
11 West St, Walworth Rd (1857-58) 4 Penton Place, Kennington Rd (1859)

BOVERI, Francis. w1822-43. Looking glass M. 9 Eyre St Hill, London

BOWEN, David. w1849-76. Clock & watch M. Alfreton
He made large wheel barometers with a clock above the dial.

BOWLEY & Co. e1815-35. Salop

BOWLEY, William. w1809-18. Engraver. Wyle Cop, Shrewsbury

BOXELL, T. w1851-78. Clock & watch M. Brighton

BOXER, John. b1779-d1852. Clock & watch M. Folkestone

BOYLE, Robert. b1627-d1691. Inventor & author. Oxford and London
Appears to have been the first person to introduce the barometer to England. He was a prolific author, writing on science, philosophy and theology. He was a student in Italy during the period of the Torricellian Experiment and studied the writings of Galileo. On his return to England, he established a private laboratory in Oxford and carried out his own experiments. He developed the experiment into a practical barometer by being the first to use a graduated scale to record the height of the mercury in the tube. He built a water barometer outside his house in 1669. (See Fig. 9.)

BRABY, J. w1866. e1850-70. Clock & watch M. Tunbridge Wells.

BRACEGIRDLE e1840-60. London
Produced almost identical free-standing wheel barometers. A siphon tube is contained within a fluted column with a Corinthian capital and on a plinth with square-stepped base. An open silvered dial is above the column.

BRACHER, George. fl.1826-36. Opt. math. & phil. IM. 19 King St, Commercial Rd, London
Mrs M. BRACHER is recorded as working at this address in 1843.

BRACKER & SYDENHAM e1865-85. Reading

Fig. 9 Robert Boyle (1627-91)

BRADFORD, Isaac. e1850-70. Opt. & math. IM. 136 Minories, London

BRADFORD, Isaac & John. fl.1795-1822. Math. IM. London
87 Bell Dock, Wapping (1795-1800) 69 Bell Dock, Wapping (1805-15) 136 Minories (1817-22)
Isaac Bradford is known to have made marine barometers at 136 Minories.

BRADSHAW, James. w1834-58. Clock & watch M. Blackburn

BRAENDLIN, Francis A. w1859-62. Math. & phil. IM. London
65 Newman St (1859) 32 Newman St (1860)

BRAGONZI, P. e1835-55. Hereford

BRAHAM, James. e1820-40. Clock & watch M. Torquay
Moved from Liverpool to Torquay early in the nineteenth century and became clockmaker to the Duchess of Clarence.

BRAHAM, John. w1830-56. Opt. & math. IM. Bristol, Bath, Torquay and Cheltenham
42 College Green, Bristol (1830) 10 St Augustine's Parade, Bristol (1833-42) 17 Augustine's Parade, Bristol (1842-56) 8 Pulteney Bridge, Bath (1833) 5 York Buildings, Bath (1837)
John Braham sold the business to N. W. Dunscombe in 1856, and it is said that the deal was struck on the top deck of a London tram!

BRAITHWAITE e1815-35. Halifax
Made barometers with paper plates.

BRAMALL, W. H. e1870-90. Manchester

BRAMWELL, Thomas. w1869-79. Clock & watch M. Alston

BRANCHI, G. e1855-75. Edinburgh

BRANDER, C. G. & Son. w1864-66. Opt. & naut. IM. 82 Minories, London
Marine barometers.

BRANDER, Colin George. w1859-63. Opt & naut. IM. 82 Minories, London

BREESE, James. w1830. Wisbeach

BREGAZZI, A. & J. e1810-30. Carvers & gilders. Ashburn

BREGAZZI, C. e1840-60. Hanley

BREGAZZI, Innocent & Peter. w1825-40. Carvers & gilders. High Pavement, Nottingham
Peter was working on his own after 1840. (See Fig. 10.)

BREGAZZI, J. e1820-40. Dursley

BREGAZZI, Peter. w1840-43. Carver & gilder. Looking glass M. Bridlesmith Gate, Nottingham
Formerly a partner in Innocent & Peter Bregazzi. He made large clock/barometers with a large wall clock, with pendulum, mounted above the barometer dial and a curved thermometer in place of a spirit level.

BREGAZZI, Samuel. w1816-30. e1816-45. Carver & gilder. Queen St, Derby

BREGAZZI, S. & Co. w1809. e1805-25. Willow Row, Derby

BRICE, Francis Henry. w1875. Clock & watch M. Chippenham
Sold Admiral Fitzroy barometers.

BRIDGER, Richard. fl.1707-17. Math. IM. Hind Court, Fleet St, London
Apprenticed to Francis Hauksbee (senior) who died in 1713 and Bridger traded from Hauksbee's last address; advertisements suggest that Bridger continued the business for the benefit of Hauksbee's widow. Bridger sold 'All sorts of weather-glasses, whether barometers, thermometers, marine barometers, portable thermometers, or hygrometers'.

BRIGHT, Philip. b1784-d1841. Clock & watch M. Doncaster

BROAD, John Butler. w1856-73. Clock & watch M. Wadebridge

BROADBELT, Michael. w1797. Clock & watch M. Knaresborough

BRODERICK, William. w1835-76. e1820-76. Clock & watch M. Boston

BROGGI, Gillando. fl.1826-30. e1815-45. Math. IM. Moulsham, Chelmsford

BROMLEY, John. w1804-39. Clock & watch M. Horsham

BRONCHETI, J. e1820-40. 15 Spear St, Manchester
The surname could be Roncheti, but there is no record of a Roncheti at this address.

BROOKS, Alfred. w1848-62. Opt. math. & phil. IM. London
41 Ludgate St (1853-61) 48 Holborn Hill (1862)

BROSONI, M. e1830-50. Brighton

BROWN e1820-40. Paddington

BROWN, B. e1790-1820. Edinburgh
He made double barometers similar to those made by Balthazar Knie.

BROWN, Charles. w1848. Clock & watch M. Bridport

BROWN, Edward. w1874-75. Phil. IM. 17 Ormsby St, Kingsland Rd, London

BROWN, Ferdinand William. w1874-79. Phil. IM. 59 Myddelton St, London

Fig. 10 Advertisement of Innocent and Peter Bregazzi
(City of Nottingham Public Library)

BROWN, James. w1871-1900+. Opt. math. & phil. IM. 76 St Vincent St, Glasgow
He worked for Gardner & Co. of 53 Buchanan St for nine years before setting up on his own. His stock included mercurial barometers and barographs, and he advertised aneroid barometers from pocket size upwards, with and without a scale for measuring heights.

BROWN, John. fl.1648-95. Math. IM. London
Dukes Place (1661) Sphere and Sun Dial, Minories
A well-regarded instrument-maker whose intruments included barometers. He also wrote textbooks on the use of his instruments.

BROWN, John & Son. w1838-74. Opt. math. & phil. IS. Newcastle upon Tyne
Grey St (1838-46) 68 Grey St (1847-50) 98 Grey St (1865-74)

BROWNBILL, Henry R. w1767-90. e1767-1810. Clock & watch M. Leeds

BROWNING & Co. w1871-72. Opt. math. & phil. IM. 111 Minories and 6 Vine St, London

BROWNING, J. e1835-55. Walton, Glastonbury

BROWNING, John. w1862-1900+. Opt. math. & phil. IM. London
111 Minories (1868-75) 6 Vine St (1868-76) 63 Strand (1872-97) 7 Southampton St (1877-82) 22 & 23 Exeter St (1880-81)
'Optical and Physical Instrument-maker to Her Majesty's Government, The Royal Observatory and Kew Observatory'. Obtained a Prize Medal in 1862, and in 1870 claimed to have been in business for 100 years.

BROWNING, Louis P. w1894. Opt. math. naut. & phil. IM. 147 Holborn Bars, London

BROWNING, S. e1850-70. Portsmouth

BRUCE, John Lewis. w1884-1900+. Opt. IM. 56 Clerkenwell Rd, London

BRUFORD & Son. e1860-80. Eastbourne

BRUGGER & HOFFMEYER w1822. Clock M. Norfolk St, Lyme Regis

BRUGGER, Lorenz & A. w1837-44. Looking glasses. 79 High Holborn, London
Became Brugger & Straub in 1844.

BRUGGER & STRAUB w1844-75. Clock & watch M. 79 High Holborn, London

BRUNER, J. w1866. Clock & watch M. Brentwood

BRUNNER, Ignatius. w1835-54. Musical boxes, clocks & watches. 66 Edgbaston St, Birmingham

BRYER & Sons. w1878-88. Naut. IM. 104 Minories, London

BRYNE, Arthur Ethelbert. w1853-76. Opt. IM. London
71 & 72 Fountain Court, Strand (1853-57) 35 Carey St, Lincoln's Inn (1858) 27 Drury Lane (1874-76)

BRYSON, James Mackay. w1850-93. Opt. IM. Edinburgh
65 Princes St (1850-53) 24 Princes St (1854) 60 Princes St (1855-66) 60A Princes St (1867-93)
After an apprenticeship with George Buchanan, which ended in 1843, Bryson went to Germany for seven years where he studied instrument-making in Hamburg and Munich.

BUCHAN, Laurence. w1835. Manchester

BUCHANAN, David. w1837-42. Opt. IM. Glasgow
169 Hill St, Garnethill (1837-40) 93 Hill St, Garnethill (1841-2)

BUCK, J. W. w1853-57. Math. IM. 36 High St, Wapping, London
Marine barometers.

BUCKLEY, Joseph. w1832-59. Opt. math. & phil. IM. 14 Lower Sackville St, Dublin

BUDD e1835-55. Banbury

BUDGE, W. w1856. Clock & watch M. Callington
Also Mrs Elizabeth BUDGE. w1873. Widow of W. Budge.

BUIST, James & Co. w1859-86. Spirit level & opt. IM. Edinburgh
91 South Bridge (1859) 5 Nicolson St (1860-84) 67 South Bridge (1885-6)
Business previously owned by J. J. Liddell.

BUIST, James & Sons. w1887-1900+. Spirit level & opt. IM. 67 South Bridge, Edinburgh

BULL, John. w1830-54. Clock & watch M. Bedford

BULL, William. w1770-1804. Clock & watch M. Stratford, Essex

BULLA, A. e1810-30. Exeter

BULLA, A. & Co. e1810-30. Exeter

BULLA, GRASSI & FONTANA w1830. 134 Fore St, Exeter

BULLOCECH e1815-35. Bradford

BULLOCK, Thomas. w1842-75. Clock & watch M. Corsham

BUNDOCK, C. e1810-30. Clock M. London
Made barometers with a clock above the main dial . See also HORROD & BUNDOCK.

BUNSTON, Joseph. w1861-83. Clock & watch M. Chard

BURN, David. w1798. Clock & watch M. Edinburgh

BURNETT e1850-70. Dublin

BURNETT, William. w1851-56. Clock & watch M. Durham

BURNS e1850-70. Epsom

BURROW e1850-70. Malvern

BURROW, James. w1861-75. Clock & watch M. Wellington, Somerset

BURTON e1850-70. Malvern

BURTON, Edward. w1853-64. Opt. math. & phil. IM. 47 Church St, Minories, London

BURTON, George. fl.1772-1815. Opt. IM. 136 High St, Borough, Southwark, London
A notable instrument-maker whose instruments were taken on Captain James Cook's second voyage of discovery in 1772. They comprised two portable barometers, six thermometers, a theodolite, level and a Gunter's chain, for which he was paid £79.13s by the Navy Board. William Gooch also took a portable barometer by Burton on his voyage to South America in 1792.

BURTON, George. c1830. Opt. math. & phil. IM. 3 Devonshire Buildings, Great Dover St, London

BURTON, James. c1830-46. Opt. math. & phil. IM. London
10 Western St, Pentonville. 25 Pleasant Row, Pentonville

BURTON, Mark. fl.1730-50. Math. IM. Euclid's Head, near New Church, Strand, London
He worked for John Bird, who was renowned for his accurate scales, and this is probably why Burton specialised in scale-dividing. He also made barometers and thermometers.

BURTON, W. e1880-1900. Grimsby
Made aneroid barometers.

BUSS & ADKINS w1860-62. Naut. IM. 3 Upper East Smithfield, London

BUSS, Thomas Odempsey. w1863-1900+. Opt. math. & naut. IM. London
3 Upper East Smithfield (1863-68) 33 Hatton Garden (1866-95) 48 Hatton Garden (1896-1900+)

BUTLER e1795-1815. London

BUTLER, Alfred. w1890. 37 Skinner St, Clerkenwell, London

BUTLER, Edward. w1795-1828. Clock & watch M. Tutbury

BUTLER, John. w1854. Clock & watch M. Reading

BUTTI, BARNASCHINA & Co. e1815-35. Newcastle upon Tyne

BUTTI & Co. w1836. Carvers & gilders. 2 Ronaldson's Buildings, Edinburgh
This name appears to have been used by Louis Joseph Butti when he took over the business of A. Waterson & Co. The name only appeared for a single year.

BUTTI, James A. w1854-93. Carver, gilder & looking glass M. Edinburgh
14 Hanover St (1854-57) 1 Queen St (1857-68) 7 Queen St (1868-93)
The son of Louis Joseph Butti who initially shared the same premises at 14 Hanover St. He took his own son into partnership in 1893.

BUTTI, J. A. & Son. w1893-1900+. Carvers, gilders & looking glass M. 7 Queen St, Edinburgh
The firm eventually became fine art dealers.

BUTTI, Joseph. w1830-42. Hardware storekeeper. Taunton

BUTTI, Louis Joseph. w1825-67. Looking glass M. Edinburgh
232 Cowgate (1825-6) 2 Springfield Gardens (1849-53) 14 Hanover St (1853-67)
Born in Italy and emigrated to Scotland. He first appeared in the Edinburgh street directory in 1823 when he began a partnership with John Zenone.

BYRNE, Arthur Ethelbert. w1853-66. Opt. IM. London
7½ Fountain Court, Strand (1853-58) Savoy St (1859-66)

BYWATER, John DAWSON & Co. w1819-35. Opt. naut. & math. IM. 20 Pool Lane, Liverpool
Wholesalers and retailers and agents for Adie's sympiesometers.

C

CADE, Simon. w1688-1735. Math. IM. Charing Cross, London
Apprenticed to Henry Wynne in 1680 who was one of the earliest barometer makers.

CADENAZZI, M. e1835-65. Alresford

CADOLA e1810-30. Clock & watch M. Wincanton

CADOLA, J. e1845-65. Taunton

CADONE e1810-30. Salisbury

CADSBY, W. e1875-95. London
Admiral Fitzroy barometers.

CAHILL, Patrick. w1876-86. Opt. IM. $17^{1/2}$ Wellington Quay, Dublin

CAHILL, Patrick (junior). w1884-1904. Opt. & math. IM. Dublin
$17^{1/2}$ Wellington Quay (1884-98) 13 & $17^{1/2}$ Wellington Quay (1898-1904)

CAHILL, Patrick & Co. w1887. Opt. IM. $17^{1/2}$ Wellington Quay, Dublin

CAHILL, Patrick & Son. w1888-91. Opt. IM. $17^{1/2}$ Wellington Quay, Dublin

CAIL, John. w1825-65. Opt. & math. IM. Newcastle upon Tyne
2 New Bridge Street (1825-37) 44 Northumberland St (1838-9) 61 Pilgrim St (1841-53) 45 Quay St (1841-53) 21 Gray St (1855-58) 8 Gray St

CAIL, S. A. w1857-84. Math. IM. 42 & 43 Quay Side, Newcastle upon Tyne

CAIRNS e1850-70. 12 Waterloo Rd, Liverpool
A carved solid walnut marine barometer with a sympiesometer and incorporating an aneroid barometer is signed by Cairns.

CALDERARA, Serafino Antonio Maria. w1831-74. Phil. IM. London
16 Kirby St (1831-33) 78 Leather Lane (1834-51) 42 Baldwins Gardens (1852-74) 2 Kings Terrace, Bagnigge Wells Rd (1854-55) 5 Cross St, Hatton Garden (1872) 20 Baldwins Gardens (1867-71) 10 Cross St, Hatton Garden (1874)

CALDERARA, Serafino & Alfred. w1875-1900+. Hydrometer & saccharometer M.
10 Cross Street, Hatton Garden, London

CALLAGHAN e1845-65. Preston

CALLAGHAN, William & Co. e1860-1900. Opt. IM. London
25 New Bond St. 23 New Bond St. 23A New Bond St (1894)
Maker of stick, wheel and aneroid barometers and barographs.

CALLCOTT, John. b1753-d1830. Clock & watch M. Cotton, Salop
Appears to have been in the habit of losing watches! Three reported lost. In the *Salopian Journal* 1 February 1817 'Lost between Whixall Moss and Whixall Chapel. A silver watch, maker's name John Callcott, Cotton, No. 2525. Whoever has found the said watch and will bring it to Mr Callcott, shall receive a reward of half a guinea. Whosoever shall conceal the said watch after the date of this notice will be punished to the utmost rigour of the law.' He died, it was said in the same journal, 'after a long and protracted illness, which he bore with true christian fortitude and pious resignation ... as a neighbour his acquaintance was generally counted and esteemed, and as a mechanic his genius was of more than ordinary class.'

CALLCOTT, John. b1777-d1853. Clock & watch M. Cotton, Salop
Son of John Callcott.

CALLIEU & BARTLETT w1882-96. Phil. IM. 11A Featherstone Buildings, London

CAMBLE e1830-50. Oswestry

CAMERON, Alexander. w1818-48. Chronometer & naut. IM. Dundee
4 High St (1818-24) 120 Overgate (1829-48)
Acted as agent for Alexander Adie's sympiesometers.

CAMERON & BLAKENEY w1853-60. Math. naut. & opt. IM. Glasgow
76 Great Clyde St (1853-55) 102 Great Clyde St (1856-59) 94 & 96 Great Clyde St (1860)
A partnership between Paul Cameron and John Blakeney.

CAMERON, James. w1863-87. Phil. IM. Edinburgh
69 Adam Square (1863-67) 71 Adam Square (1868-70) 39 South Bridge (1871-84) 94 South Bridge (1885-87)

CAMERON, John R. w1851. e1850-70. Chronometer & watch M. 54 South Castle St, near the Customs, Liverpool

CAMERON, Paul. w1851-54. Math. opt. & phil. IM. 87 London St, Glasgow
Exhibited four instruments at the Great Exhibition in 1851.

CAMERON, Paul & Co. w1861-69. Math. & naut. IM. Glasgow
11 & 19 Howard St (1861-64) 25 Howard St (1866-67) 2 York Place (1868) 178 Broomielaw (1869)
The business was known as Houston & Cameron in 1865.

CAMINADA, L. e1820-60. Manchester

CAMINADA, Peter. e1820-45. High St, Taunton

CAMOTTA, Ann. w1860. 14 Bull Green, Halifax
Widow of Richard Camotta.

CAMOTTA, Richard. w1830-41. e1830-60. Carver, gilder & opt. IM. Halifax
14 Bull Close (1830) 12 Bull Green (1841)

CAMOZZI, Charles. w1830-50. e1815-50. General hardware dealer, jeweller, ironmonger & clock & watch M. Bicester
Market End (1830) Market Place (1832-50)

CAMOZZI, Eleanor. w1852. Hardware shopkeeper. Market Place, Bicester

CAMPBELL, J. e1830-50. Gatehouse

CAMPBELL, J. w1870-90. Opt. IM. Perth
Maker of aneroid barometers.

CAMPBELL, John. e1860-80. 6 & 7 South Castle St, Liverpool

CAMPI, John. e1840-60. Wolverhampton

CAMPION, B. & Co. e1820-40. Belfast

CAMPIONE e1760-1820. Oxford

CAMPIONI, P. e1820-50. Edinburgh
Also CAMPIONI & Co. e1835-55.

CAMPONOVO e1820-40. Summers Town, Oxford

CAMPONOVO, Angelo. w1846. St Thomas's Parish, Oxford

CANOVA, John. w1879. Clock & watch M. Halesworth

CANOVA, P. e1835-55. Huntingdon

CANOVA, Peter. e1825-45. Clock & watch M. Halesworth

CANTI e1825-45. Charles St, Hatton Garden, London

CANTI, C. A. e1815-45. Town Malling, Kent

CANTI, C. A. e1820-40. Clock & watch M. 4 Cross St, Hatton Garden, London

CANTI, C. A. (junior). e1820-40. 59 Shoe Lane, Holborn, London

CANTI, C. A. e1830-60. 30 High Holborn, London

CANTI, C. A. & Son. e1820-50. 16 Brooke St, Holborn, London

CANTONI, Brazio Carfax. w1839. e1820-45. Clock & watch M. Horsham

CAPADURO, Domenico. w1830. Opt. IM. Deal and Margate

CAPELLA, David. c1854. 46 Pershore St, Birmingham

CAPELLA, G. e1880-1900. London

CAPELLA, J. w1868-75. Clock & watch M. Newport, Mon. and at Nantgarw, Glam.

CAPELLA, Michael. w1854. 53 Edgbaston St, Birmingham

CAPELLA, V. e1840-65. Coventry

CAPLATZI, Anthony. w1878-1900. Opt. math. & phil. IM. London
3 Chenies St, Bedford Square (1878-1900) 22 Charlotte St (1878-82, 1894-1900)

CAPLATZI, James. w1874. Math. & opt. IM. 16 Chenies St and 22 Charlotte St, London

CAPLATZI, James & Anthony. w1875-77. Math. & opt. IM. 16 Chenies St and 22 Charlotte St, London

CAPNER, Henry Morgan. w1878-82. Phil. IM. London
20 Northampton Square (1879-81) 59 Myddelton St (1881-82)

CAPO, Anthony. w1810-20. Mirror M. 154 Millfield, Belfast

CAPODURO & Co. e1790-1810. Opt. IM. Margate

CAPPI, William. w1844-50. Barometer case M. 11 Bakers Row, Clerkenwell, London

CAPPO, Anthony. w1839-54. Clock, watch & opt. IM. Belfast
164 Millfield (1839-40) 168 Millfield (1843-46) 160 Millfield (1850-54)

CAPPO, Joseph. w1835-41. w1856-80. Chemical & phil. IM. Belfast
168 Millfield (1835) 202 North St (1839) 164 Millfield (1840) 147 Millfield (1856)
24 Portland St (1858) 14 Portland St (1860-61) 5 Portland Place (1863-80)
Cappo moved to Glasgow and worked there between 1847 and 1853 (see below), but he returned to Belfast and was in business again by 1856.

CAPPO, Joseph. w1847-53. Hydrometer & phil. IM. Glasgow
Buchanan Court, 75 Argyll St (1847-52) 404 Parliamentary Rd (1853)
Cappo was in business in Belfast until 1841 (see above) and he returned there to continue in business in 1856.

CAPPO, Mary. w1884. Phil. IM. 5 Portland Place, Belfast
Probably the widow of Joseph Cappo.

CAPPRANI, G. & Co. e1815-35. Norwich

CAPRAINI, P. w1828. 5 Leopard's Court, Baldwins Gardens, London

CAPRANI, L. e1835-55. Leicester

CAPUS, Peter. e1800-30. Brecknock

CARACCIA e1815-35. Clock & watch M. London

CARACIA, C. e1835-55. Edenbridge
Also CARACIA, Joseph. e1835-55.

CARINALLI, John. e1820-40. Gloucester
He made large wheel barometers with a clock above the dial.

CARIOLI, A. w1839. e1815-40. Clock & watch M. Whitby

CARIOLLI & Co. e1810-1830. Scarborough

CARLILE, John. w1755. General merchant. At entry to Bell's Wynd above the Cross, Glasgow, at the Sign of the Rose. Wholesale or Retail.

CARMAN e1840-60. London
He made a free-standing wheel barometer with open dial above a Corinthian column.

CARNOVA, P. e1810-30. Charlesworth

CARNOVA, P. w1846. Halesworth

CARPENTER, Philip. w1817-37. Opt. math. & phil. IM. Birmingham and London
Bath Row, Birmingham (1817) 111 New St, Birmingham (1829) 33 Navigation St, Birmingham (1829) 24 Regent St, London (1827-37)
Name changed to Carpenter & Westley around 1837.

CARPENTER & WESTLEY w1835-1900+ Opt. math. & phil. IM. Birmingham and London
111 New St, Birmingham (1835) 24 Regent St, London (1838-1900+)
The original proprietor was Philip Carpenter. Exhibited at the Great Exhibition in 1851.

CARR, Andrew. w1865. Clock & watch M. Belfast

CARREW, John W. w1833-66. Math. naut. & phil. IM. London
18 Wapping Lane (1838) 13 Wapping Wall (1840-66)

CARRORI, B. w1854. Clock & watch M. Buckingham

CARRORI, Benjamin. w1830-54. Clock & watch M. High Wycombe

CARTER, George. w1839-52. Optician & jeweller. 252 High St, Exeter

CARTER, Henry. b1795-d1876. Clock & watch M. Ripon
Son of William Edward Carter.

CARTER, John. w1829-d1878. Clock & watch M. 61 Cornhill, London
A Lord Mayor of London.

CARTER, N. e1800-20. Salisbury

CARTER, William Edward. b1760-d1842. Clock & watch M. Ripon
Moved to London in 1829 and a son, Henry Carter, carried on the business.

CARTO, Joseph. w1828-39. Clock & watch M. Putney

CARTWRIGHT, Thomas. w1834-37. Clock & watch M. Halifax

CARUGHI, Paul. w1839-62. Looking glass M. London
15 Brooke St (1839) 128 Holborn (1841-43) 16 Charles St, Hatton Garden (1844-45) 38 Brooke St (1846-47) 139 High Holborn (1852-62)

CARUGHI, Paul & Co. w1846-47. Looking glass M. 38 Brooke St, Holborn, London

CARY, George & John. w1821-25. Opt. & math. IM. 86 St James St, London
Two sons of John Cary the cartographer and nephews of William Cary whose business they took over in 1825. They continued to use the William Cary business name rather than their own. See William CARY & Co.

CARY, PORTER & Co. w1897-1900+. Math. & opt. IM. 7 Pall Mall, London

CARY, William. w1789-d1825. Opt. & math. IM. London

272 Strand (1786) 182 Strand (1794) 181 Strand (1794-1825)
The younger brother of John Cary the cartographer and the uncle of George and John Cary. He was a pupil of Jesse Ramsden and became a renowned instrument-maker. His two nephews took over the business when he died in 1825 but because of his very high reputation they retained the name of William Cary.

CARY, William & Co. w1825-1894. Opt. & math. IM. 181 Strand, London
A partnership between George and John Cary which they started in 1821 in their own name but then changed to William Cary in 1825 when they took over their uncle's business. The name was changed from William Cary to William Cary & Co. after 1843.

CASARTELLI e1790-1810. London

CASARTELLI, A. e1835-55. 2 Fade St, Dublin

CASARTELLI, Anthony. w1863-d1881. Opt. & phil. IM. Liverpool
43 South Castle St (1863-65) Swift Court (1866-76) 54 Old Hall St, and St John's Lane (1876-81)
The younger brother of Joseph Casartelli who left the business at 20 Duke St to start up in business on his own. His widow carried on the business at 39A South Castle St after his death in 1881.

CASARTELLI, Anthony & Joseph. w1845-52. Opt. & phil. IM. 20 Duke St, Liverpool
A partnership between Anthony John and Joseph Lewis Casartelli. Joseph left in 1852 and moved to Manchester to marry Harriet Ronchetti and take over the business of John B. and Joshua Ronchetti.

CASARTELLI, Joseph. w1881-83. Math. IM. 34 Hatton Garden, London

CASARTELLI, Joseph Lewis. w1852-96. Opt. & math. IM. 43 Market St, Manchester
Married Harriet Ronchetti in 1852 and moved from Liverpool to take over the business run by John B. and Joshua Ronchetti.

CASARTELLI, J. & Son. w1896-1900+. Opt. & math. IM. 43 Market St, Manchester
A partnership between Joseph Lewis and his son Joseph Henry. The elder Joseph died in 1900 and his son carried on the business until his death in 1925.

CASARTELLI, Lewis. b1784-d1860. Opt. & math. IM. Liverpool
37 King St (1812-32) 132 King St (1832-43) 133 King St (1830-37) 20 Duke St (1837-45)
The nephew of Baptista Ronchetti, he emigrated from Tavernerio, near Lake Como, Italy around 1787. He worked for several barometer makers before setting up in business and traded from various addresses in King St and Duke St. Anthony and Joseph Casartelli took control of the business in 1845.

CASELLA, Louis & Co. w1848-1857. Opt. & phil. IM. 23 Hatton Garden, London
This name was used by Louis Casella when the partnership between him and Caesar Tagliabue appears to have ended in 1848. It could be that Tagliabue retained an interest in the business but took no active part in its management. The firm expanded rapidly and became instrument-makers to the Admiralty and governments abroad until the name was changed to Louis Casella.

CASELLA, Louis Pascal. c1858-1900+. Opt. math. & phil. IM. London
23 Hatton Garden (1858-71) 147 Holborn Bars (1871-1900+)
The business was run by Louis Pascal Casella and barometers are signed 'CASELLA', 'L. CASELLA', 'LOUIS CASELLA' and 'L. P. CASELLA'. He married the daughter of Caesar Tagliabue in 1837 and became his partner in 1838 under the name of Tagliabue & Casella. Other partnerships followed until he was on his own around 1860. His catalogue issued in 1871 shows that he produced a full range of instruments and was 'maker to the Admiralty, Board of Trade, Board of Ordnance and the Governments and Observatories of India, Russia, Spain, Portugal, the United States and the Brazils'. Casella became one of the largest makers of barometers in England and still trades today in the name of C. F. Casella & Co. Ltd.

CASELLA & TAGLIABUE w1846-47. Opt. & phil. IM. 23 Hatton Garden, London
A partnership between Louis Casella and Caesar Tagliabue. It was called Tagliabue & Casella from 1838 to 1846 and then changed to Louis Casella & Co. in 1848.

CASSERA, Genera. e1815-45. Hardware dealer. Stourbridge

CASSERA, J. e1830-50. Brierley Hill

CASSINELLO, George & Co. w1856. 23-4 West Smithfield, London

CASSNA, B. e1820-40. Banff

CASTELETI, Job. e1830-50. Leicester

CASTELETI, John, also spelt 'CASTELLETTI'. w1841. e1815-41. High St, Leicester

CASTELLI, J. w1824. Waterford

CASTELLO, Joseph. w1854-91. Opt. IM. 42 Wellington Quay, Dublin

CASTELLO & Son. w1891-1900+. Opt. IM. 42 Wellington Quay, Dublin

CASTILIONI, James. e1830-50. Whitley

CATELLI, C. & Co. e1815-45. Hereford

CATELLI & Co. e1810-30. Worcester

CATLIN, Daniel. w1784. e1784-1820. Clock & watch M. King's Lynn

CATMUR, B. w1863. Math. IM. 50 Devonshire Rd, Upper Holloway, London

CATMUR, Benjamin. w1838-43. Opt. math. & phil. IM. 28 Chamber St, Goodman's Fields, London

CATTANEO e1820-40. Bristol

CATTANEO, Austin, Henry & John. e1810-35. Clock & watch M & opt. IM. Kings

Staith, York
They traded individually and in various partnerships which included Peter Ballarini and Joseph Fattorini.

CATTANEO, Charles. e1830-50. Huddersfield

CATTANEO & Co. w1848. Clock & watch M & jewellers. 12 Castlegate, York
A partnership between Henry and Philip Cattaneo and Joseph Fattorini.

CATTANEO & Co. w1866. e1840-66. Clock & watch M. 135 Briggate, Leeds

CATTANEO, H. & Co. c1845. Clock & watch M. 12 Castlegate, York
A partnership between Henry and Joseph Cattaneo.

CATTANEO, Henry. w1837-58. Clock & watch M. optician & jeweller. York
12 Castlegate (1837-48) 2 St Martin's Lane (1849-58)

CATTANEO, Joseph. w1851. Clock & watch M & opt. IM. 1 South Entrance, York
He was made bankrupt in 1849 but was in business again in 1851.

CATTANEO, Joseph. w1858-74. Clock & watch M. Folkestone

CATTANEO, Pasqual. w1839-55. Clock & watch M. Croydon

CATTANEO, Peter. w1851. Clock & watch M. Croydon

CATTANEO, Peter & Co. w1839. Clock & watch M. Reigate

CATTANEO, Philip. w1848. Clock & watch M & jeweller. 12 Castlegate, York

CATTANIO, A. w1829. e1825-50. Worcester

CATTANIO, Anthony. w1840-58. Clock & watch M. Market Place, Malton

CATTANIO, Anthony. e1840-65. Blackhall St, Kidderminster

CATTANIO, C. & DOTTI e1820-40. Braintree

CATTANIO, Natal. w1850. Clock & watch M. Kidderminster

CATTANIO, P. e1810-30. Chester

CATTANIO, S. c1831. Watch M. Stockton

CATTANIO, V. e1805-45. Worcester

CATTANIO, Vincent. w1851-56. Clock & watch M. Stockton

CATTANIO, William. w1866. Clock & watch M. Market Place, Malton

CATTELLI & Co. w1810-30. Worcester

CATTELLI, G. & Co. also G. & Son. e1820-45. Hereford

CATTELY & Co. e1830-50. Hertford

CATTELY, S. & Co. e1810-30. 81 Holborn, London

CAVENS e1820-40. Carlisle

CAVERHILL & Co. e1840-60. Berwick-on-Tweed

CAWDLE, William. c1830-50. Clock M. Torquay

CEALEY, WOHLMANN & BRADSHAW w1899-1900+. Naut. & opt. IM. 22 New North Rd, London

CEPPI, Lewis. e1820-45. Chichester

CEPPI & SHELBOURNE e1830-50. Grantham

CERLETTI, L. e1810-30. Manchester

CERUTTY, John. e1800-20. At the Tuns Lodging House, Bath

CERUTTY, Peter. e1810-30. Tavistock

CETTA & Co. e1825-45. Stroud

CETTA, G. & Co. e1810-30. Dursley

CETTA, J. e1835-55. Stroudwater

CETTA J. & J. e1830-50. Stroud

CETTA, John. w1838-60. Looking glass M. London
7 Union Court, Black Hill, Holborn (1838) 15 Brooke St (1839-44) 14-15 Brooke St (1845-6) 40 Hatton Garden (1847-60)

CETTA, John & Co. w1859-60. Looking glass M. 40 Hatton Garden, London

CETTA, L. e1835-55. Stroudwater

CETTA, P. e1840-60. Gloucester

CETTI e1820-40. Henley

CETTI e1825-45. Stroud

CETTI e1835-55. Dudley

CETTI, A. e1810-30. Reading

CETTI & Co. e1800-20. Leeds

CETTI, Edward. w1853-69. 11 Brooke St, Holborn, London

CETTI, Edward. w1880-95. Phil. IM. London
11 Brooke St, Holborn (1880-82) 31 Brooke St, Holborn (1880-81) 36 Brooke St, Holborn (1883-95)

CETTI, Edward (junior). w1896-98. London
19 Brookes Market (1896-97) 71 Hatton Garden (1898)

CETTI, Edward & Co. w1870-79. Phil. IM. London
11 Brooke St, Holborn (1870-79) 13 Brooke St, Holborn (1874) 31 Brooke St, Holborn (1876-79)

CETTI & GATTY e1805-25. Belfast

CETTI, J. e1815-35. 81 High Holborn, London

CETTI, John. w1842-54. Clock & watch M. Buckingham

CETTI, John & Co. w1840-48. Looking glass M. 25 Red Lion St, London
Successor to Joseph Cetti & Co.

CETTI, Joseph & Co. w1802-39. Looking glasses & prints. London
3 Long Lane, Smithfield (1802) 54 Red Lion St (1803-15) 25 Red Lion St (1816-39)

CETTI, P. e1835-55. Kendal

CETTI, Paul & Co. w1841-79. Clock & watch M. New St, Wellington, Salop

CETTI, Romano. w1896. 2 Beauchamp St, Holborn, London

CETTI, Romano & Co. w1897. 2 & 3a Beauchamp St, Holborn, London

CETTI, William. w1843. Watch M. Buckingham

CHADBURN Bros. fl.1837-c1875. Opt. math. & phil. IM. Sheffield and Liverpool
Albion Works, 26 Nursery St, Sheffield. 71 Lord St, Liverpool
Notable makers and retailers of instruments, some of which were purchased from London and continental makers. Instrument-makers to Prince Albert. Exhibited at the Great Exhibition at the Crystal Palace in 1851. (See Fig. 11.)

CHADBURN, Charles Henry. w1845-57. Opt. IM. 71 Lord St, Liverpool
Optician to the Prince Consort. Received an honourable mention at the Great Exhibition at the Crystal Palace in 1851.

CHADBURN & Co. w1830-33. Opt. math. & phil. IM. Sheffield
40 Lady's Bridge, Nursery St (1830) 23 Nursery St (1833)

CHADBURN & Son. e1857-75. Opt. IM. 71 Lord St, Liverpool

CHADBURN, William. w1816-30. Opt. math. & phil. IM. Sheffield

Fig. 11 Trade card of Chadburn Bros *(Science Museum, London)*

81 The Wicker (1816-17) Albion Works, 27 Nursery St, Lady's Bridge (1830)

CHADBURN & WRIGHT w1830. Opt. math. & phil. IM. Sheffield
40 Nursery St. 85 The Wicker

CHADBURNS e1875-85. Opt. IM. Liverpool

CHADBURNS Ltd. e1875-1900+ Opt. math. & phil. IM. 47 Castle St, Liverpool

CHAMBERLAIN e1800-20. Portsea
Made wheel barometers in the style of, and as a companion to, a grandfather clock.

CHAMBERLAIN, James Bradley. w1830-52. Opt. IM. London
37 Broad St, Bloomsbury (1830-39) 203 High Holborn (1845-52)

CHAMBERLAIN, J. B. & Son. w1848-74. Opt. IM. 203 High Holborn, London

CHAMBERS, George. w1859-75. Clock & watch M. Warminster

CHAMPION e1810-30. Belfast

CHAMPION e1820-50. Glasgow

CHAMPIONI, Andrea. e1780-1805. London

CHANCE e1880-1900. Selby
Marine barometers.

CHANCELLOR, John & Sons. e1820-40. Clock & watch M. Dublin

CHAPMAN e1835-55. Alresford

CHAPMAN, William. w1849-76. Clock & watch M. Lincoln

CHARINETTI, D. e1825-55. Gloucester

CHAVE, Samuel. w1841. e1841-55. Goldsmith, silversmith & jeweller. 38 High St, Taunton
Commenced in business in 1841 and advertised: 'Samuel Chave earnestly solicits the attention of the Gentry and Public of Taunton and its Vicinity, and would recommend those who have hitherto sent their orders, in the various departments of his Business, to London or elsewhere, under an idea that it could not be properly executed in Taunton, to afford him a trial.'

CHESSA e1790-1810. Manchester

CHICK, Edward. w1884-1900+. Phil. IM. London
24 Woodbridge St, Clerkenwell (1886-96) 8 & 9 Clerkenwell Green (1897-1900+)

CHICK, Peter. w1878. e1855-78. Clock & watch M. Worthing

CHICKIE, Francis. w1827-29. Specialist barometer M. Aberdeen
127 Broad St (1827) 127 Gallowgate (1828) 48 Broad St (1829)

CHIESA e1810-30. St Albans

CHIESA, A. e1820-40. Puckeridge

CHIESA, Joseph. e1810-30. Manchester

CHIESA, Joseph. e1815-35. Macclesfield

CHIESA, Joseph. e1820-40. Liverpool

CHILDE, Henry. w1830-43. Opt. math & phil. IM. London
3 Barrett St, Lambeth. 66 Vauxhall Walk

CHISLETT, Alfred. w1838-56. Opt. math. & phil. IM. London
8 Postern Row, Tower Hill (1838-44) 27 Greenhill St, Commercial Road East (1847)
Some barometers signed 'A. Chislett late Gilkerson' or 'A. Chislett late Gilkerson & MaCall'.

CHRISTENSON, F. J. w1848. Clock & watch M. Ventnor

CHRISTENSON, Frederick J. w1859-78. Clock & watch M. West Cowes

CHRISTENSON, P. w1839-48. Clock & watch M & chronometers. West Cowes

CHRISTENSON, Peter. e1830-50. Clock & watch M. Newport, Isle of Wight

CHRISTIAN, J. & Co. e1830-50. Deal

CHRISTIE, Andrew. w1890-1900+. Chronometer & naut. IM. 27-28 Clyde Place, Glasgow
Previously employed by D. McGregor & Co.

CHRISTIE, Elizabeth. w1838. Opt. math. & phil. IM. 32 Warner St, New Kent Rd, London

CHRISTIE, William. w1839-81. Clock & watch M. 25 Hanway St, London

CIAPPESSONI, F. w1862. Clock & watch M. Eastbourne

CICERI & Co. w1875. Carvers & gilders. Frederick St, Edinburgh

CICERI MANTICA & TORRE e1830-41. Carvers & gilders. 81 Leith St, Edinburgh

CICERI & PINI w1841-58. Carvers & gilders. 81 Leith St, Edinburgh

CICERI PINI & Co. e1825-45. Carvers & gilders. London

CICERI PINI & Co. w1842. e1842-60. Carvers & gilders. 8-9 Carlton St, Edinburgh
A branch of the London firm.

CIVATTI, C. e1810-30. 281 Holborn, London

CIVATTI, Charles & Co. e1820-40. 280 Holborn, London

CLARE, Peter. fl.1772-1844. Watch & math. IM. Manchester

CLARK e1840-60. South Molton

CLARK e1870-90. 20 Old Bond St, London

CLARK, Frederick. w1851-70. Opt. IM. 13 Parkside, Knightsbridge, London

CLARK, Jno. e1790-1810. Chester
Produced angle barometers.

CLARK, John. w1749-96. Goldsmith, jeweller & opt. IM. Edinburgh
Luckenbooths (1749) Parliament Close (1751-55) Opposite the Guard (1773-82) At the Cross (1786-88) 13 Parliament Close (1793-96)
The first Edinburgh instrument-maker to advertise his instruments in the press. He insisted on a down-payment with each order and when he had fifty orders he commenced their manufacture.

CLARK, R. H. (Mrs). w1854. Clock & watch M. Birmingham

CLARK, Robert. w1836-45. London
2 Whartons Place, High Holborn. 27 Brooke St, Holborn Bars

CLARK & Son. e1845-65. Greenock
Marine barometer with sympiesometer.

CLARK, Thomas. w1846-57. 20 Kirby St, London

CLARKE w1840-60. South Molton

CLARKE, C. F. w1847-64. Clock & watch M. St Ives, Hunts.

CLARKE, E. & Co. w1823-32. Opt. math. & phil. IM. 83 Dame St, Dublin

CLARKE, Edward. w1810-21. Opt. IM. Dublin
18 Lower Sackville St (1810-12) 10 Lower Sackville St (1819-21)

CLARKE, Edward Marmaduke. w1804-49. Opt. math. & phil. IM. London
11 Lowther Arcade, Strand (1838-40) 9 Agar St, West Strand. 428 Strand (1840-51)
Rodney Iron Works, Battersea

CLARKE, F. W. e1860-80. London

CLARKE, N. & Co. e1850-70. London

CLEAVER, Samuel. w1845-50. Hydrometer M. London
30 Theobalds Rd (1845-47) 56 Hatton Garden (1848-50)

CLEMENT, Elizabeth. w1828. Clock & watch M. Tring

CLERKE, Frederick William. w1863-81. Clock & watch M. London

CLERKE, G. J. w1839-44. Clock & watch M. 27 Lombard St, London

CLEWLEY, R. W. e1880-1900. Rolfe St, Smethwick, Birmingham

CLIFT, Charles. w1843. e1840-60. Opt. IM. 3 New Inn Yard, Shoreditch, London

CLUSKEY, J. e1810-30. Boston

COATES e1835-55. Devizes

COCHRANE, George. w1872-75. Phil. IM. 7 Drummond St, Edinburgh

COE, A. E. & Sons Ltd. e1890-1900. Norwich
Barographs.

COGGS, John (senior). fl.1690-1740. Math. IM. The Globe & Sun, Fleet St, London
Advertised 'weather-glasses of all sorts'.

COGGS, John (junior) fl.1730-59. Math. IM. The Globe & Sun, Fleet St, London
The son of John Coggs (senior). He also advertised weather-glasses 'to the greatest Exactness and at the most reasonable prices'.

COHEN, David. w1821-58. Opt. & math. IM. Newcastle upon Tyne
5 Collingwood St (1821-37) 1 Grey St (1838-44) 76 Grey St (1847-51) 30 Mosley St (1853) 9 Mosley St (1855-58)

COHEN, J. w1861. e1840-65. Clock & watch M. Louth

COHEN, Jacob & Co. w1868-79. Math. opt. & phil. IM. London
52 Hatton Garden (1868-72) Charterhouse St & 36 & 37 Ely Place (1873-79)

COHEN, Simeon Phineas. w1844-53. Math. opt. & phil. IM. Glasgow
82 Queen St (1844) 105 Buchanan St (1845-49) 121 Buchanan St (1850-51) 51 St Vincent St (1852) 136 Buchanan St (1853)
He was the manager of the Glasgow branch of A. Abraham & Co. of Liverpool and took over the business in 1844. He was made bankrupt in 1853 and still owed Abraham Abraham £1,960.

COIFFIER, Alexandre. w1859-81. Math. opt. & phil. IM. London
37 Hatton Garden (1859-64) 28 Wilmington Square (1865-67) 36 Brooke St, Holborn (1868-73) 13 Hatton Garden (1874-81)

COLE, Benjamin (senior). b1695-d1766. Opt. math. & phil. IM. London
Popping Court, Fleet St. Ball Alley, Lombard St (1744) The Orrery, 136 Fleet St (1748-66)
Took over the business of Thomas Wright when he retired in 1748 and was in partnership with a son, Benjamin, by around 1751.

COLE, Benjamin (junior). b1725-d1813. Opt. math. & phil. IM. 136 Fleet St, London
Apprenticed to his father, Benjamin, and was in partnership with him by around 1751. The partnership lasted until the father died in 1766 and the son continued on his own until 1782 when he retired, having sold the business to J. & E. Troughton.

COLE, Benjamin & Son. w1751-66. Opt. math. & phil. IM. 136 Fleet St, London
A partnership between Benjamin Cole and his son Benjamin. The partners advertised 'barometers of all sorts, nicely adjusted'.

COLEMAN, Ann. w1831-34. 11 Vineyard Walk, Clerkenwell, London
The widow of Charles Coleman who carried on the business after his death.

COLEMAN, Charles. w1823-30. London
7 Dorrington St, Clerkenwell (1823-28) 11 Vineyard Walk, Clerkenwell (1829-30)

COLES, William. w1884-89. 19 Bakers Row, Farringdon Rd, London

COLLA, A. e1820-40. 8 Albermarle St, Clerkenwell, London

COLLIER & BARTLETT w1889-94. London
Maker of aneroid barometers.

COLLIER, Benjamin. e1850-70. London

COLLINGS, C. W. w1845-47. Phil. IM. London
16 Mortimer St, Cavendish Square (1845-46) Royal Polytechnic Institute (1847)

COLLINGS, James. c1830. Opt. math. & phil. IM. Skinner St, Clerkenwell, London

COLLINGS, John. w1850. Clock & watch M. Stroud

COLLINGWOOD & Co. e1865-85. 46 Conduit St, London

COLLINGWOOD & Co. w1898. Clock & watch M. West Hartlepool

COLLINGWOOD & Son. e1870-90. Newcastle upon Tyne

COLLINS, Charles. w1863-1900+. Math. phil. opt. & naut. IM. London
77 Great Titchfield St (1863-70) 157 Great Portland St (1871-1900+)

COLLINS, Charles William. w1845-60. Math. opt. & phil. IM. 16 Mortimer St, London

COLLINS, Robert. e1810-50. Paisley

COLLIS, William Humphrey. w1858-79. Clock & watch M. Bury St Edmunds

COLOMBA, A. e1810-30. Salisbury

COLOMBA, Andrew. w1842-67. London
37 Charles St, Hatton Garden (1842-59) 89 Chancery Lane (1846) 16 Charles St, Hatton Garden (1860-67)

COLOMBA, Andrew. w1876-79. 45 Hatton Garden, London

COLOMBA, F. e1815-35. Deal

COLOMBA & HARE w1844-49. London
37 Charles St, Hatton Garden (1844-48) 89 Chancery Lane (1846)

COMBERBACH, Edward Stephen. w1858. Clock & watch M. Blackburn

COMBES, Fisher. e1690-1710. Math. IM. The Mariner & Globe, Broad St, London

COMBS, Oliver. w1693-1747. Opt. IM. London
The Spectacles, St Martin's Court, Leicester Fields. Second House from Essex St, near Temple Bar
Was apprenticed to Edward Scarlett and when he was in business on his own he advertised himself as 'Oliver Combs (from Mr Scarlett)'. The advertisement included barometers and thermometers.

COMITTI, Joseph. e1800-20. Banff

COMITTI, O. w1870-76. 2 Black Hill, Hatton Garden, London

COMITTI, O. & Son. w1878-1900+. Phil. IM. London
24 Great Warner St, Clerkenwell (1878) 19 Great Warner St, Clerkenwell (1878-89) 19 Hatton Garden (1879-80) 67 & 69 Mount Pleasant (1890-1900+)
Advertised as 'Patentees of the "Visible" aneroid dial barometers and sole manufacturers of the Torricelli barometer'. Still trading today.

COMOLI, J. also COMOLLI e1810-30. Aberdeen

COMOLI, J. w1825-26. 82 St Mary's Wynd, Edinburgh

COMOLI, J. & NOZZI e1820-45. 82 St Mary's Wynd, Edinburgh
Also J. COMOLI & Co.

COMOLI, Peter, Andrew & John. w1817-30. e1815-50. High St, Dudley
Barometers signed 'P. COMOLI & Co.', 'P. & A. COMOLI' and 'P. & A. COMOLI & Co'.

COMOZZI, C. e1810-30. Aylesbury

COMOZZI, C. e1835-55. Buckingham

COMYNS, Henry. w1820-45. Opt. math. & phil. IM. 17 King's Rd, Chelsea, London

CONCONI, Louis. w1832-66. Clock & watch M. Margate

CONNELL, William. w1839-69. Clock & watch M. Cheapside, London

CONTI, Chas. e1820-40

CONTI, Jno. e1790-1810

CONYERS, John. fl.1673-79. Apothecary & amateur IM. By Holborn Bridge, London
He kept a weather diary and made experiments with air pressure using instruments that he designed and made himself.

COOK e1795-1815. London

COOKE, Laban. c1825. Math. & phil. IM. 21 Crown Court, Soho, London

COOKE, Thomas. w1837-68. Math. IM. York
50 Stonegate (1837-38) 12 Coney St (1843-51) 26 Coney St (1860-68)

COOKE, T. & Sons. w1869-1900+. Opt. math. & phil. IM. York
This would appear to be a partnership between the sons of Thomas Cooke after he died in 1868. It expanded rapidly and a factory was established at Buckingham Works, York. Later a London office was established at 3 Broadway, Westminster. A branch office was opened in Cape Town, South Africa and there were agencies around the world. An illustrated catalogue shows that stick, marine, wheel and aneroid barometers and barographs were made.

COOKE, William. e1865-85. Opt. IM. Skipton Rd, Keighley, Yorks

COOMBES, J. w1889. Devonport

COOMBS, Henry Joseph. w1896-99. 9 St James's Walk, London

COOPER, D. A. & Co. w1868-76. Clock & watch M. Worcester

COOPER, George. w1811. London

COOPER, R. e1820-40. Paisley

COOPER, William. w1808-24. Clock & watch M. Hamilton

CO-OPERATIVE SCIENCE SUPPLY, The. w1883-88. Math. opt. & phil. IM. 22 Charlotte St, Fitzroy Square, London

COPINI & GATINI w1832-49. Carvers & gilders. London
217 High St, Shoreditch (1832-41) 280 High Holborn (1839-41) 37 Norton Folgate (1842-49)

COPODURO, D. e1810-30. Cirencester

COPPLE, Richard. e1790-1810. Sankey

COPPOCK, Charles. w1867-1900+. Math. opt. & phil. IM. London
100 New Bond St (1884-87) 36 Davies St, Berkeley Square (1888-90) 26 Maddox St (1891-1900+)
He was previously a partner in R. & J. Beck.

CORBETTA, I. e1830-50. 11 Brooke St, Holborn, London

CORBY, J. e1830-50. London

CORDONI, Lorenzo. e1790-1810. Salisbury

CORFIELD e1820-40. Cheltenham

CORNELL, Charles. w1840-77. Clock & watch M. Royston

CORNISH, W. H. e1820-40. Okehampton

CORRALL, William. w1822-41. Clock & watch M. Church St, Lutterworth

CORSBIE e1845-65. Camden Town, London

CORT & Co. e1800-20. Ironmongers. Market Place, Leicester
Barometer signed 'Jno CORT' c1790.

CORTI e1835-55. Warwick

CORTI, A. e1810-40. 7 Greville St, London
Barometer signed 'G. CORTI' with this address.

CORTI, Antoni. w1833-45. Glassworker, carver & gilder. Glasgow
97 Nelson St (1833-41) 38 Candlerigg St (1841-44) 54 Glassford St (1844-45) 77 Bell St (1845)

CORTI, F. e1810-30. Newcastle

CORTI, G. e1810-30. Aberdeen

CORTI, G. A. e1820-40. Inverness

CORTI, J. e1800-30. Colchester

CORTI, J. e1810-30. Union Court, Hatton Hill, London

CORTI, James B. 1800-50. Glasgow

CORTI, Jno. e1800-40. 94 Holborn Hill, London
Barometers signed 'CORTI & Son' with this address.

CORTI, John. w1809-36. Math. IM. London
27 Leather Lane (1809-25) 35 Eyre St, Hatton Garden (1826-36)
Sold barometers and thermometers 'wholesale, retail and for exportation'.

CORTI, Joseph. e1810-30. Ipswich

CORTI, P. e1810-30. Burton

CORTI, Paul. w1850. e1830-60. 5 Market St, Exeter
Barometers signed 'P. CORTI & Son' with this address.

CORTI, Peter. w1845-50. 30 Eyre St Hill, London

CORTI, S. e1810-30. Warrington

CORTY e1820-40. Bristol

COSAR, Alfred Charles. w1892-98. London
Red Lion St (1892) 67 Farringdon St (1897-98)

COSSA e1820-40. Glasgow

COSSA RABALIO & Co. e1820-40

COSTALA, Thomas. w1781-84. Watch M. Liverpool

COULDREY, Joseph. w1819-51. Math. & phil. IM. London
Church Passage, Tooley St (1819-29) 26 St Thomas St East, Borough (1830-51)

COULSELL, Elizabeth. w1838. Opt. math. & phil. IM. 153 Union St, Borough, London
Probably the widow of Thomas Coulsell.

COULSELL, Thomas. w1810-27. Math. IM. 153 Union St, Southwark, London

COULSELL, William. w1815-58. Math. IM. 9 Castle St, Borough, London

COULSON, Daniel. w1838-43. Math. IM. 58 Charles St, City Rd, London

COULTAS, William Padget. w1867-94. Math. IM. Bradford
Ashley St (1867-71) Croft St (1872-94)

COUNSELL, Edwin. w1854-77. Clock & watch M. Farringdon

de la COUR, George. w1823-55. Clock & watch M. 327 & 59 High St, Chatham

de la COUR, W. w1861. Clock & watch M. Bath

COURTI & EVE e1835-55. London

COURTI, Paul. w1856-57. Clock & watch M. Exeter
38 1/2 South St (1856) 7 High St (1856-57)

COUSENS, Basil R. w1887. e1860-87. Clock & watch M. Swansea
Marine barometers.

COWAN, S. e1880-1900. Clock & watch M & silversmith. Market Place, Manchester

COWAN, William. w1806-22. Clock & watch M. Glasgow

COWLAND, C. H. & C. e1865-85. Sunderland

COX e1835-55. Cheltenham

COX e1865-85. Devonport and Plymouth

COX & COOMBES e1845-65. Devonport and Plymouth

COX, Frederick. w1844-1900+. Clock & watch M & opt. IM. London
100 Newgate St (1844-72) 98 Newgate St (1873-1900+)
Sympiesometers.

COX, Frederick J. w1877-78. Phil. IM. 26 Ludgate Hill, London

COX, George. w1845. e1820-45. Opt. math. & phil. IM. London
100 Newgate St. 128 Holborn Hill. 5 Barbican.

COX, James. w1830-51. Opt. math. & phil. IM. 5 Barbican, London

COX, Joseph. e1820-40. The Barbican, London

COX, S. W. w1849-55. Clock & watch M. Market Harborough

COX, William. w1806. Math. IM. Plymouth Dock, Devon
Supplied nautical instruments to the Naval College.

COX, William Charles. w1822-57. Chronometers, opt. math. & phil. IM. Plymouth
86 Fore St (1822-39) 89 Fore St (1852-56) 24 Southside St (1856) 83 Fore St (1857)

COXALL, Samuel. b1734-d1815. Clock & watch M. Royston
Made a large square dial wheel barometer as a companion to a wall clock.

CRAIGHEAD & WEBB w1851-63. Clock & watch M. Royal Exchange, London

CREMON, I. e1810-30. London
Purchased barometer cases from William Lacy.

CREMON, Joseph. e1770-90. London

CREMONINI, A. e1810-30

CREMONINI, C. e1845-65. Bilston

CREMONINI, F. e1850-70

CREMONINI, P. e1845-70. Wolverhampton

CREMONY, G. e1800-20. Dorchester

CRICHTON Bros. w1871-77. Math & phil. IM. 11 Billiter St, London
Sympiesometers.

CRICHTON, James. w1785-1835. Chronometer & phil. IM. Glasgow
Grammer School Wynd (1785) 129 Gallowgate (1789) Charlotte St (1790-1811) 5 Charlotte St (1812) 2 Charlotte St (1813-18) 9 Charlotte St (1819) 2 Charlotte St

(1820-25) 5 Charlotte St (1826-35)

CRICHTON, John. w1820-32. Math. IM. 32 Fore St, Limehouse, London
J. F. Daniel, scientist and Professor of Chemistry at King's College, London, wrote in 1832 about a standard barometer, with attached thermometer, as 'a very delicate instrument made by Crichton'.

CRICHTON, John. w1831-66. Opt. math. & phil. IM. 112 Leadenhall St, London
Acted as agent for Adie's sympiesometers.

CRICHTON, John & Son. w1867-70. Math. & naut. IM. London
112 Leadenhall St (1867-69) 11 Billiter St (1870)

CROCE, A. e1810-30. Lewis

CROCE, G. e1820-55. York

CROCE, Joseph. e1810-30. 212 or 242 Holborn, London

CROCE, Joseph. w1847. York

CROCE, Joshua. w1823-d1841. Artificial flower M. 15 Grape Lane, York

CROCKER Bros. w1878. Clock & watch M. Kingston, Surrey

CROCKER, S. e1835-55. Kingston

CROSTA CETTI e1860-80. Nottingham

CROSTA & Co. w1853-60. Carvers & gilders. Bridlesmith Gate, Nottingham

CROSTA & Co. e1860-80. London

CROSTA, Joseph. w1876. Clock & watch M. Wednesbury

CROTCHIE, Charles. e1835-55. Inverness

CROUCH, Henry. w1868-90. Opt. math. & phil. IM. 66 Barbican, London

CROUCH, Henry Ltd. w1891-1900+. Opt. math. & phil. IM. 66 Barbican, London

CROW, Francis. w1780-1822. Math. & phil. IM. Faversham (1780-95)
Also at Gravesend and 37 Windsor Terrace, City Rd, London.

CROWDEN & GARROD e1850-70. London

CRUDDAS, John. w1834. Clock & watch M. Durham

CRUDDAS, John & Son. w1851-60. Clock & watch M. Durham

CRUNDWELL, Samuel. w1847-74. Clock & watch M. High St, Tunbridge Wells

CUFF, John. b1708-d1772. Opt. IM. At the Sign of the Reflecting Microscope and Spectacles, against Serjeants Inn Gate, Fleet St, London
An important instrument-maker who was apprenticed to James Mann (junior). He called himself 'an optician, spectacle and microscope maker, who makes and sells, wholesale and retail, all manner of optical instruments.' These included barometers and thermometers.

CUIATI, Charles. e1810-30. 281 Holborn, London

CULPEPER, Edmund. b1660-d1738. Opt. & math. IM. London
Cross Daggers, Moorfields (1706-31) Black and White Horse, Moorfields. Royal Exchange (1725)

CULYER, George. w1866-74. Clock & watch M. Halstead

CUMINE, James A. w1852-81. Photographic, opt. & phil. IM. Belfast
168 North St (1852-61) 29 High St (1863-68) 27 High St (1870) 57 Upper Arthur St (1877) 48 Upper Arthur St (1878-80) 40-42 Upper Arthur St (1881)

CUMMIN, J. w1851-80. Opt. & phil. IM. London
7 Cobham Row, Coldbath Square (1851) 1 Newcastle Place, Clerkenwell (1852-57) Phoenix Place, Gray's Inn Rd (1858-80)

CUMMING, Alexander. w1754-d1814. Clock M & math. IM. London
12 Clifford St, Bond St (1785) 75 Fleet St
A notable clockmaker who made three barograph clocks. One was for George III which still stands in Buckingham Palace. He was paid £1,178 for it and also £150 a year for its maintenance. In 1766 he published *Elements of Clock and Watch Work* which he dedicated to the King with the words 'Your bounty has afforded me the leisure to pursue my researches'. Cumming was born in Edinburgh in 1732 and went to London when a young man and set up in business as a clockmaker; he was a founder member of the Royal Society in Edinburgh and was made an Honorary Freeman of the Clockmakers' Company.

CUMMINS, Charles. e1820-45. Opt. & phil. IM. 148 Leadenhall St, London
In 1840 he was granted a patent for a sympiesometer using sulphuric acid instead of almond oil.

CUROTTI, J. e1810-30

CURROTTY, J. e1830-50

CURTIS & HORSPOOL e1875-95. Leicester
Aneroid barometers.

CURTIS, Joseph. e1780-1800. Bristol

CUSHEE, E. fl.1729-68. Globe & math. IM. London
Globe and Sun, between St Dunstan's Church and Chancery Lane. The Orrery, Water Lane, Fleet St
The son of Richard Cushee whose business he took over.

CUSHEE, Richard. fl.1708-32. Globe & math. IM. London
Globe and Sun, between St Dunstan's Church and Chancery Lane
The father of E. Cushee to whom the business passed.

CUTHBERT, Charles. w1830-51. Opt. math. & phil. IM. London
81-2 Garnault Place, Spitalfields, Clerkenwell (1830-37) 9 Clerkenwell Green (1842-51)

CUTHBERT, John. w1783-1810. Math. IM. London

CUTLER, Richard. w1782-87. Engraver, clock & watch M. Youghal and Carrickfergus

CUTTS, John P. w1825-45 Opt. math. & phil. IM. Sheffield
58 Norfolk St (1825) 43 Division St (1828-45)
His trade card shows that he manufactured spectacles, telescopes, opera glasses, mathematical and nautical instruments, barometers, thermometers etc. 'By special appointment Optician to Her Majesty Queen Adelaide'.

CUTTS, J. P., SUTTON & Son. w1845-69. Opt. math. & phil. IM. Sheffield and London
43 Division St, Sheffield. 14 Bridge Rd, Lambeth, London
A partnership between John P. Cutts and George Sutton who were instrument manufacturers and wholesalers.

D

DALGARNO, Alexander. e1830-d1851. Clock & watch M. Aberdeen

DALGLEISH, Laurence. w1771-1821. Clock & watch M. Edinburgh

DALLAWAY e1820-40. Bath

DALLAWAY e1835-55. Opt. IM. Cheltenham

DALLAWAY, Joseph James. w1802-09. Opt. IM. London
4 George Lane, Botolph Lane (1802) 147 Tottenham Court Rd (1805-09)

DALLY e1835-55. Wokingham

DALTON, John. w1850-56. Clock & watch M. Hartlepool

DANCER, John Benjamin. w1838-78. Opt. math. & phil. IM. 13 Cross St, King St, Manchester
In partnership with Abraham Abraham under the name of Abraham & Dancer between 1841 and 1845, and then he continued the business alone. He was in business

previously, having succeeded to the business of Josiah Dancer in 1835. Dancer concentrated on microscopes. His trade card included the statement 'By appointment to Her Majesty's Commissioners. Prize Medal 1862'.

DANCER, Josiah. w1812-35. Opt. IM. Liverpool
Succeeded by John Benjamin Dancer.

DANEGAN, PETTER & Co. e1820-40

DANGELO & CADENAZZI e1800-40. Winchester

DANGELO, G. e1820-40. Basingstoke

DANIELL & LUND w1872. 12 Brooke St, Holborn, London

DANIELS & BOUCHETTE w1876-78. Phil. IM. 48 Windsor Terrace, City Rd, London

DANIELS & Co. w1885-86. Phil. IM. 48 Windsor Terrace, City Rd, London

DANIELS, John. w1887-1900+. 14 Smith St, Clerkenwell, London

DARBYSHIRE, J. e1880-1900+. Sheffield

DARCY e1820-40. London

DARTON, Francis & Co. w1834-1900+. Opt. math. & phil. IM. London
102 St John St (1872) 72 St John St (1873-77) 45 St John St (1878-91) 142 St John St (1892-1900+)
Still trades today in the name of F. Darton & Co. Ltd.

DAVENPORT, Stephen. w1720-37. Math & phil. IM. London
Against the Distillers in High Holborn, near Drury Lane
An advertisement includes: 'Weather glasses of all sorts, viz. portable, diagonal, horizontal, wheel and marine barometers; which shew the various alterations in the weight of the air, and foretel the changes of weather consequent thereon.'

DAVEY, G. M. & T. w1862. Clock & watch M. Lewes

DAVIDSON, Alexander. w1876-1900+. Opt. math. & phil. IM. Glasgow
144 London St (1876) 107 London St (1877-78) 77 London St (1879-81) 47 London St (1882-1900+)

DAVIES, Edward. w1853-1900+. Opt. math. & phil. IM. Leeds
34 Boar Lane (1853) 35 Boar Lane (1861-67) 1 Albion St (1866) 74 Albion St (1870-87) 22 Albion St (1893-99) 2 Aire St (1899-1900+)
Succeeded Gabriel Davies.

DAVIES, Edward. w1879. Clock & watch M. Shrewsbury

DAVIES, Gabriel. w1822-53. Opt. & math. IM. Leeds
20 Boar Lane (1822) 34 Boar Lane (1826-53)

Succeeded by Edward Davies of Leeds.

DAVIES, John. e1810-30. Clock & watch M. St Harmons, Wales

DAVIES, John. w1848-57. Clock & watch M. Chester

DAVIES, J. & Son. e1840-60. Derby

DAVIES, Owen. w1835-57. Clock & watch M. Llandidloes

DAVIES, Thomas. w1850-75. Clock & watch M. Llandovery

DAVIES, William. w1805-14. Clock & watch M. Liverpool

DAVIS, Alfred. e1785-95. 5 Charlotte St, London

DAVIS, C. & Co. e1830-50. London

DAVIS, Clara. c1830. Opt. math. & phil. IM. 12 South St, Finsbury, London

DAVIS & Co. w1869. 163 Fenchurch St, London

DAVIS, D. w1823-32. Math & opt. IM. Glasgow
110 Nelson St (1823-25) 98 Trongate (1826-32)

DAVIS, E. e1825-45. Opt. IM. Shrewsbury

DAVIS, G. e1825-45. Opt. IM. Leeds

DAVIS, Henry. w1799-1817. Opt. & math. IM. 8 Macclesfield St, Soho, London

DAVIS, James. w1835. Opt. IM. 51 Paradise St, Liverpool

DAVIS, Jno. e1830-50. Opt. IM. Cheltenham

DAVIS, John. e1830-60. Opt. & math. IM. 14 Iron Gate, Derby

DAVIS, John. w1836-42. Math. opt. & phil. IM. Edinburgh
64 Princes St (1836-40) 78 Princes St (1841-42)
On moving to 78 Princes St in 1841 he advertised: 'Reductions as formerly, viz. 25% from the Original Prices of every article of Optical, Mathematical and Philosophical Instruments'. He was made bankrupt in the following year.

DAVIS, Joseph & Co. w1871-93. Royal Polytechnic Institution, 6 Kennington Park Rd, London
The sole manufacturer in England of the Royal Polytechnic barometer; it has paper register plates with the Royal Coat of Arms and the Prince of Wales Feathers and is annotated 'Design Copyright and Title Registered'.

DAVIS, J. & Son. e1860-1900+. Opt. & math. IM. London and Derby
Also J. DAVIS & Sons.

DAVIS, Messrs. w1835-42. Math. opt. & phil. IM. Liverpool and Cheltenham
65 Bold St, Liverpool (1835) 101 High St, Cheltenham (1842)

DAVIS, William. w1822-42. Clock & watch M. High St, Shiffnall
His obituary in the local paper read: 'A man universally respected and deeply lamented'.

DAWSON e1750-70. Perth

DAWSON, Matthew. w1798-1843. Clock & watch M. Haddington

DAWSON & MELLING e1820-40. Liverpool

DAWSON, Nathan. e1810-30. London
Also Nathan DAWSON & Co. e1830-50.

DAWSON, William. w1830-58. Clock & watch M. Fakenham. Also at Foulsham

DAY, F. e1800-20. 37 Poultry, London

DEACON, Frederick. w1822. Watch & clock M. Leicester

DEACON, John. w1795-c1830. Clock & watch M. Leicester

DEACON, Samuel. w1771-d1816. Clock & watch M. Barton

DEAN, Alfred. w1876-82. Hydrometer M. 22 Cross St, Hatton Garden, London

DEAN, Peter. w1830. Opt. math. & phil. IM. Bear Yard, Lincoln's Inn, London

DECK e1770-90. Leamington

DECK, I. e1830-50. Cambridge

DEE, J. e1835-55. Skipton

DEEBLES, J. H. & Son. e1880-1900. Falmouth
Aneroid barometers.

de la COUR, see COUR

DELANDER, Daniel. b1674-d1733. Clock & watch M. London
Devereux Court (1699-1712) Temple, Fleet St (1712-33)
A famous clockmaker who was apprenticed in 1692 and was elected to the Clockmakers' Company in 1699. He worked for a time for Thomas Tompion and appears to have made far more clocks than barometers.

della BELLA, see BELLA

della TORRE, see TORRE

del VECCHIO, see VECCHIO

DEMERIA, J. e1830-50. Taunton

DENNIS, John C. c1839-65. Math & phil. IM. London
118 Bishopsgate Within (1839-49) 122 Bishopsgate St (1850-65)

DENSHAM, W. T. e1880-1900+. Holsworthy
Admiral Fitzroy barometers.

DENT, Edward John. w1844-51. Clock & watch M & chronometers. London
He was the first to sell the Vidie aneroid barometer in England in 1847. In 1849 he published *A Treatise on the Aneroid, a Newly Invented Portable Barometer.* He exhibited at the Great Exhibition at the Crystal Palace in 1851 when the Vidie barometer was awarded a Council Medal.

DENT, M. F. w1863. Chronometer, clock & watch M. 33-34 Cockspur St, London
Also M. F. DENT & Co. w1869-81.

DENTON, Joseph. w1779-1814. Clock & watch M. Hull

DENTON, Samuel George. w1882-94. 25A Hatton Garden, London

DERBY e1835-55. Fareham

DERBY, Edward. e1780-1800. Phil. IM. Union Court facing St Andrew's Church, Holborn, London
His trade card notes: 'Successor to the Ingenious Mr Joseph Hickman'.

DERRY, Charles. w1838-57. Math & phil. IM. London
7 Leigh St, Burton Crescent (1838-54) 74 Judd St, Brunswick Square (1855-57)

DESAGULIERS, John Theophilus. c1683-1744. Channel Row, Westminster, London
He came to England at the age of two with a Huguenot refugee family. He lectured on experimental philosophy and improved the design of the instruments used for his lectures; these included barometers, thermometers and microscopes. In 1714 he was elected a Fellow of the Royal Society.

DESBOIS, Daniel. w1844-75. Clock & watch M. Brownlow St, London
Also Daniel DEBOIS & Sons. w1881-1900+.

DI MARIA, J. e1860-70. Taunton

DIMMICK, James. w1878. e1850-80. 147 High St, Ryde, Isle of Wight. Also at West Cowes

DIPPLE, C. & E. w1858-60. 36 Great Hampton Row, Birmingham

DISCACIATI, A. e1835-55. High St, Newport

DIXEY e1840-60. Norwich

DIXEY w1860. e1850-70. Opt. IM. 21 King's Rd, Brighton

DIXEY, Charles Wastell. w1838-62. Opt. math. & phil. IM. 3 New Bond St, London
Previously in partnership with his twin brother George who died in 1838. The partnership was in the name of George & Charles Dixey and was formed when they succeeded their father Edward Dixey. The original business was established in 1777. Dixey's trade card shows that he was 'Optician & Mathematical Instrument Maker to Her Majesty; the King and Queen of Hanover; their Royal Highnesses the Dukes of Sussex and Cambridge; the Princesses Augusta and Sophia; the Duchesses of Kent, Cambridge and Gloucester; the King of Belgium Etc Etc'.

DIXEY, C. W. & Son. w1863-1900+. Opt. math. & phil. IM. 3 New Bond St, London
A partnership between Charles Wastell Dixey and his son Adolphus.

DIXEY, Edward. c1808-43. Opt. IM. London
370 Oxford St (1808) 335 Oxford St (1821-43) 3 New Bond St (1825)
Apprenticed to George Linnell in 1771 and took over the business of William Hawks Grice in 1825 at 3 New Bond St. When Edward handed over the 3 New Bond St business to his two sons it appears that he retained the business at 335 Oxford St.

DIXEY, George & Charles. w1821-38. Opt. math. & phil. IM. London
335 Oxford St (1821) 78 New Bond St (1822-23) 3 New Bond St (1825-38)
A partnership between twin brothers who were the sons of Edward Dixey. George died in 1838 and Charles continued the business on his own. Opticians to the King.

DIXEY, L. w1843. e1830-50. Opt. IM. 62 King's Rd, Brighton
His trade card states: 'Son of Mr G. Dixey, Optician to the Royal Family, Bond Street, London'.

DIXEY, William. w1843-74. Opt. IM. 241 Oxford St, London

DIXEY, William & Son. w1874-1900+. Opt. IM. London
241 Oxford St (1874-81) 552 Oxford St (1882-1900+)

DIXON e1880-1900. Norwich

DIXON, John. w1857-66. Math. opt. & phil. IM. 95 Lillington St, Vauxhall Bridge Rd, London

DOBBIE, Alexander. w1841-85. Chronometer & naut. IM. Glasgow
20 Clyde Place (1841-56) 24 Clyde Place (1857-72) 24-25 Clyde Place (1873-85)

DOBBIE, Alexander & Son. w1886-95. Chronometer & naut. IM. Glasgow
24 & 25 Clyde Place (1886-88) 18 & 19 Clyde Place (1889-91) 44 & 45 Clyde Place (1893-95)

DOBBIE, Alexander & Son Ltd. w1896-1903. Chronometer & naut. IM. 44 & 45 Clyde Place, Glasgow
Branches in Greenock and South Shields were established in 1897 and a Cardiff branch was opened in 1899 in the name of DOBBIE, HUTTON & GEBBIE Ltd. In 1894 a branch in London was opened under the name of DOBBIE, SON & HUTTON.

DOBBIE, William. w1821-60. Clock & watch M. High St, Falkirk
Noted for copying John Russell's wheel barometer. The *Alloa Monthly Advertiser* of 7 February 1845 reported: 'Has just completed two of Russell's splendid and celebrated royal Barometers (now scarce), warranted identical with those made by the original constructor. The dial presents two indexes, the one of common range and the other indicating the thousands of an inch in the rise or fall of the Mercury.' Clockmaker to the Queen.

DOBSON, John. w1830-46. Opt. math. & phil. IM. London
13 Newington Causeway (1830) 54 Newington Causeway (1838-46)

DOBSON, John. w1850-66. Math. opt. & phil. IM. London
268 High Holborn (1850-53) 1 Union Rd, Camberwell Rd (1854-66)

DOBSON, John Thomas. w1867. Opt. math. & phil. IM. 254 Camberwell Rd, London

DOBSON, Jonathan. e1815-35. Clock & watch M. Finsbury St, Finsbury Square, London

DODD, Andrew. w1837-47. Opt. math. & phil. IM. Glasgow
70 Hutcheson St (1837) 36 Glassford St (1838-46) 88 Glassford St (1847)

DOLLOND & Co. w1870-1900+. Opt. math. & phil. IM. London
1 Ludgate Hill (1870-91) 62 Old Broad St (1889-1900+) 35 Ludgate Hill (1892-94) 32 Ludgate Hill (1895-1900+) 5 Northumberland Avenue (1894-1900+)

DOLLOND, George. b1774-d1856. Opt. math. & phil. IM. London
59 St Paul's Churchyard (1804-56) 61 Paternoster Row (1854-56)
His real name was George Huggins but he changed it to Dollond, the name of his famous uncle, Peter Dollond. He was apprenticed to Peter in 1788 and became his partner in 1804 when another uncle, John Dollond, died. John had been in partnership with Peter, his brother. George was one of sixteen instrument-makers who exhibited at the Great Exhibition at the Crystal Palace in 1851; he was instrument-maker to William IV and Queen Victoria. Peter Dollond died in 1820 and George continued the business.

DOLLOND, Peter. b1730-d1820. Opt. IM. London
Vine St, Spitalfields (1750) Golden Spectacles and Sea Quadrant, near Exeter Exchange, Strand (1752-63) 59 St Paul's Churchyard (1769-1820) 35 Haymarket (1784)
The son of John Dollond, a Huguenot silk weaver, but when he was only twenty he started in business as an optician. He became a brilliant instrument-maker and was appointed optician to King George III and the Duke of York. His father (see Fig. 7) was in partnership with him from 1752 to 1761 and his brother John joined him in 1766 until John died in 1804. Peter made instruments of high quality, and it is said that he went down to the glasshouse regularly and picked out all the flawless pieces of flint glass for his workshop. Most of the Dollond barometers are just signed 'DOLLOND London' so it is difficult to attribute them accurately.

DOLLOND, Peter & George. w1804-20. Opt. IM. 59 St Paul's Churchyard, London
A partnership between Peter and his nephew George.

DOLLOND, Peter & John. w1752-61. Opt. IM. Golden Spectacles and Sea Quadrant, near Exeter Exchange, Strand, London
A partnership between Peter and his father John.

DOLLOND, Peter & John. w1766-1804. Opt. IM. 59 St Paul's Churchyard, London
A partnership between Peter and his younger brother John.

DOLLOND, William. w1868-71. Opt. math. & phil. IM. 59 St Paul's Churchyard and 61 Paternoster Row, London

DONEGAN e1810-30. Leicester

DONEGAN, A. e1820-40. Edinburgh

DONEGAN & Co. e1820-40. Newcastle

DONEGAN, F. e1810-30. Stafford

DONEGAN, Francis. e1810-30. Carver & gilder. Lad Lane, Newcastle under Lyme
Emigrated to Canada.

DONEGAN, John. e1810-30. Bristol

DONEGAN, John. w1839. Clock & watch M. Dublin

DONEGAN, Joseph. w1830-35. e1822-40. Lad Lane, Newcastle under Lyme

DONEGAN, L. e1810-30. Newcastle

DONEGAN, L. & Co. e1815-35. 3 Long Lane, London

DONEGAN, Peter. w1805. Picture frames. 7 Union Court, Holborn, London

DONEGAN, Peter. e1820-40. 94 Holborn Hill, London
Also DONEGAN & Co. at this address. e1810-30.

DONEGAN, Peter & Co. e1810-40. London

DONEGAN & REVE e1835-55. Edinburgh

DONEGANI e1850-70. Tamworth

DONEGANI, J. e1820-40. Newcastle under Lyme

DONEGON, J. & Co. e1820-40. Bristol

DONEVAN e1820-40. Edinburgh

DONEVAN, P. e1810-30. London

DONKIN, B. e1780-1800. London

DORRINGTON e1810-30. Devonport

DORRINGTON, Theophilus Lutey. w1873. e1850-75. Clock & watch M. Truro

DOTTI e1830-50. Pontypool

DOTTI, G. e1810-30. Carlisle

DOTTI, G. e1820-40. Bath

DOUBLET, T. & H. w1849-1900+. Opt. math. & phil. IM. London
City Rd, Finsbury (1853-68) 7 Moorgate St (1861-68) 6 Moorgate St (1869-78) 11 Moorgate St (1879-1900+)

DOUBLOTT, Hannah. w1830. Opt. math. & phil. IM. 14 Shepperton Place, New North St, London

DOWLER, George. w1858-60. 90 Great Charles St, Birmingham

DOWLING, William. w1822-29. Opt. math. & phil. IM. West Gateway of Lincoln's Inn, Serle St, Lincoln's-Inn-Fields, London
Manufactured and sold all kinds of instruments, including barometers, 'of the best Workmanship and according to the latest Improvements'.

DOWNES e1770-90. Yarmouth

DRAYTON, Thomas. e1820-40. Clock & watch M. Chard

DRESCHER, John. w1823-58. Clock & watch M. 21 Mytongate, Hull

DRESCHER, M. Pius. w1838-58. Clock & watch M. 66-67 Mytongate, Hull

DRING & FAGE w1798-1900+. Opt. math. & phil. IM. London
6 Tooley St, Southwark (1798) 248 Tooley St, Southwark (1800) 20 Tooley St, Southwark (1822-45) 10 Duke St, Tooley St (1843) 19-20 Tooley St, London Bridge (1846-70) 145 Strand (1862-1903) 546 Stamford St (1903+)
The original partners were John Dring and William Fage. An important firm which specialised in hydrometers, saccharometers and gauging instruments and were makers to 'H.M. Customs, Inland Revenue, Colonial Governments and the Honourable Victualling Board for H.M. Navy'. Made wheel barometers with a square dial looking like longcase clocks.

DRITCHLER, John & Co. w1804. Clock & watch M. Manchester

DRITCHLER, P. e1805-30. Salford Bridge, Manchester

DUBINI e1800-20. 8 North Place, Brunswick Place, London

DUBINI e1810-30. 25 Little College St, West Camdentown, London

DUBINI, F. e1835-55. 23 Baldwins Gardens, London

DUBINI, J. e1815-35. Ship Little Turnstile, Holborn, London

DUBINI, J. e1815-35. 14 Union Court, Holborn Hill, London

DUBINI, L. e1815-35. Cross St, Hatton Garden, London

DUBINI, Peter. w1832-70. London
11 Beauchamp St, Leather Lane (1832-33) 8 Beauchamp St (1835) 12 Beauchamp St, Leather Lane (1836) 47 Red Lion St (1853-70)

DUFF, Daniel. w1836. Clock & watch M. Paisley

DUNCAN, James. w1860. e1845-65. Clock & watch M. Aberdeen

DUNCAN, William. w1841-49. Math. opt. & phil. IM. Aberdeen
46 Dee St (1841) 92 Union St (1842-49)

DUNGAN, L. e1810-30. Newcastle upon Tyne

DUNKIN e1770-90. Penzance

DUNN, John. w1824-42. Math. opt. & phil. IM. Edinburgh
7 West Bow (1824) 25 Thistle St (1825-27) 52 Hanover St (1828-31) 50 Hanover St (1832-42) A branch was opened in Glasgow at 157 Buchanan St in 1840; it moved to 28 Buchanan St in 1841
An important maker who was Curator of the Museum of the Society of Arts from 1833 until he died in 1841; this involved demonstrating instruments to the members.

DUNN, Thomas. w1843-67. Opt. math. & phil. IM. Edinburgh
50 Hanover St (1843-66) 106 George St (1867)
Continued the business of his brother, John Dunn, for whom he had worked since 1825. Exhibited at the Great Exhibition at the Crystal Palace in 1851.

DUNSCOMBE, N. W. w1856-1900+. Opt. & math. IM. 17 St Augustine's Parade, Bristol
N. W. Dunscombe purchased the business from John Braham in 1856 and it is said that the deal was struck on the top deck of a London tram! The firm became N. W. DUNSCOMBE Ltd in 1872.

DYASON, John Sanford. e1870-90. Marylebone, London

E

EAGLAND, Joseph. w1850-72. London
3 Wellington Row, Bethnal Green (1856-59) 9 Kirby St, Hatton Garden (1868-70) 13 Red Lion St, Clerkenwell (1871-72)

EAGLAND, Joseph. w1881-1900+. London
20 Warner St, Clerkenwell (1881-83) 152 Farringdon Rd (1890-1900+)

EAGLAND, Thomas, w1885. 20 Warner St, Clerkenwell, London

EAMES, Jacob. w1861-66. Clock & watch M & jeweller. Bath

EAMES, Jacob & Sons. w1875-83. Also known as 'EAMES Bros', Bath
30 & 31 Broad St. 7 Quiet St
A partnership between Jacob Eames and his sons.

EASTMOND, William P. w1878. Clock & watch M. Redhill

EBSWORTH, Richard. w1819-20. Opt. IM. 68 Fleet St, London

EDGECUMBE e1840-60. Plymouth

EDGEWORTH, Henry. w1775-87. Math. phil. & opt. IM. Bristol

EDKINS, James. w1832-39. Clock & watch M. Kensington, London

EDMENCE, T. e1820-40. Engraver. London

EDMONDS, T. w1861-75. Clock & watch M. Bath

EDNEY e1870-90. Lowestoft

EDWARD, George. w1860. e1860-85. Clock & watch M. Glasgow

EDWARDES & HUNTER w1839-44. Clock & watch M. Cornhill, London

EDWARDS e1780-1800. Hanham

EDWARDS, John. e1835-55. Menai Bridge

EDWARDS, Matthew. w1891-93. Opt. IM. 209 Sauchiehall St, Glasgow

EDWARDS, William. w1819-50. Clock & watch M. Bishops Castle

EIDMANS, Joseph S. & Co. w1889-1900+. Opt. math. & phil. IM. 15 Bartlett's Buildings, London

ELEY, Hodson. w1861-76. Clock & watch M. Wide Bargate, Boston

ELLICOTT, John. b1706-d1772. Clock M. 7 Sweetlings Alley, Royal Exchange, London
Ellicott, who was one of the most famous clockmakers, also made barometers. One or two of his longcase clocks have barometers fitted to their doors; these were of the wheel type and he also made complete wheel barometers, but not of the banjo type. In 1738 he was elected a Fellow of the Royal Society and later became clockmaker to George III. His son Edward was made a partner in 1769 and continued the business on the death of John.

ELLINETT, Thomas. c1740. Charing Cross, Norwich

ELLIOT, John. w1846-72. Phil. IM. 14 Stacey St, Soho, London

ELLIOT, John. w1846-72. Phil. IM. 14 Stacey St, Soho, London

ELLIOTT Bros. w1853-1900+. Opt. & electrical IM. London
56 Strand (1853-57) 5 Charing Cross (1857-58) 112 St Martin's Lane (1864-78) 449 Strand (1864-86) 101 & 102 St Martin's Lane (1878-1900+) 30 Strand (1859-63)
A partnership between Frederick Henry and Charles Alfred Elliott formed to take over the business of William Elliott & Sons when their father died in 1853. In 1857 the business of Watkins & Hill was taken over and the enterprise expanded rapidly. It is now part of the GEC-Elliott Automation Group.

ELLIOTT, George. w1866. Clock & watch M. Ashford

ELLIOTT, John. w1805. Clock & watch M. Ashford

ELLIOTT, T. e1835-55. 20 Haberdashers Walk, Hoxton, London

ELLIOTT, Walter Frederick. w1873-74. 10 Frith St, Soho, London

ELLIOTT, William. w1800-30. Opt. IM. Sash Court, Gray's Inn, London
He started in a small room of a house in Sash Court working for the trade as a maker of drawing instruments. Very soon he moved to the upper floor of a house in Holborn, and by 1807 he had expanded the business sufficiently to lease a shop and workshop in High Holborn. He had outgrown these premises by 1830 when he moved to 56 Strand and took his two sons, Frederick Henry and Charles Alfred, into partnership under the name of 'William Elliott & Sons'.

ELLIOTT, William. 1815-49. Opt. math. & phil. IM. 268 High Holborn, London

ELLIOTT, William Edward. c1825. Math. & phil. IM. 19 Upper East Smithfield, London

ELLIOTT, William & Sons. w1830-53. Opt. & electrical IM. 56 Strand, London
A partnership between William Elliott and his two sons, Frederick Henry and Charles Alfred. They were awarded a Bronze Medal at the Great Exhibition at the Crystal Palace in 1851; the exhibits included 'wheel and pediment barometers carved to illustrate the four seasons'. The father died in 1853 and the name was changed to Elliott Bros.

ELLIS e1825-45. Plymouth

ELLIS, Henry. e1820-50. Clock & watch M. Exeter

ELLIS, John. w1756-57. In St Peter of the Bayly, Oxford

ELLISON e1840-60. Norwich

ELLISON, T. e1810-30. 4 Little Bath St, London

ELLISON, Thomas. w1851-69. Clock & watch M. London

ELMER, A. e1865-85. High Wycombe

EMANUEL, E. e1830-50. Peterborough

EMANUEL, E. w1851. e1835-55. Jeweller. Upper Hill St, Wisbech

EMANUEL, E. & E. w1859-67. Clock & watch M. The Hard, Portsmouth
Also at Portsea. w1859-78.

EMANUEL, H. M. & Sons. w1878-93. Clock & watch M. 12 & 13 Ordnance Row, Portsea

EMBERSON, Thomas. e1805-25. Long Sutton, Lincs

EMMERTON, James. w1866-88. Hydrometer M. London
32 Kirby St, Hatton Garden (1866-69) 33 Kirby St, Hatton Garden (1870-72) 14 Kirby St, Hatton Garden (1873-80) 13 Kirby St, Hatton Garden (1881-88)

ENDERSBEE, William. w1810-30. Math. IM. 1 Little Tower St, Tower, London

ENDERSBEE, William & Son. w1830-43. Math. IM. London
335 High St, Wapping (1830-43) 28 Wapping (1843)

ENDICOTT, John. w1832-50. London
10 Norwich Court, Fetter Lane (1832-33) 23 Little Saffron Hill (1844-50)

ENGLISH e1855-75. Pocket sympiesometers. Brighton
Also ENGLISH & Sons. e1865-85. Brighton & Lewes

ENOCK, Henry. w1835-60. Clock & watch M. Warwick

ENOCK, William. w1828-50. Clock & watch M. Warwick
Also William ENOCK & Son. w1854-80.

ESCHLE, Felix. w1868-87. Clock & watch M. Commercial Place, Aberdare

ESPLIN, George. w1831-58. Watch M & jeweller. Wigan

ESTHER, Henry. w1854-58. Clock & watch M. Morpeth

EVANS, Charles. w1851-69. Clock & watch M. London

EVANS, Frederick. w1830-38. Opt. math. & phil. IM. 12 Denzell St, London

EVANS, John. w1800-01. Opt. IM. 88 Bishopsgate Within, London

EVANS, John. w1856-74. e1840-75. Clock & watch M. Welshpool

EVANS, Thomas. e1815-35. Clock & watch M. Usk

EVE, George Frederick. w1851-90. Phil. IM. London
4 Charles St, Hatton Garden (1851-53) 90 1/2 Holborn Hill (1854-69) Earl's Buildings, Featherstone St (1869-90)

EVENS, Nicholas. w1823-50. Clock & watch M. Totnes

EVERALL, John B. w1878-80. Phil. IM. 81 St George's Rd, London

EVERINGTON, A. or E. e1880-1900. Nottingham

EYLAND, Joseph. w1881. 20 Warner St, Clerkenwell, London

EZEKIEL, Cath & America. w1809-30. Goldsmiths. Fore St, Exeter

F

FACCINI, A. e1810-30. Bedford

FAGERIO, J. e1810-30. 4 Cross St, Hatton Garden, London

FAGGIOLI, A. e1835-55. Peterborough

FAGIOLI, A. e1820-40. 68 Red Lion St, Clerkenwell, London

FAGIOLI, D. e1835-55. 117 Baldwins Gardens, Leather Lane, London

FAGIOLI, Dominic. w1834-40. 3 Gt Warner St, Clerkenwell, London

FAGIOLI, D. & Son. w1840-54. London
3 Gt Warner St, Clerkenwell (1840-51) 10 Gt Warner St, Clerkenwell (1851-54)
A partnership between Dominic Fagioli and his son. Prolific makers.

FAGIOLI, J. e1795-1815. 5 Union Terrace, London

FAGIOLI, J. e1835-55. 30 Gt Warner St, Clerkenwell, London

FAGIOLI & Son. e1830-50. 9 Gt Warner St, Clerkenwell, London

FAIREY, John & Son. w1828-32. Opt. math. & phil. IM. 22 Ratcliff Highway, London

FAIREY, Joseph. w1817-22. Opt. math. & phil. IM. 20 Ratcliff Highway, London

FAIREY, Joseph & Son. w1823-46. Opt. math. & phil. IM. 8 Northumberland Place, Commercial Rd, London

FAIREY, Richard & Joseph. w1790-1827. Opt. math. & phil. IM. 150 Tooley St, Borough, London

FAIT, William. e1835-55. Boston

FALCIOLA, B. & Co. w1839-45. 53 Edgbaston St, Birmingham

FALCIOLA, G. e1810-30. Nottingham

FALCIOLA, I. e1810-30. Nottingham

FALLER e1840-60. Canterbury

FALLER, P. w1868. e1850-70. Clock & watch M. Coventry

FALLON, Thomas. e1835-55. Manchester

FALLOW, Joseph. w1827-36 Clock & watch M. 127 Pilgrim St, Newcastle upon Tyne

FANCOURT, James, w1881-93. London
17 Wynyatt St (1881-83) 6 Wynyatt St (1884) 12 Skinner St, Clerkenwell (1888-91)
58 Clerkenwell Rd (1892-93)

FARELLI, C. e1810-30. Northampton

FARMER e1835-55. Christchurch

FARONE e1810-30. Bristol

FARONE, A. e1835-55. Dundee

FASANA e1815-35. 35 Milsom St, Bath

FATORINI e1830-50. Hammersmith

FATORINI, M. e1810-30. Chichester

FATORINI, M. e1820-40. 24 Charles St, Hatton Garden, London

FATTORINI, Antonio. w1831. Clocks. Como House, Harrogate

FATTORINI, A. & Son. w1866. Clock & watch M. 14 Regent Parade, Harrogate

FATTORINI, A. & Sons. w1826-71. e1826-90. Clock & watch M. 24 Kirkgate, Bradford

FATTORINI, Innocent. w1866-71. Clock & watch M. Caroline Square, Skipton

FATTORINI, Joseph. w1838-48. 12 Castlegate, York

FAVERIO, F. & Co. e1810-30. Lincoln

FAVERIO, J. e1820-40. Andover

FAYRER & Bros. w1850-54. Math. IM. 66 White Lion St, Pentonville, London

FAYRER, James. w1838. Math. & phil. IM. 40 White Lion St, Pentonville, London

FAYRER, James & J. w1855-68. Math. IM. 66 White Lion St, Pentonville, London

FAYRER, John. w1869-73. Math. IM. 66 White Lion St, Pentonville, London

FAYRER, J. & Son. w1841-49. Math. IM. 66 White Lion St, Pentonville, London

FAZANELLI e1810-30. Bishops Castle

FEARNS, Francis Henry & Co. w1878-85. Opt. math. & phil. IM. London
Rose Works, Peckham (1878) Trafalgar Rd, Old Kent Rd (1883-85)

FEATHERS, P. A. & Son. w1874-1909. Chronometer, naut. & opt. IM. Dundee
40 Dock St (1874-76) 43 Dock St (1877-1909)

FEATHERS, Peter Airth. w1840-73. Chronometer, naut. & opt. IM. Dundee
73 High St (1840-44) 10 Dock St (1845-50) 26 Dock St (1853-68) 40 Dock St (1869-74)

FELTHAM, William. w1839-75. Clock & watch M. Stowmarket
Also at Harleston. w1813-58.

FENTON e1840-60. Lancaster

FERARI, B. e1810-30. Colchester

FERARI, B. e1810-30. Ipswich

FERELLI, G. & Co. e1810-30. Barnstable

FERGUSON, Alexander. w1849-50. Clock & watch M. Belfast

FERONI, Alexander. w1804-10. Carver & gilder. 49 Fleet St, Dublin

FERRARI, B. e1835-55. Wisbech

FERRIER, William Thornton. w1820-51. Clock & watch M. Hull
11 Queen St (1820-42) 5 Nelson St (1846-51)

FERRIS, James. w1810-24. Clock & watch M. Poole

FESTE, L. e1810-30

FETTANI, T. e1820-40

FIDLER, Robert. w1800. Opt. & math. IM. 31 Wigmore St, Cavendish Square, London

FIELD & Co. e1865-85. 10 New St, Birmingham

FIELD, H. & Son. e1850-70. Birmingham
Used a Gay-Lussac type tube on domestic barometers.

FIELD, John. c1765-1830. Opt. math. & phil. IM. 74 Cornhill, London
His trade card described him as 'late apprentice to Mr Nairne'.

FIELD, J. W. e1840-60. 11 Newington Causeway, London

FIELD, Robert. w1830. Opt. & math. IM. 33 Navigation St, Birmingham

FIELD, Robert & Son. w1845-63. Opt. IM. 113 New St, Birmingham

FIELD, Thomas. w1773-1812. Clock & watch M. Bath

FIELD, Thomas White. w1832-69. Clock & watch M. Aylesbury

FIELD, W. w1819. Clock & watch M. Bath

FILLINGER, G. w1846-58. Clock & watch M. Ely

FILLINGER, G. & Co. w1858-65. Clock & watch M. Ely

FINLAY, Robert. w1846-50. Opt. math. & phil. IM. Glasgow
46 John St (1846-47) 225 George St (1848) 87 London St (1849-50)

FINNEY, Joseph. w1770-1826. Opt. & math. IM. Liverpool
Angle barometers.

FINNIE, Joseph. w1818-25. Opt. IM. Edinburgh
5 Bank St (1818) 3 North Bank St (1819-25)

FINNIE & LIDDLE w1826-27. Opt. IM. 3 North Bank St, Edinburgh
A partnership between Joseph Finnie and William Liddle.

FIORA e1810-30. London

FIORA, J. w1814-15. e1814-30. Looking glasses. Long Row, Nottingham

FISHER w1870-90. 188 Strand, London
Maker of aneroid barometers.

FITTON, Alexander. w1787. Opt. math. & phil. IM. 60 Paul St, Cork

FITTON, Francis. w1783-95. Ship-chandler & math. IM. 36 Paul St, Cork

FITTON, William. w1773. Math. IM. Cork

FITZROY, Admiral Robert. b1805-d1865. Meteorologist. London
Although not a barometer maker, Fitzroy was responsible for improvements to the Kew pattern marine barometer which he considered to be too delicate for marine use. He was also concerned for the safety of fishermen and other mariners, and was responsible for the free issue of fishery or sea-coast barometers around the coast. The

Fig. 12 Admiral Robert Fitzroy (1805-65)

Admiral Fitzroy barometer was named after him; it is claimed that he suggested its construction and his words were certainly used as weather indications on the scale and his 'Rising and Falling' remarks were recorded below the scale. (See Fig. 12.)

FLAIG & ALEXANDER e1840-60. Bath

FLEMING, William. w1862-72. Naut. IM. Glasgow
182 Broomielaw (1862-66) 27 James Watt St (1868-72)

FLETCHER, J. & Sons. e1840-60. Opt. & phil. IM. 148 Leadenhall St, London
Sold sympiesometers patented by Charles Cummins.

FLETCHER, Thomas. e1840-60. Gloucester

FLOCKHART, Andrew. w1811-32. Clock & watch M. 5 King St, Covent Garden, London

FOLETTI, Michael. w1844-73. Looking glasses. London
88 Curtain Rd (1844-46) 4-5 Batemans Row (1847-49) 64 Banner St (1851-52) 89 Old St (1853-73)

FONTANA, B. w1856. e1840-60. Cowick St, St Thomas, Exeter

FONTANA, B. & J. e1825-50. Kettering

FONTANA, Charles. w1839-77. Clock & watch M. High Wycombe

FONTANA, E. e1825-50. High Wycombe

FONTANA, L. e1810-30. Cliff, Lewes

FONTANA, M. e1810-30. High Wycombe

FORD, Alfred. w1836-1900. Clock & watch M. Newtown, Mon.

FORD, William. w1770. Clock & watch M. London

FORDHAM e1810-30. Bishops Stortford

FORDISON e1810-30. London

FORRE & Co. e1815-35. London

FORSTER, Clement w1670-94. Clock & math. IM. At Mr Davis's, near Painter's Coffee House, in Salisbury Court, Fleet St, London
Advertised that 'he makes all manner of Mathematical instruments as well as weather-glasses (priced from 12s. to 50s.)'.

FOSANELLI, Peter. e1810-30. Bishops Castle

FOSSELL, David. e1790-1820. Hinkley

FOSTER, Charles. e1820-40. Halifax
Made angle and double-angle barometers with paper plates similar to those made by Samuel Lainton and Charles Howorth, both of Halifax.

FOSTER, J. e1850-70. Opt. & math. IM. South Castle St, Liverpool

FOWLE, Henry. w1862-78. Clock & watch M. Redhill

FOWLE, William. w1828-70. Clock & watch M. Uckfield

FOX, Charles. w1883. e1855-85. Clock & watch M. Yeovil

FOX, Edmund. w1846-75. Clock & watch M. Ely & Soham

FRANCIS & Co. e1855-75. Southampton St, Strand, London

FRANCIS, George. w1830-42. Opt. math. & phil. IM. 93 Berwick St, London

FRANCO, Teodoro. w1854-56. London
2 Brookes Market, Leather Lane (1854) 39 Charles St, Hatton Garden (1855) 11 Cross St, Hatton Garden (1856)

FRANKHAM, Richard & Henry. w1829-55. Engravers. 12 Wilson St, Grays Inn Rd, London

FRANKHAM, Richard William. w1872-1900+. Math. IM. London
40 Baker St, Clerkenwell (1872) 5 Little James St (1887-89) 28 Anwell St (1895-1900+)

FRANKHAM & WILSON w1856-70. Engravers. 12 Wilson St, Grays Inn Rd, London
Previously traded as Richard & Henry Frankham.

FRANKLIN e1825-55. 44 High St, Bloomsbury, London

FRANKLIN, A. & Co. w1824-34. Opt. math. & phil. IM. 20 St Ann's Square, Manchester

FRANKLIN & HARE e1880-1900. Taunton
Also FRANKLIN & HARE Ltd.

FRANKS, Ben. e1880-1900. Market St, Manchester. Also at Hull and 39 Piccadilly, Hanley

FRANZONI, B. w1857-64. Barometer case M. 36 Charles St, Hatton Garden, London

FRASER, A. & H. w1816. Opt. IM. 3 New Bond St, London

FRASER & Son. w1799-1815. Opt. & math. IM. 3 New Bond St, London
A partnership between William Fraser and a son. It lasted until the father died in 1815.

FRASER, William. born c1720-d1815. Opt. & math. IM. 3 New Bond St, London
Mathematical instrument-maker to the King and the Prince of Wales. In partnership with a son from 1799.

FRAZER, Alexander. w1879-1900+. Phil. IM. Edinburgh
5 Elder St (1879-80) 7 Lothian St (1881-87) 22 Teviot Place (1888-1900+)
Worked for Adie & Son from 1863 before setting up on his own.

FREDERICK, Leonard. w1842. Clock & watch M. Bilston

FREEMAN, Charles. w1871-91. e1845-91. London
25 Gt Warner St, Clerkenwell (1871-74) 25 Sekforde (1888-90) 39 Woodbridge St (1891)

FREEMAN, Henry. w1817-38. Opt. math. & phil. IM. London

FRENCH, Santiago James Moore. w1810-44. Clock & watch M. London
Royal Exchange and Sweetings Alley (1810-40) 80 Cornhill (1840-44)
Well known for his clocks, watches, chronometers and barometers, some of which he exported to Spain and America. He made large barometers with twelve inch circular dials and pendulum clock above.

FRIGERIO, J. e1815-45. 4 Cross St, Hatton Garden, London

FRIGERIO, J. or G. e1800-25. 281 High Holborn, London

FRITH, Peter & Co. w1853-88. Opt. & math. IM. Sheffield and 5 Bartletts Buildings, Holborn, London

FRODSHAM & BAKER w1809-11. Clock & watch M. Gracechurch St, London

FRODSHAM, George. w1857-69. Clock & watch M. 84 Strand, London

FRODSHAM, Henry. w1828-51. Opt. & math. IM. 38 Castle St, Liverpool

FRODSHAM, John. e1810-40. Clock & watch M. 33 Gracechurch St, London

FRODSHAM & KEEN e1840-70. Liverpool
Became FRODSHAM & KEEN Ltd around 1870.

FROGGATT, Samuel. w1827-46. Opt. math. & phil. IM. London
14 Kirby St, Hatton Garden (1827-38) 27 Bridgehouse Place, Newington Causeway (1839-46) 13 Charterhouse (1839-46)

FROGGATT, Thomas. w1822-30. Opt. IM. Sheffield
Walk Mile, Pickle (1822-30) Savile St (1822-30)

FROST, John. w1830-34. Clock & watch M. Penrith

FROST, NOAKES & Co. w1851-57. 195 Brick Lane, Spitalfields, London

FROWD, William. w1839-74. Clock & watch M. Hemel Hempstead

FRY, Samuel. e1810-30. Clock & watch M. Dublin
Fitted wheel barometers to the doors of some of his longcase clocks.

FULLER, CALTENBACK & Co. e1830-50. 77 Blackman St, Borough, London

FULLER, Joseph. w1830. Math. & phil. IM. 2 St James's Walk, Clerkenwell, London

FUSY e1840-60. Sympiesometers. Hull

G

GABALIO, P. w1808-17. 3 Long Lane, London

GABORY e1800-20. 125 Holborn, London
Made wheel barometers with a square dial at the top of the case as a companion to a longcase clock.

GABORY, J. w1794. e1780-1800. 123 Holborn, London

GABRIELE, William. w1875-81. Clock & watch M. 61 Cornhill, London

GABRIELLI, James Vincent. e1825-45. Clock & watch M. London

GADOLA J. e1840-60. Taunton

GAFURIO & Co. e1810-30. Chester

GAFURIO, Joseph. e1810-30. Chester

GALE, Joseph. w1828-41. Looking glass M. 46 Knight St, Manchester

GALETI, C. e1810-30. Montrose

GALI, J. e1820-40. Lincoln

GALIMBERTI, J. e1845-65. 3 Bugle St, Southampton

GALLATTI, Anthony. w1830-37. Opt & math. IM. 10 Castle St, Liverpool

GALLENKAMP, Adolf & Co. w1894. e1880-1900. 2, 4 & 6 Cross St, Finsbury, London

GALLETTI, Antoni. w1805-50. Carver & gilder, opt. & math. IM. Glasgow
10 Nelson St (1805-28) 21 Nelson St (1826-28) 24 & 25 Argyle Arcade (1829-50)
He was succeeded by his son John.

GALLETTI, Charles. w1807. Carver & gilder. 82 Glassford St, Glasgow

GALLETTI, John. w1850-94. Carver & gilder, opt. math. & phil. IM. 24 Argyle Arcade, Glasgow
Took over the business of his father Antoni.

GALLEY, P. P. & Co. e1855-75. Dudley

GALLI e1800-20. London

GALLI e1835-55. Kingston

GALLI. Charles. w1860-82. Looking glass M. 68 Hatton Garden, London

GALLI, F. e1805-25. Sheffield

GALLI, G. e1825-50. 5 Waterloo Place, Edinburgh

GALLY e1815-25. Manchester

GALLY e1820-40. 152 Holborn, London

GALLY, A. e1800-30. Glasgow

GALLY, C. e1820-40. Leith

GALLY, C. w1852-54. Looking glass M. 68 Hatton Garden, London
Also Charles GALLY & Co. at this address.

GALLY, D. e1800-20. 263 High Holborn, London

GALLY, G. e1815-35. Glasgow

GALLY, John. e1810-30. Exeter
Also John GALLY & Co. at this address.

GALLY, John & Co. e1820-40. Manchester

GALLY, John & MAGGI e1810-30. Exeter

GALLY, P. e1800-20. Bristol

GALLY, P. e1800-30. Cambridge

GALLY, P. e1820-40. Cranbrook

GALLY, P. w1837-62. Jeweller. Leeds
89 Kirkgate (1837-62) 97 Kirkgate (1841)

GALLY, Paul & Peter. w1809-61. Looking glass & picture frame M. London
8 Turnmill St, Clerkenwell (1809-11) 9 Turnmill St, Clerkenwell (1815-25) 50 Exmouth St, Spitalfields (1826-48) 68 Hatton Garden (1849-61) 3 Upper North Place, Grays Inn Rd (1852-54)

Some barometers signed 'GALLY & Co.' from the 9 Turnmill St address.

GALLY, Peter & Charles. w1832-46. Phil. IM. London
50 Exmouth St, Spitalfields (1832-39) 9 Turnmill St, Clerkenwell (1840-46)

GALLY, P. P. & Co. w1829-61. Looking glass M. 50 Exmouth St, Spitalfields, London

GALLY TARONE & Co. e1790-1810. Grevil St, Holborn, London

GALOPIN Bros & Co. w1877-79. 30 Grafton St, Fitzroy Square, London

GANDOLA, P. e1810-30. 12 Little Saffron Hill, London

GANTHONY, Richard Pinfold. w1821-45. Clock & chronometer M. 83 Cheapside, London

GAPP, C. e1830-70. London

GARACCIA, Joseph. e1830-50. Edenbridge

GARDEN, Alexander. w1824. Chemical & phil. IM. Oxford St, London
Also in partnership with Frederick Accum as ACCUM & GARDEN.

GARDENER, S. H. w1877. e1875-1900+. Clock & watch M. Reading

GARDINER, George. w1879-80. Math. phil. & naut. IM. 34 Aldgate, London

GARDNER & Co. w1837-83. Math. opt. & phil. IM. Glasgow
44 Glassford St (1837-38) 21 Buchanan St (1839-59) 53 Buchanan St (1860-82) 53 St Vincent St (1883)
A partnership between T. R. & William Gardner. Opticians to Queen Victoria.

GARDNER & Co. w1891-1900+. Math. opt. & phil. IM. Glasgow
53 St Vincent St (1891-98) 36 West Nile St (1899-1900+)
This was the business name for T. R. Gardner (junior).

GARDNER & DOWLING w1827-30. Clock & watch M. 57 High St, Belfast
A partnership between Henry Gardner and James Dowling.

GARDNER, Henry. w1809-35. Clock & watch M, opt. & math. IM. Belfast
27 High St (1809-19) 65 High St (1819-24) 57 High St (1824-35)
Appears to have been able to turn his hand to many trades as he was variously described as 'dentist, clock and watch maker, silversmith and jeweller, optical and mathematical instrument-maker and money exchange broker'.

GARDNER, James. w1830. Math. & phil. IM. 5 Somerset Place, Whitechapel, London

GARDNER JAMIESON & Co. w1819-22. Math. & opt. IM. 43 Bell St. Glasgow
A partnership between John Gardner (senior), Margaret Rankine and Robert Jamieson.

GARDNER, J. & J. w1799-1818. Math. & opt. IM. Glasgow
Bell St (1799-1801) 43 Bell St (1803-18)
A partnership between John Gardner and his son John who died in 1818.

GARDNER, John. w1773-92. Land surveyor, math. opt. & phil. IM. Glasgow
Crawford's Land, Bell's Wynd
Was senior journeyman for James Watt before founding the firm which was to become known as 'Gardners of Glasgow'. The firm was a prolific maker of barometers and as early as 1773 Gardner advertised in the *Glasgow Mercury* 'Barometers on the most improved principles, so as to admit of being carried to any distance with the greatest safety. Likewise Barometers, for measuring the height of hills, which have a peculiar adjustment to regulate the lower surface of the Mercury in one place, and have the mercury boiled in the tube.'

GARDNER & LAURIE w1792-99. Math. opt. & phil. IM. Corner of Bell's Wynd, Glasgow
A partnership between John Gardner and James Laurie.

GARDNER & LYLE w1883-91. Math. opt. & phil. IM. 53 St Vincent St, Glasgow
A partnership between T. R. Gardner (junior) and James Lyle.

GARDNER, M. & Co. w1821-22. Math. opt. & phil. IM. 43 Bell St, Glasgow
A partnership between John Gardner, who died in 1822, and Margaret Rankine.

GARDNER, M. & Sons. w1822-37. Math. opt. & phil. IM. Glasgow
43 Bell St (1822-25) 92 Bell St (1826-31) 44 Glassford St (1832-37)
A partnership between Margaret Rankine, T. R. and William Gardner.

GARDNER & NEILL w1809-18. Opt. & math. IM, clock & watch M. 27 High St, Belfast
A partnership between Henry Gardner and Robert Neill.

GARDNER, William. w1846-64. Math. opt. & phil. IM. Glasgow
3 Royal Bank Place (1846-55) 56 Gordon St (1856-61) 134 Buchanan St (1862-64)

GARGORY, James. w1830-c1875. Opt & math. IM. Birmingham and Wolverhampton
4 Bull St, Birmingham (1830-35) 5 Bull St, Birmingham (1850-56) 41 Bull St, Birmingham

GAROF, O. & Co. e1810-30. Edinburgh

GAROF, P. & Co. e1825-45. Edinburgh

GASPER & JOSEPH e1780-1800. Manchester

GATH, Thomas. w1830-79. Clock & watch M. Small St, Bristol

GATTI, C. e1815-35. 48 Port Pool Lane, Clerkenwell, London

GATTI, Charles. w1817-22. Looking glass M. 89 Leather Lane, Holborn, London

GATTI, O. e1810-30. 48 Port Pool Lane, Clerkenwell, London

GATTI, T. e1820-40. 53 Grays Inn Lane, London

GATTY, A. e1810-30. Fish Lane, London

GATTY, Andrew. w1796-1800. Dublin
18 Fishamble St (1796-1798) 1 Smock Alley (1799-1800)

GATTY, Andrew. w1815-24. Dublin
1 Smock Alley (1815-19) 45 Fishamble St (1820-22) 7 Smock Alley (1823-24)

GATTY, Antony. e1800-20. Glasgow

GATTY, Antony. e1810-40. Royal Oak, Fisher Row, Reading
Also barometers signed 'A. GATTI' and 'GATTY & Co.' at this address.

GATTY, B. e1810-30. Reading

GATTY, Charles. e1810-30. London

GATTY & Co. e1820-40. 89 Leather Lane, Holborn, London

GATTY, D. e1815-35. Lewis

GATTY, Domco. e1790-1830. 94 High Holborn, London

GATTY, Dominico. w1826. e1820-45. 111 Broad St, Reading
Barometers signed 'D. GATTI' with this address.

GATTY, James. e1780-1815. London
130 High Holborn. 132 High Holborn. 237 High Holborn
One of the earliest Italian immigrants who appears to have set up in business as a barometer maker in London at least by 1780. He made some stick and double barometers, but is best known for his very attractive wheel barometers which are of a very high quality. Very many good examples still survive.

GATTY, Jno. e1810-45. Manchester
Some barometers signed 'Jno GATTY & Co.'

GATTY, Joseph. w1801-14. Dublin
1 Smock Alley (1801-07) 25 Fishamble St (1808) 1 Smock Alley (1809-14)

GATTY & MALACRIDA w1803-17. 104 High Holborn, London
A partnership between Charles Gatty and Charles Malacrida.

GATTY, Thomas. w1844-73. Clock & watch M. Bodmin

GATWARD, Benjamin. w1795. Clock & watch M. Hitchen

GATWARD, John. w1828-51. Clock & watch M. Hitchen

GATWARD, Thomas. b1802-d1863. Clock & watch M. Saffron Walden

GAUDIN, Henry. w1865-76. 64 Hatton Garden, London

GAY, Thomas. w1668-1732. Opt. IM. At the Sign of the Golden Spectacles, by the Sun Tavern behind the Royal Exchange, London
His instruments include 'telescopes, microscopes, reading glasses, magic lanterns and weather glasses'.

GAYDON, Francis. w1866-78. Clock & watch M. Upper Norwood

GEBHARDT & ROTTMAN Co. w1863-89. Opt. math. & phil. IM. London
7 Lawrence Lane (1863) 24 Lawrence Lane (1864-89)

GEORGE, Robert (late Dicker). w1890-1900+. Math. IM. 652 Commercial Rd, London

GERDINO, D. e1815-35. 2 Great Warner St, Clerkenwell, London
Also spelt 'D. GEROLINO'.

GERLETTI, Charles. w1828-48. Looking glass M. Glasgow
156 Saltmarket (1828-32) 153 Saltmarket (1833) 145 Saltmarket (1834-39) 10 Candleriggs St (1840-48)

GERLETTI, Dominick. w1849-58. Opt. IM and firework artist. Glasgow
10 Candleriggs St (1849-55) 24 Glassford St (1855-57) 44 Trongate (1857-58)

GERLETTI, John. w1853-58. Looking glass M. Glasgow
95 Candleriggs St (1853-54) 55 St Enoch's Wynd (1854-58)

GERONIMO, P. e1815-50. Bristol

GESTRA, John. e1810-30. Newport

GESTRA, J. & SCHENA e1810-30. Newport

GIANELLONE, A. or GIANETTONE, A. e1830-50. Merthyr Tydfil

GIANI e1810-30. London

GIANNA, Lewis. w1809-16. Opt. IM. Market Place, Shrewsbury
The Salopian Magazine of March 1816 noted his passing: 'Death. Mr Lewis Gianna, barometer maker of Shrewsbury: his death is imputed to his having slept in a damp bed.' In 1809 Gianna had inserted an advertisement in the same paper which read: 'A Farmer or Grazier without a weather glass is just like a mariner without a compass.'

GIASANI e1810-30. Wolverhampton

GIBB, Ernest. w1896-1900+. 11 Powell St, Goswell St, London

GIBBONS, W. e1850-70. 38 Hampton St, Birmingham

GIBBS e1860-80. 13 Chester Terrace, Pimlico, London

GIBBS, Thomas. w1828-54. Clock & watch M. Stratford-upon-Avon

GIBURGER, G. e1835-55. Repairer. Clapham, London

GIERDELI, P. e1810-30. 7 Brooks Market, London
Also spelt 'P. GIARDELI'.

GILARDI, A. or J. e1835-55. Bristol

GILARDONI, A. e1830-50. 6 Nicholas St, Bristol

GILARDONI, B. w1816. e1810-30. Jeweller. Fore St, Exeter
Barometers signed 'G. GILARDONI & Co.' and 'GILARDONE & Co.' at this address.

GILBERT, Edward. w1843-53. e1840-60. Clock & watch M. Belfast

GILBERT & GILKERSON w1793-1819. Math. IM. 8 Postern Row, Tower Hill, London

GILBERT, Jesse. w1839. e1830-50. Clock & watch M. Lydd

GILBERT, John (senior). w1717-52. Math. opt. & phil. IM. The Mariner, Postern Row, Tower Hill, London
His trade card includes a drawing of a stick barometer with a bayonet tube, thermometer and hygrometer. (See Fig. 13.)

GILBERT, John (junior). w1752-91. Math. opt. & phil. IM. The Mariner, Postern Row, Tower Hill, London
The son of John Gilbert (senior), he succeeded to his business. He was also in a partnership styled 'Gregory, Gilbert & Wright' for a short time.

GILBERT & Sons. w1806-18. Math. IM. 148 Leadenhall St, London

GILBERT, William & Son. e1830-60. Clock & watch M. Belfast

GILBERT & WRIGHT w1790-92. Math. IM. 148 Leadenhall St, London

GILBERT & WRIGHT w1802-05. Math. IM. 148 Leadenhall St, London

GILBERT, WRIGHT & HOOKE w1794-1801. Math. IM. 148 Leadenhall St, London

GILBERT, W. & T. w1819-31. Math. IM. 148 Leadenhall St, London
A partnership between William and Thomas Gilbert, the sons of William Gilbert who was the brother of John Gilbert (junior). The firm became instrument-makers to the East India Company in 1820.

GILKERSON & Co. w1809-27. Opt. IM. London
8 Postern Row, Tower Hill. The Navigation Warehouse, 148 Leadenhall St

Fig. 13 Trade card of John Gilbert *(Trustees of the British Museum)*

GILKERSON, James. w1817. Opt. IM. 8 Postern Row, Tower Hill, London

GILKERSON & MACALL w1770. Math. IM. Tower Hill, London

GILLHAM, W. w1878. e1850-80. Clock & watch M. Eastbourne

GILMOUR, J. e1840-60. Glasgow

GINOCCHIO e1775-1825. Cork

GIOBBI & SALA e1790-1810. London

GIOBBIO, G. B. e1810-30. Burnley

GIOBBIO, G. B. e1810-30. Shipton

GIOBBIO, G. B. e1810-45. Trowbridge and Devizes
Produced a large number of wheel barometers, also angle barometers. Some instruments have Trowbridge or Devizes as the address and some are signed 'GIOBBIO & Co.'

GIOCCOMELLI, G. e1800-30. Belfast

GIREARO, J. e1820-40. Ely

GIRONIMO, B. e1820-40. London

GIRONIMO, B. e1835-55. Bristol

GIRONIMO & CATTELY e1810-30. London

GIRONIMO, J. e1820-40. Bristol

GIRONIMO, Laurence. w1843-45. Looking glass M. 93 Leather Lane, London

GISCARD, Jeremiah. w1840. Clock & watch M. Ely

GISCARD, William. w1830-36. Clock & watch M. Downham

GITTINS, William. w1786-1806. Pride Hill, Shrewsbury
Made stick barometers, also angle barometers with paper plates.

GIUDICE, A. & Co. e1820-50. Stroud Water

GIUSANI, John. e1805-25. 92 Salop St, Wolverhampton

GIUSANI, Peter. w1835. e1810-45. Carver & gilder. Cock St, Wolverhampton
Barometers also signed 'P GIUSANI & Sons, Wolverhampton & Bilston'. See also P. GUISANI and P. GUISANI & Sons.

GLADSTONE John. b1772-d1851. e1820-40. Clock & watch M. Biggar

GLASE, Thomas. w1828-50. Clock & watch M & gunsmith. Bridgnorth

GLOYN, John Pugh. w1860. Math & phil. IM. 143 Strand, London

GLYNNE, Richard. w1705-23. Math. IM. Sign of the Hercules and Atlas, facing Salisbury Court, Fleet St, London
His trade card shows that he made 'Mathematical Instruments, either for Land or Sea, and Apparatus for Experimental Philosophy.' It is believed that he worked for a time with Henry Wynne.

GOBBI, A. e1835-55. Clock & watch M. Swaffham

GOBBI, A. e1840-60. Liverpool

GOBBI, D. e1810-30. Leather Lane, Holborn, London

GOBBI, G. e1845-65. Liverpool

GOBBI, L. e1845-65. Liverpool

GOBBI, P. e1840-65. Stroud
Barometers signed 'P. GOBBI & Son' and 'GOBBI & Sons' with this address.

GOBBO, G. e1820-40. York

GOGERTY, Robert. w1838-d1856. Math. opt. & phil. IM. London
32 Kings St, Smithfield (1838-48) 72 Fleet St (1848-56)

GOLDMAN & Co. w1897-98. Opt. IM. London
5 Wood St Square (1897) 3a Bradford Avenue (1898)

GOLDMAN & Co. Ltd. w1899-1900+. Math. opt. & phil. IM. London
12 Old St (1899) 42 Goswell Rd (1900+)

GONDOLA, P. e1835-55. 12 Little Saffron Hill, London

GONSKI & DAVIS e1840-60. Northampton

GOOD, J. e1840-60. 19 High St, Hull

GOODALL, Charles. w1795-1824. Clock & watch M. Brydges St, opposite York St, Covent Garden, London

GOODALL, George. w1780-1807. Clock & watch M. Tadcaster

GOODMAN, David. e1840-60. Cardiff

GOODMAN, David. w1844-68. Clock & watch M. Taff St, Pontypridd

GOODMAN, John. w1861-75. Clock & watch M. Taunton

GOODYEAR, William. w1862-66. Opt. IM. London
9 Lower Copenhagen St, Islington (1862-64) 76 Lower Copenhagen St, Islington (1864-66)

GORDELLI, P. e1800-20. Dundee

GORE, A. J. e1870-90. Norwich

GORLAND e1830-50. London Wall, London

GOTZ, John Rodolphe. w1886-97. Opt. math. & phil. IM. London
19 Buckingham St, Strand (1886-94) 150 Shaftesbury Avenue (1895) 215 Shaftesbury Avenue (1896-97)

GOUGH, Walter. w1799-1810. Opt. math. & phil. IM. 21 Middle Row, Holborn, London

GOULD, F. J. e1875-95. Barographs. London

GOVER, Edward Thomas. w1876. 28 Camomile St, London

GOWLAND e1845-65. Enfield

GOWLAND, Clement. w1851. Clock & watch M. Sunderland

GOWLAND, James. w1832-75. Chronometers. 11 Leathersellers Buildings, London Wall, London

GRACE, G. e1810-30. York

GRAFTON, Henry. w1841-53. Math. & phil. IM. London
80 Chancery Lane (1841-53) 36 Holborn Hill (1849-53)

GRAFTON, Henry (senior). w1840-41. Math. IM. 18 Barbican, London

GRAFTON, Henry (junior). w1840-41. Math. & phil. IM. 18 Barbican, London

GRAGGARY, J. e1810-30. Macclesfield

GRAHAM, George. b1673-d1751. Math. IM. London
The Dial and Three Crowns, at the corner of Water Lane, Fleet St, London (1713-20) The Dial and One Crown, Fleet St (1720-51)
Honest George Graham - as he was known - was born in Cumberland and tramped to London as a boy when he could just about read and write. He was apprenticed in 1688 to Henry Aske and became a member of the Clockmakers' Company in 1695. He became one of Thomas Tompion's assistants in 1696 and, having married his niece, became his partner in 1711. Tompion died in 1713 and Graham succeeded to the business. He became the leading maker of clocks but made very few barometers; he spent his life in scientific enquiry and the manufacture of suitable astronomical instruments for the Astronomer Royal of Greenwich Observatory. One of them, James Bradley, wrote of him: 'I am sensible that, if my own endeavours have, in any respect

been effectual to the advancement of Astronomy, it has principally been owing to the advice and assistance given to me by our worthy member, Mr George Graham, whose great skill and judgement in mechanics, joined with a complete and practical knowledge of the uses of astronomical instruments enabled him to contrive and execute them in the most perfect manner.' (See Fig. 14.)

GRAHAM, Harriet. w1832-34. 25 Baldwins Gardens, London

GRAHAM, John. w1851. e1845-65. Clock & watch M. 1 New Wapping, Liverpool

GRANGER, Francis. w1864-76. e1850-80. Clock & watch M. Nottingham

GRANT Bros. e1850-70. Exeter and Torquay

GRANT, Henry. w1844-55. Cardiff
Maker of sympiesometers. Emigrated to Canada.

GRANT, John. w1781-d1810. Clock & watch M. 75 Fleet St, London

GRANT, John. w1863-65. Naut. & opt. IM. 45 Regents Quay, Aberdeen
This business was taken over from Smith & Ramage.

GRASSI, BERGNA & ORIGONI w1830-34. 34 Dean St, Newcastle

GRASSI & FONTANA e1815-50. Exeter

GRASSI, J. e1835-55. Exeter

GRASSI, L. & Co. e1835-55. Newcastle

GRASSI, S. e1840-60. 42 Queen St, Wolverhampton

GRASSICK, James. w1862-65. Opt. IM. Edinburgh
44 Cumberland St (1862-64) 10 Hanover St (1865)
He started work as a clerk with Adie & Son and was promoted to managing clerk in 1860; two years later he started his own business.

GRAVELL, William & Son. w1828-57. Clock & watch M. 29 Charterhouse Square, London

GRAY & GRIERSON e1860-80. Aneroid barometers. Dumfries.

GRAY, John. w1805-62. Naut. math. & opt. IM. Liverpool
10 East Side, Dry Dock (1813-20) 11 East Side, Dry Dock (1821) 25 Bridgewater St (1828-29) 3 Chester St (1839) 25 Strand St (1841-62)

GRAY, John. e1810-30. Clock & watch M. Belfast

GRAY, John. w1830-38. Opt. math. & phil. IM. 4 Upper East Smithfield, London

GRAY, John. w1867-75. e1840-75. Clock & watch M. Trowbridge

Fig. 14 George Graham (1673-1751)

GRAY, John & KEEN w1847-51. Naut. math. & phil. IM. 25-6 Strand St, Liverpool

GRAY, Stephen. w1694-1701. Amateur IM. Canterbury
In 1698 he suggested fitting a microscope and micrometer to the barometer so that readings could be taken to the accuracy of a thousandth of an inch.

GRAY, W. w1849-64. Clock & watch M. Leicester

GRAY, W. e1850-70. 16 Crocked Lane, London Bridge, London

GREATOREX, Ralph. b1625-d1712. Math. IM. The Sign of Adam and Eve in the Strand, London
A notable instrument-maker who made a weather glass for Samuel Pepys in 1663, although this may have been a thermometer.

GRECHI, C. A. e1810-30. Shaftesbury
Some barometers signed 'Cs. CRECHI'.

GREEN, Edward. e1840-60. Opt. IM. Southampton
Maker of marine barometers.

GREEN, William. w1828-76. Clock & watch M. Grantham

GREEN, William. w1844-48. Math. opt. & phil. IM. Glasgow
5 Franklin St (1844-45) 87 London St (1846-48)

GREENALL, William Webb. w1822. Phil. IM. 31 Old Compton St, London

GREENWOOD, William. w1823-47. Clock & watch M. Rochester

GREGGI, G. e1820-40. Liverpool

GREGO, A. w1817. e1810-30. Looking glass M. 27 Leather Lane, London

GREGORY, GILBERT & WRIGHT w1789-92. Opt. & math. IM. The Navigation Warehouse, 148 Leadenhall St, London

GREGORY, Henry. w1750-92. Math. & opt. IM. London
The Azimuth Compass, near the East India House, Leadenhall St (1761) 148 Leadenhall St (1763-92)

GREGORY, Samuel. w1761-62. Sycamore Alley, Dublin

GREGORY & Son. e1770-92. Math. & opt. IM. 148 near the India House, London
A partnership between Henry Gregory and his son. Some barometers are signed 'Gregory & Son, 148 India Way, London'.

GREGORY, William. w1866-91. Math & opt. IM. 51 Strand, London

GREGORY, William & Co. w1891-1900+. Opt. math. & phil. IM. 51 Strand, London
Instrument-makers to 'Her Majesty's Government, War Department, London County

Council and the National Rifle Association'. Barometers also signed 'William Gregory & Son'.

GREGORY, William Tucker. w1850. e1835-55. Clock & watch M. Gloucester

GREGORY & WRIGHT w1783-92. Opt & math. IM. The Navigation Warehouse, 148 Leadenhall St, London
A partnership between William Gregory and George Wright.

GREGSON, H. e1845-65. Church

GRICE, William Hawks. w1815-25. Opt & math. IM. 3 New Bond St, London
Succeeded William Fraser at this address when he died in 1815. Appointed instrument-makers to 'Their Majesties and the Royal Family'.

GRIFFIN & HYAMS e1830-50. Cornhill, London

GRIFFIN, John Joseph. w1855-66. Phil. IM. London
119 & 120 Bunhill Row (1855-66) 10 Finsbury Square (1855)

GRIFFIN, John J. & Sons. w1867-90. Phil. IM. 22 Garrick St, London

GRIFFIN, John J. & Sons Ltd. w1891-1900+. Phil. IM. London
22 Garrick St (1891-98) 2 Long Acre (1894-98) 20-26 Sardinia St, Lincoln's Inn Fields (1899-1900+)

GRIFFIN & TATLOCK e1830-60. Manchester

GRIFFIN, William. w1844. Clock & watch M. 27 Lombard St, London

GRIFFITHS, William Henry. w1850. Clock & watch M. Bishops Castle
Also at Ludlow. w1856-70.

GRIGGI, J. e1805-30. Liverpool

GRIGGIARI & ANZAN e1830-50. Pelham St, Nottingham

GRIGIONI, G. e1880-1900. Liverpool
Marine barometers with sympiesometer.

GRIMALDI, Dominic. e1815-50. Opt. IM. London
82 Leather Lane (1814-16) 12 Baldwins Gardens, Holborn
His barometers were 'Warranted to go well'. Made barometers with a clock above the dial.

GRIMALDI, H. & Co. w1857-73. Opt. & phil. IM. 31 Brooke St, Hatton Garden, London

GRIMALDI, Henry. w1839-57. Math. & phil. IM. London
16 Brooke St, Hatton Garden (1839-42) 4 Charles St, Hatton Garden (1844) 24 Greville St, Hatton Garden (1845-47) 31 Brooke St, Hatton Garden (1850-57)

GRIMSHAW, Aaron. e1790-1820. London

GRITTINS e1760-80. Salop

GROCE, G. e1810-30. York

GROCE, J. e1860-80. Maker and repairer. York

GROVER & WOOD w1885-89. 62 Glengall Rd, Old Kent Rd, London

GRUBB, Henry G. & Co. w1854-57. Phil. IM. Charlemont Bridge Works, Dublin

GRUBB, Henry S. w1855-61. Phil. IM. Grand Canal Bank, Rathmines, Dublin

GRUNDY & GOADSBY e1800-20. Looking glasses. 4 Exchange St, Manchester

GRUNDY, John Clowes. w1834-48. Looking glasses. Opt & math. IM. 4 Exchange St, Manchester

GUANELLA, A. e1820-40. Clock M. Bristol

GUANZIROLI, G. & L. w1845-52. Looking glasses. 106 Hatton Garden, London
A partnership between Guiseppe and Luigi Guanziroli.

GUANZIROLI, Guiseppe (Joseph). e1853-65. Looking glasses. Artificial flowers. 106 Hatton Garden. London

GUANZIROLI, Luigi (Lewis). e1853-60. Looking glasses. London

GUARNERIO, A. e1820-50. St Ives, Cambs

GUARNERIO, G. w1863. Clock & watch M. London

GUARNERIO, Gasper. w1866. Clock & watch M. 4 Newborough St, Scarborough

GUARNERIO, G. & Co. w1878. Clock & watch M. Peckham

GUARNERIO, Peter. w1839-54. Clock & watch M. Huntingdon

GUDGEON, George. w1830-39. Clock & watch M. Bury St Edmunds

GUDGEON, John. w1830. e1815-35. Clock & watch M. Abbey Gate St, Bury St Edmunds

GUGERI, A. e1810-30. 74 Leather Lane, London

GUGERI, A. e1835-55. Blandford

GUGERI, Andrew. w1829-59. Looking glasses. London
15 Upper Union Court, Holborn (1829) 16 Charles St, Hatton Garden (1830-59)

GUGERI & BELLOTTI e1820-45. 15 Union Court, Holborn Hill, London

GUGERI & BELOTTI w1838-43. 16 Charles St, Hatton Garden, London

GUGERI & CARUGHI w1844-45. 16 Charles St, Hatton Garden, London

GUGERI, Dominic. w1835-42. e1815-45. Clock & watch M, silversmith & jeweller. Market Place, Boston

GUGERI, E. e1835-55. Blandford

GUGERI, Felix. w1854-59. 93 Leather Lane, London

GUGERI, J. e1820-40. Boston

GUGGIARI, Charles. w1828. e1800-30. 32 Church St, Sheffield

GUGGIARI, Charles. w1858. e1830-60. 25 Digbeth, Birmingham

GUGGIARI, D. & ANZIANI w1832-60. Carvers & gilders. Pelham St, Nottingham

GUGGIARI, Dominic. w1835-41. Carver & gilder. Pelham St, Nottingham

GUIDICE, A. or GULDICE, A. e1835-55. Bristol

GUISANI, P. e1820-40. Carver & gilder. 42 Cock St, Wolverhampton

GUISANI, P. & Sons. e1840-60. Carvers & gilders. 42 Cock St, Wolverhampton

GULLIFORD, William. w1866-83. Clock & watch M. Porlock
Also at Luccombe. w1875-83.

H

HAAS & HURTER w1787. Math. IM. London
Developed barometers and other meteorological instruments for scientists.

HAAS, Jacob Berhard. w1789-99. Math. IM. London
Developed, with J. H. Hurter, an ivory float for the cistern tube barometer.

HADDOW, Thomas. e1880-1900. Opt. IM. 2 Maitland St, Edinburgh

HAGUE & Son. e1870-90. Bath

HAIR e1830-50. Winchester

HAIR, William E. w1849-50. Clock & watch M. Boston

HALDEN, J. & Co. Ltd. e1870-90. Manchester and Hamburg

HALIFAX, J. e1740-60. Southampton Buildings, London

HALLAM, & Son. w1849-55. Clock & watch M. Nottingham

HALLETT, F. H. w1848. e1845-65. Clock & watch M. Fore St, Trowbridge
Also at Melksham.

HALLIFAX, George. b1725-d1811. Clock M. Doncaster
The fourth son of the noted clockmaker, John Hallifax of Barnsley. He moved to Doncaster before his father died in 1750 and became a successful clockmaker and was twice Mayor of Doncaster. He made a limited number of barometers similar in design to those of his father, and it is possible that he was using up surplus or unwanted parts from his father's stock on the death of his brother Joseph in 1762.

HALLIFAX, John. b1694-d1750. Clock M. Barnsley
John was the son of a vicar and he started in business in 1711; he soon became a notable clock and barometer maker and a number of his barometers survive. They are all of distinctive form, and the design of the cases and dials was influenced by the shape and line of his longcase clocks. He was regarded as one of the leading provincial clockmakers of his day and this was acknowledged on the engraving on his tombstone: 'Whose abilities and virtue few in these times have attained. His art and industry were such as his ingenious inventions will be a lasting monument of his merit - such as recommended him to the favour and esteem of all good men that knew him.'

HALLPIKE, H. e1865-85. Aneroid barometers. Shepherd's Bush Green, London

HALSE & Son. e1820-40. London

HALSTAFF & HANNAFORD e1890-1900. 228 Regent St, London

HAMBLETON, Thomas. w1857-78. Clock & watch M. Birkenhead

HAMLIN, William. w1792-1814. Math. IM. 111 Leadenhall St, London

HAMMOND e1850-70. South Molton

HAMMOND, George & Thomas. w1848-51. Clock & watch M. Manchester
Made large wall clocks with a wheel barometer and thermometer.

HANCOCK, E. e1855-75. Westgate St, Bath

HANCOCK, I. W. e1830-50. Yeovil
Some barometers have clocks above the dial.

HANCOCK, James. w1840. Clock & watch M. Yeovil

HANCOCK, John. c1840. Opt. & math. IM. 30 City Rd, Finsbury, London

HANCOCK, John. w1894. Opt IM. 61 City Rd, Finsbury, London

HANCOCK, J. & Sons. e1835-55. Yeovil

HAND e1810-30. Farringdon

HANNAH, Adam. e1800-20. Fleet St, London

HANNY, James. w1835-79. Clock M. Shrewsbury

HANSFORD, John. w1861-83. Clock & watch M. Ilminster

HANSON e1840-60. Marine barometers. Hull

HANSON, William. w1830-64. Clock & watch M. 30 High St, Windsor

HARDT, Harry. w1881. Clock & watch M. London

HARDT, William. w1885-1900+. Math. & phil. IM. 165 Pentonville Rd, London

HARDY, Edward. c1770-90. Clock & watch M. Hull

HARDY, William. w1800-30. Clock & watch M. 171 Holborn, London

HARGRAVES, Robert. c1830. e1820-40. Clock & watch M. Skipton

HARGRAVES, Thomas. w1790-1834. Clock & watch M. Settle
Produced very unusual barometers with slender rectangular cases, with a quadrant or fan-shaped painted and glazed dial on one side of the case. The dial pointer is operated by a pivot mechanism.

HARKER, George. e1805-25. Clock & watch M. London

HARLING, William Henry. w1874-1900+. Math. IM. London
9 London Place, London Fields (1874-81) 40 Hatton Garden (1877-89) 47 Finsbury Pavement (1890-1900+)

HARMAN, William, w1820. Math. & phil. IM. 1 Halfman Crescent, White Conduit Fields, London

HAROCASTLE, I. e1820-40. 53 Blackburn St, Borough, London

HARRIMAN, John. w1835-62. Birmingham
58 Church St (1835-49) 60 Church St (1854) 100 Pritchett St (1858-62)

HARRIS e1865-85. Southampton

HARRIS, A. O. w1850. London
Proposed the use of carbon dioxide as the gas and mercury as the liquid for an improved sympiesometer.

HARRIS, Clement. w1828-44. Chronometers, clock & watch M. 76 Cornhill, London

HARRIS, Elias & Co. w1874-75. Aneroid barometers. 63 Hatton Garden, London

HARRIS, H. w1848. Clock & watch M. Westbury

HARRIS, J. C. e1805-25. Spalding

HARRIS, John. w1822-41. Opt. IM. 22 Hyde St, Bloomsbury, London

HARRIS, John. e1840-60. Clock & watch M. Witney

HARRIS, Joshua. w1809-31. Clock & watch M. Witney
Advertised that he sold 'Sheraton' banjo-cased barometers.

HARRIS, Joshua. e1825-45. Clock & watch M. Burford

HARRIS, J. & Son. e1770-90. London

HARRIS, Philip & Co. w1875-95. Physical apparatus M. Bull Ring, Birmingham
Also Philip HARRIS & Co. Ltd. w1896-1900+. 144 & 146 Edmund St, Birmingham

HARRIS, Thomas. w1780-c1806. Opt. IM. Bloomsbury, London
The founder of the firm Thomas Harris & Son which advertised in 1894: 'Originally established opposite British Museum 1780'.

HARRIS, Thomas. e1780-1825. Clock & watch M. Southgate St, Bath

HARRIS, Thomas & Son. c1806-1900+. Opt. IM. London
140 Fleet St (1806) 20 Duke St (1808) 30 Hyde St, Bloomsbury (1810-17) 52 Great Russell St, Bloomsbury (1817-87) 50 High Holborn (1846) 144A Oxford St (c1845) 32 Gracechurch St (1888-1900+)
There was also a branch in Hamburg. Opticians to the Royal Family.

HARRIS, William. w1799-1814. Opt. math. & phil. IM. 47 High Holborn, London
Worked for David Brewster of Edinburgh before starting on his own in London. The name was changed to William Harris & Co. in 1814.

HARRIS, William. w1814-41. Opt. IM. Great Russell St and 63 King St, London

HARRIS, William & Co. w1814-40. Opt. math. & phil. IM. 50 High Holborn, London
The name was changed to William Harris & Son in 1840.

HARRIS, William Henry. w1875. e1875-95. Clock & watch M. East Dereham

HARRIS, William & Son. w1840-55. Opt. math. & phil. IM. 50 High Holborn, London
Produced the improved sympiesometer that was patented by A. O. Harris in 1850.

HARRISON, Francis. w1834-58. Clock & watch M. Hexham

HARRISON, John. w1847-e1875. Phil. math. & opt. IM. London
3 Raquet Court, Fleet St (1847) 36 Kirby St, Hatton Garden (1853) 29 Kirby St, Hatton Garden (1856-60) 68 Red Lion St, Clerkenwell (1869-75)

HARRISON, John & Son. w1876-98. Clock & watch M. Darlington

HARRISON, W. e1840-60. Hexham

HARRISONS e1880-1900. Opt. IM. Arcade, Birmingham
Aneroid barometers.

HARROD, William Thomas. w1834. 1 Bakers Row, Clerkenwell, London

HARRODS e1875-1900+. Retailer. Knightsbridge, London

HARROP, J. e1870-90. Manchester.

HART, N. e1835-45. Woolwich

HART, Samuel. w1830-75. Clock & watch M. Devizes

HART, Stephen & Maurice. w1799-1818. Clock & watch M. London

HART, William D. w1855-93. Electric bell & phil. IM. Edinburgh
6 Young St (1855) 7 North College St (1856-61) 8 North College St (1862-69) 8 North College St & 549 Castle Hill (1870-72) 549 Castle St (1873-93)

HARTNALL, Thomas. w1830-50. Clock & watch M. Cirencester

HARVEY & PEAK w1884-1900+. Opt. math. & phil. IM. London
6a Beak St, Regent St (1884-89) Sandringham Buildings (1890) 56 Charing Cross Rd (1891-1900+)

HASKELL, James. w1842-75. Clock & watch M. Salisbury

HASSARD, W. J. w1894. Opt. & phil. IM. 209 Sauchiehall St, Glasgow

HASSFELD Bros. w1878-81. Math. opt. & phil. IM. London
34 London Wall (1878-80) 76 Newgate St (1881)

HAUKSBEE, Francis (elder). w1700-d1713. Math. & phil. IM. London
Giltspur St. Wine Office Court, Fleet St. Hind Court, Fleet St
An important instrument-maker who was noted for his surgical cupping glasses, air pumps and barometers. He gave lectures on meteorology and pneumatics, and was elected a Fellow of the Royal Society in 1705. He invented a type of inverted angle barometer described by John Harris in his *Lexicon Technicum* of 1704 as follows: 'The ingenious Mr Hauksbee shewed me a Baroscope where the mercury rose and fell 60 inches with very great ease, and without breaking or dividing; and it may very easily be made for 100 or 200 inches, if a strait small thin glass tube can be blown and drawn of that length, and that it were as easily manageable.' He had a nephew of the same name.

HAUKSBEE, Francis (younger). b1687-d1763. Math. & phil. IM. In Crane Court, near Fetter Lane, Fleet St, London
An instrument-maker who produced a similar range of instruments to those of his uncle Francis Hauksbee. He was almost certainly apprenticed to his uncle and was working

on his own by 1712. His trade card showed him to be a maker of pumps and hydrostatic apparatus, whilst his advertisements indicated that he made and sold 'Several sorts of barometers constructed according to their latest and best improvements'. These included stick, wheel and angle barometers. His instruments were recommended by the Secretary of the Royal Society.

HAW, T. e1830-50. York

HAWES, Alfred. e1815-35. Clock & watch M. London

HAWES, Alfred. w1894. Opt. IM. London
79 Leadenhall St and 7 Great Marylebone St

HAWES, William. w1843. Opt. IM. 95 Cheapside, London

HAWES, William. w1869-81. Clock & watch M. London

HAWKES, John. w1883-92. Math. IM. London
294 Albany St, Camberwell (1877-78) 74 Green St, Bethnal Green (1880) 2 Albany St, Camberwell (1883-92)

HAWKINS, Joseph. w1830. e1830-70. Clock & watch M. Southampton

HAWKINS, Thomas. c1820. Math. & phil. IM. 16 Percy St, King's Cross, London

HAY, John. e1840-60. Carver & gilder. Market St, Aberdeen

HAY & LYALL w1856-91. Carvers & gilders. Aberdeen
2 Market St (1856-90) 97 Union St (1891)
Barometers also signed 'HAY & LYLE'.

HAYMAN e1835-55. Launceston

HAYNES, Thomas. w1822-28. Clock & watch M. Stamford

HAYTON, Daniel. w1879. e1850-80. Clock & watch M. Hereford

HAYWARD, Edward. w1847-74. Clock & watch M. Ashford

HEADLAM e1840-60. 4 Silver St, Stockton-on-Tees

HEALD, Alfred. w1840-75. Watch, clock & opt. IM. High St, Wisbech

HEARN, C. e1840-60. Montrose

HEATH e1865-90. 8 George St, Plymouth
Admiral Fitzroy barometers.

HEATH & Co. w1883-87. Naut. & phil. IM. 28 Fenchurch St, London

HEATH & Co. Ltd. w1888-1900+. Math. opt. phil. & naut. IM. London

115 & 117 Cannon St (1891-97) 2 Tower Royal, Cannon St (1898-1900+) 28 Fenchurch St (1888-89) Observatory Works, Crayford (1888-1900+)

HEATH & STONEMAN e1870-90. London

HEATH, Thomas. w1714-d1773. Math & phil. IM. At the Hercules and Globe next door to ye Fountain Tavern in the Strand, London
The son of William Heath, a yeoman, and apprenticed to Benjamin Scott. Heath was a distinguished instrument-maker whose advertisements show that he made globes, spheres, weather-glasses, mathematical instruments with books on how to use them. Around 1750 he formed a partnership in the name of Heath and Wing with his former apprentice, Tycho Wing, who was also his son-in-law.

HEATH, W. e1845-65. 4 George St, Plymouth

HEATH, William. c1830. Math. IM. Devonport

HEATH, William & Thomas Cornish. w1850-57. Opt. & math. IM. Devonport
46 Fore St (1850-52) 116 Fore St (1857)

HEATH & WING w1750-73. Math. & phil. IM. Hercules and Globe, Exeter Exchange, Strand, London
A partnership between Thomas Heath and his former apprentice Tycho Wing who became his son-in-law. The partnership lasted until Heath died in 1773 when Wing retired and sold the business to Thomas Newman, an apprentice of Tycho Wing. (See Fig. 15.)

HEATHCOTE, P. e1810-30. Burnley

HEIGHWAY e1850-70. Cambridge

HEMINGWAY, Robert. w1848-49. 18 Brooke St, London

HEMSLEY, Henry. w1828-60. Opt. IM. London
138 Ratcliffe Highway (1828-45) 140 St George St (1846-60)

HEMSLEY, Thomas. w1820-53. Opt. math. & phil. IM. 11 King St, Tower Hill, London

HEMSLEY, Thomas & Son. w1857-98. Naut. IM. London
4 Tower Hill (1857-98) 4 King St, Tower Hill (1887-98)

HENDERSON, Angus. w1861-84. Math. & opt. IM. Edinburgh
23 Hanover St (1861-68) 69 George St (1869) 48 Frederick St (1870-73) 11 Teviot Place (1874-76) 2 South St David St (1877) 72 Gilmore Place (1878) 51 Hanover St (1882-83) 5 Cathcart Place (1884)
On his trade card he advertised himself as having been 'for many years in the Establishment of Messrs Adie & Son and Mr James Bryson'. It is said that he devised a differential barometer.

HENDERSON, Thomas. w1754-56. Opt. math. & phil. IS. Glasgow
He was agent for James Ayscough and George Sterrop.

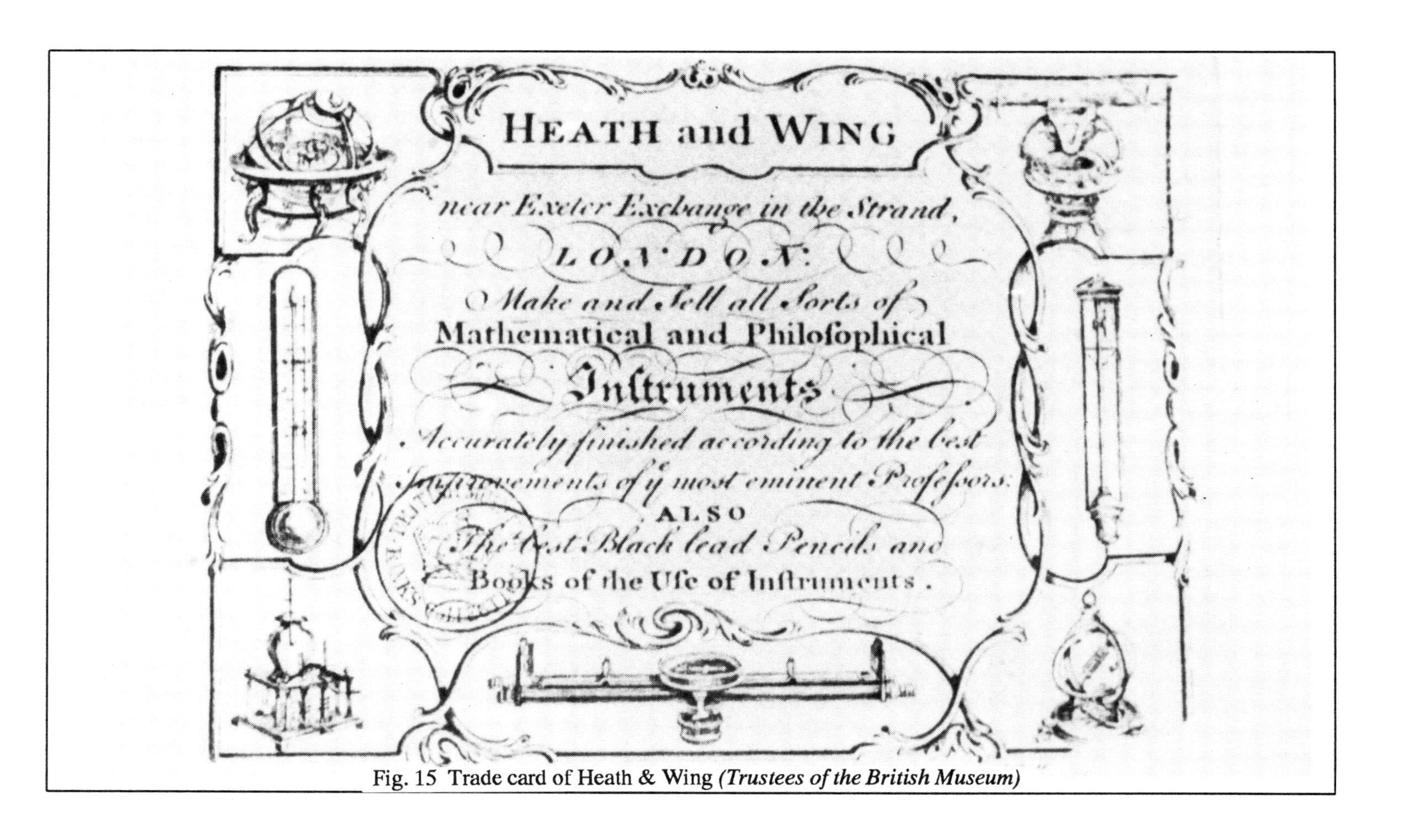

Fig. 15 Trade card of Heath & Wing *(Trustees of the British Museum)*

HENDRY, W. T. & Co. w1875-87. Hydrometer M. 2 Wilson St, Finsbury, London

HENFREY, J. & W. w1815-35. Clock & watch M. Leicester

HENLEY, William Thomas. w1844-48. Phil. IM. 28 Haydon St, Minories, London

HENRY, William. w1820-28. Clock & watch M. Islington, London
He made large wheel barometers with a clock above the dial.

HENSHAW, Isaac. e1815-35. Clock & watch M. London

HERON, David. w1827-63. Naut. & opt. IM. Glasgow
1 William St (1827-34) 128 Broomielaw (1834-36)
212 Broomielaw (1836-47) 4 Carrick St (1849-63)

HERON, David & Co. w1836-63. Naut & opt. IM. Glasgow
212 Broomielaw (1836-47) 4 Carrick St (1849-63)

HERON & JOHNSTON w1844. Naut. & opt. IM. 212 Broomielaw, Glasgow
A partnership between David Heron and James Johnston that only lasted for one year.

HESELTINE, Charles. w1830-38. e1830-50. Opt. math. & phil. IM. 5 Robert St, Gray's Inn Lane, London

HESLOP, Richard. w1850-71. Clock & watch M. Huddersfield

HEWITSON, J. e1855-75. Newcastle upon Tyne

HEWITT, Whisson White. w1847. Math. opt. & phil. IM. 26 Long Acre, London

HEYWOOD, William. w1817-40. Clock & watch M. London

HICKMAN, Joseph. w1775-81. Phil. IM. Basinghall St, London

HICKS, F. J. e1880-1900. Yeovil
Aneroid barometers.

HICKS, G. e1830-50. 42 Upper North Place, Gray's Inn Lane, London

HICKS, George. e1820-40. Gray's Inn Rd, London

HICKS, James Joseph. w1861-1900+. Opt. math. & phil. IM. London
8 Hatton Garden (1861-84) 8, 9 & 10 Hatton Garden (1885-1900+) St Peter's House, Clerkenwell Rd
Born in Ross Carbery, Co. Cork, Ireland and apprenticed to L. P. Casella in London. He made and sold, wholesale and retail, all types of barometers and the business became one of the largest in the United Kingdom. He was a staunch Catholic and presented meteorological instruments to the Vatican; he was made a Knight Commander of St Gregory.

HICKS, Joseph. w1814-22. Math. & phil. IM. London

11 Brooke St (1814-16) 17 Lambeth Walk (1817) 19 Kirby St (1817-20) 17 Bishopsgate Without (1820-22)

HIGGINS, John. w1811-23. Cabinet-maker. London
16 Saffron St, Saffron Hill (1811-19) 3 Saffron St, Saffron Hill (1822-23)

HIGHFIELD, Edward. w1857-63. e1855-75. Clock & watch M. London

HIGHLEY, Samuel. w1863-75. Opt. IM. London
70 Dean St, Soho (1863) 18 Green St, Leicester Square (1864-68) 10a Great Portland St (1869-75)

HILL, Daniel. w1843-d1884. Clock & watch M. Colchester

HILL, J. J. w1866. Clock & watch M. Castle Cary

HILL, M. w1860. 201/2 Constitution Hill, Birmingham

HILL, Nathaniel. w1746-66. Math. IM & engraver. The Globe & Sun, Chancery Lane, London (See Fig. 16.)

HILL, Peter. w1801-28. Math & opt. IM. Edinburgh
Richmond St (1801-03) 7 East Richmond St (1804-10) 9 East Richmond St (1811-12) 6 Union Place (1813-22) 7 Union Place (1823-24) 2 Greenside Place (1825-28)

HILL & PRICE e1870-90. Bristol

HILL, T. e1860-80. Aneroid barometers. 4 Haymarket, London

HILLIARD, J. e1795-1815. London

HILLS, Benjamin. w1839-58. Clock & watch M. Sudbury

HILLS, Jno. e1770-90. Bury

HILLS, William. w1847-74. Clock & watch M. Rochester

HILLUM & Co. w1854-55. Opt. math. & phil. IM. 109 Bishopsgate St Within, London

HILLUM, John. w1840. Opt. IM. 109 Bishopsgate St Within, London

HILLUM, Richard. c1810-47. Opt. math. & phil. IM. 109 Bishopsgate St Within, London

HILLUM, S. (Mrs) w1849-53. Opt. math. & phil. IM. 109 Bishopsgate St Within, London

HILSER, F. e1880-1900. Clock & watch M. Trowbridge

HINDERWILL, Matthew. w1827. Clock & watch M. Stockton

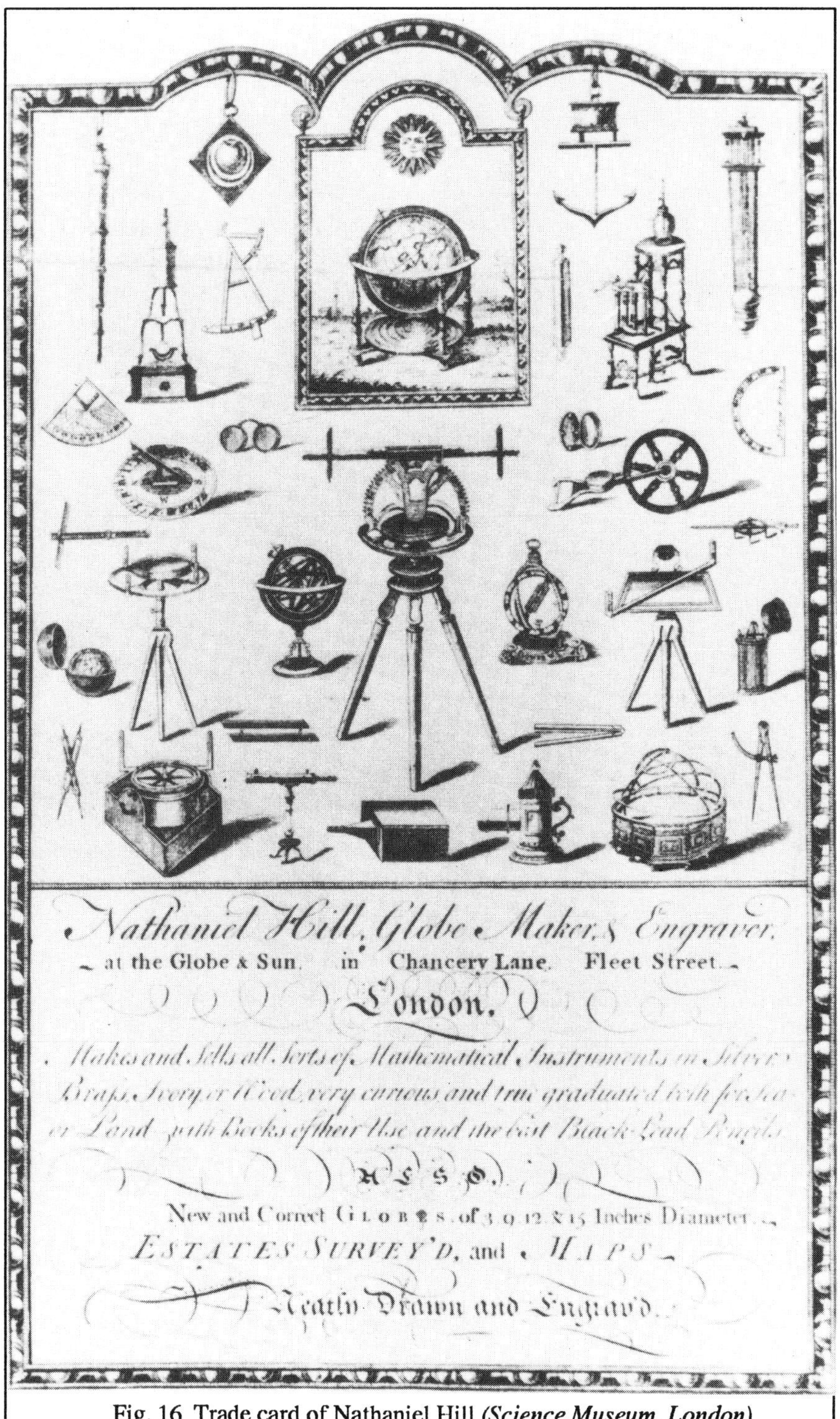

Fig. 16 Trade card of Nathaniel Hill *(Science Museum, London)*

HINTON, William. w1856-66. Frame maker. London
39 Charles St, Hatton Garden (1856-60) 21 Greville St, Hatton Garden (1865-66)

HITCH w1797. London

HOBCRAFT, William. w1822-72. Opt & math. IM. London
14 Barbican (1830-56) 91 Fleet St (1857) 419 Oxford St (1853-72)
He called himself 'senior' whilst at the Barbican premises between 1845 and 1856.

HOBCRAFT, William (junior). w1847. Opt. math. & phil. IM. London
38 Princes's St, Leicester Square (1847) 14 Great Turnstile, Holborn (1847)

HOBDAY e1770-90. Tetsworth

HOBDELL, Henry Banshard. w1832-44. Clock & watch M. Oxford

HODSON, Charles. w1850-60. Clock & watch M. Worcester

HOGG, William. w1834-46. Opt. IM. 394 Rotherhithe St, London

HOLLAND, Gabriel. e1730-50. Clock & watch M. Coventry
Angle barometers.

HOLLAND, William. w1849-71. London
14 Greville St (1849-51) 20 Greville St (1852-59) 17 Greville St (1860) 20 Greville St (1862-71)

HOLLAND & WITHERSPOON w1848. 24 Brooke St, London

HOLLIS, John. w1879-89. London
50 Corporation Row, Clerkenwell (1879-80) 52 Whiskin St (1881-89)

HOLLIWELL, William. w1795-1845. Opt & math. IM. Liverpool
14 North Side, Salthouse Dock. 79 West End, Old Dock

HOLLIWELL, William & Son. w1830-37. Opt & math. IM. Liverpool
Hurst St. 7 Salthouse Dock East

HOLLYER, Sam. e1810-30. Clock & watch M. London
Attached stick barometers to the doors of some of his longcase clocks.

HOLMAN, William. w1875-77. 4 Berry St, Clerkenwell, London

HOLME, D. w1849-55. Clock & watch M. Derby

HOLMES, F. w1890-97. Math. naut. & phil. IM. 76 Shacklewell Lane, London

HOLMES, John. w1762-1815. Clock & watch M. 156 Strand, Somerset House, London

HOLMES, John. w1811. Clock & watch M. London

HOLMES, William. e1835-55. London

HOLMES, William & Son. w1802-24. Clock & watch M. Strand, London

HONEYBONE, George. w1840-63. Clock & watch M. Fairford

HONEYBONE, Richard. w1830. e1820-40. Clock & watch M. Fairford

HOOD, John. w1840-d1888. Clock & watch M. Cupar, Fife

HOOD, Robert. w1830-55. Clock & watch M. Blandford
Also Robert HOOD (junior) w1867-75.

HOOD, Thomas Horton. w1852-64. London
4 Margaret St, Commercial Rd (1852-53) 20 Margaret St, Commercial Rd (1854-56) 6 Salmon Lane, Limehouse

HOOKE, Robert. b1635-d1703. London
Born on the Isle of Wight and went to Westminster School, London before going to Oxford as a chorister. He became assistant to Robert Boyle and soon was appointed curator of experiments to the Royal Society when it was formed in 1662. He is credited with inventing the wheel barometer and making the first hygrometer in England. He was also responsible for adapting the cistern tube barometer for marine use and for developing the double barometer. (See Fig. 17.)

HOOPER, Henry. w1860. Frame M. 17 Aylesbury St, Clerkenwell, London

HOPKINS e1835-55. London

HOPPE, Ebenezer. w1804-10. e1800-30. Math. IM. 51 Church St, Minories, London

HOPTON, James Knie. w1817. Lawnmarket, Edinburgh
The grandson of Balthazar Knie, he carried on his grandfather's barometer business when Knie died in 1817. It is known that Knie had difficulty in disposing of his stock when he announced his impending retirement in 1814; in fact he advertised a lottery at one guinea a ticket. This was unsuccessful and it could be that his grandson carried on the business solely to clear the remaining stock.

HORDEN, W. P. w1860. e1835-60. Clock & watch M. Kidderminster

HORNE & THORNTHWAITE w1853-85. Opt & phil. IM. London
123 Newgate St (1853-56) 121, 122 & 123 Newgate St (1857-66) 122 & 123 Newgate St (1867-74) 3 Holborn Viaduct (1875) 416 Strand (1876-85)
Trade cards with the Newgate St addresses show that they obtained a Medal at the Great Exhibition at the Crystal Palace in 1851 and that they were appointed photographers to the Queen.

HORNE & THORNTHWAITE w1894-1912. Opt. & phil. IM. 416 Strand, London

HORNE, THORNTHWAITE & WOOD w1845-56. Opt. & phil. IM. 123 Newgate St, London

Fig. 17 Robert Hooke (1635-1703)

Their trade card dated June 1846 noted that they were successors to Edward Palmer.

HORNE, THORNTHWAITE & WOOD w1886-93. Opt. & phil. IM. London
416 Strand (1886-87) 416 Strand and 74 Cheapside (1888-93)

HORROD & BUNDOCK e1815-35. 2 Silver St, Clerkenwell, London

HORROD, William. w1811. e1805-45. 37 Laystall St, Leather Lane, London
Some barometers signed 'C. W. HORROD' at this address. He made large wheel barometers with a clock above the dial.

HORROD, William Thomas. w1832-34. Engraver. 1 Bakers Row, Clerkenwell, London

HORTON, William. w1842. 12 Barbican, London

HOUGHTON, F. e1830-50. Chester

HOUGHTON, Thomas. w1771-d1825. Watch tool M. Farnworth

HOULISTON, James. w1839-59. Opt. IM. London
3 St Alban's Terrace, Kennington Rd (1839) 33 New Bond St (1843-50) 85 New Bond St (1851-59)

HOUSTON & CAMERON w1865. Math. & naut. IM. 19 Howard St, Glasgow

HOW, James. w1861-75. Math. opt. & phil. IM. 2 Foster Lane, Cheapside, London

HOW, James & Co. w1876-91. Math. opt. & phil. IM. London
2 Foster Lane, Cheapside (1876) 5 St Bride St (1877-79) 73 Farringdon St (1880-91)

HOWARD e1865-85. Wolverhampton

HOWARD John. e1850-70. Vauxhall Rd, 24 McGuire St, Liverpool

HOWELL, J. e1780-1800. London

HOWELL, James & Co. e1870-90. Regent St, London
Aneroid barometers and barographs.

HOWIE, James. w1869. Opt. & phil. IM. 76 Nethergate, Dundee

HOWIE, Peter. w1871. Opt. IM. 52 Barrack St, Dundee

HOWLETT, John. w1830-79. Clock & watch M. Cheltenham

HOWORTH, Charles. w1823-d1852. Halifax
A prolific maker of stick and angle barometers with paper plates. His angle barometers had one or two tubes and were identical to those made by Samuel Lainton.

HOWSE, Richard. w1842-75. Clock & watch M. Marlborough

HUDDLESTON e1850-70. Boston

HUDSON, Alfred. w1881. Math. IM. 34 Hatton Garden, London

HUDSON, Alfred & Co. w1882-85. Math. & opt. IM. 34 Hatton Garden, London

HUDSON, Arthur. e1790-1810. Bradford

HUDSON, John. w1817-37. Opt. math. & phil. IM. London
112 Leadenhall St. 7 Orange St and St Martin's Court, Leicester Square

HUDSON, John. e1835-55. Ottley

HUDSON & Son. e1800-1900. Math. opt. & phil. IM. Greenwich, London
Some barometers signed 'HUDSON, Greenwich' and some large wheel barometers have a clock above the dial. Instrument-makers to the Admiralty, the Royal Naval College and the Royal Observatory. 'HUDSON & Son' is recorded at Stockwell St, Greenwich between 1881 and 1885.

HUGGINS, J. e1835-55. Colchester
Produced large wheel barometers with brass stringing and pendulum clocks above the dial.

HUGHES, E. K. e1875-95. Gresford
Aneroid barometers.

HUGHES, Henry. w1830-76. Math. IM. 120 Fenchurch St, London
He moved into 120 Fenchurch St around 1835 where he established a Navigation Warehouse under the trade sign of 'Little Midshipman'. This became a well-known rendezvous for seamen. The street number was changed to 59 Fenchurch St in 1855.

HUGHES, Henry. w1840-42. Opt. & naut. IM. 3 Union Terrace, Commercial Rd, London

HUGHES, Henry & Son. c1876-1900+. Math. naut. opt. & phil. IM. 59 Fenchurch St, London
A partnership between Henry Hughes of Fenchurch St and his son Alexander. Alexander's son Arthur joined the business and took it into the twentieth century.

HUGHES, James. w1817-22. Opt. IM. 16 Queen St, Ratcliff Cross, London

HUGHES, James. w1842-48. Clock & watch M. Swindon

HUGHES, Joseph. c1800. Limehouse, London

HUGHES, Joseph. w1822-78. Math. naut. & phil. IM. London
16 Queen St (1822-42) 38 Queen St (1843) 37 & 38 Queen St (1844-67) 38 & 40 Queen St (1868-76) 19, 21 and 22 London St, Fenchurch St (1872-76) 104 Minories (1877-78)

HUGHES, Thomas. e1815-45. Oxford

HUME, William. w1874-1900+. Chemical & phil. IM. Edinburgh
16 South College St (1874-79) 1 Lothian St (1880-1900+)

HUMMEL, Maurice F. w1893-1900+. Opt. IM. London
23 Fenchurch St (1893-95) 73 Hatton Garden (1896-1900+)

HUMPHREY, Thomas. w1812-48. Clock & watch M. Barnards Castle

HUNT, George. e1740-60. Overton

HUNT, Harry. w1673-1713. Gresham House, Broad St, London
He was assistant to Robert Hooke until 1676 when he was appointed Operator to the Royal Society. He specialised in meteorological instruments, and when Edmund Halley was measuring the height of Snowdon in 1697 he wrote 'I could have wished for one of Hunt's portable barometers, which will certainly be accurate enough for taking the levels for bringing water from distant places.' He also made marine barometers and a weather glass for Samuel Pepys.

HUNT, Thomas (senior). w1792-1812. Opt. & math. IM. Patrick St, Cork

HUNT, Thomas (junior). w1820-28. Opt. & math. IM. Patrick St, Cork

HUNT, Thomas. w1822-25. Chronometer, clock & watch M. Tottenham Court Rd, London

HUNTER & EDWARDES w1839-44. Clock & watch M. Cornhill, London

HUNTER, W. e1780-1830. Edinburgh

HUNTLEY, R. e1820-40. 124 Cheapside, London

HUNTLEY, Robert. w1810-30. Opt. IM. London
1 Plummers Row, City Rd. 53 High Holborn. 294 Regent St. 118 Oxford St

HURT, Joseph. w1729-48. Opt. IM. Archimedes and Three Golden Spectacles, Ludgate St, London
His trade card includes 'curious portable barometers with or without thermometers'.

HURTER, J. H. w1787-93. Math. IM. London
A barometer made by Hurter was used to measure the height of Mont Blanc in 1787. He developed, with J. B. Haas, an ivory float for the cistern tube barometer.

HURTER & HAAS w1790-95. Math. opt. & phil. IM. London
Developed barometers and other meteorological instruments for scientists.

HUSBANDS e1865-90. Opt. IM. 8 St Augustine's Parade, Bristol

HUSBANDS & CLARK e1855-65. Opt. IM. 8 St Augustine's Parade, Bristol

HUSBANDS, Henry. e1840-55. Opt. IM. 8 St Augustine's Parade, Bristol
Barometers also signed 'HUSBANDS & Sons'.

HUTCHINSON, George. w1825-51. Clock & watch M. Clapham, London

HUTCHINSON, George. w1857. Clock & watch M. London

HUTCHINSON & Son. e1835-55. Glasgow

HUTCHISON, George. w1888-1900+. Math. & opt. IM. 16 Teviot Place, Edinburgh

HUTTON, John. w1863-69. Clock & watch M. London

HUXTABLE, J. w1848. e1845-65. Clock & watch M. Trowbridge. Also at Frome

HUXTABLE, W. e1860-80. South Molton

HYDE, John. w1828-61. Clock & watch M. Engraver. Southgate, Sleaford

HYDE, John M. w1848-51. 1 Broad Quay, Bristol

HYNES, John. w1830. e1815-45. Opt. IM. 98 High St, Lynn

I

ILLINGWORTH, John. e1790-1810. Halifax

IMMISCH, Moritz. w1887-88. Malden Crescent, Prince of Wales Rd, London

IMRAY, James. w1846-54. Naut. IM. London
116 Minories (1846-50) 3 Old Fish St Hill (1848-50) 102 Minories (1853)

IMRAY, James & Son. w1864-1900. Naut. IM. London
102 Minories (1864-66) 89 & 102 Minories (1867-76) 1 Postern Row (1868-72)

IMRAY & Son, REYNOLDS & WIGGINS w1859-63. Naut. IM. 102 Minories, London

INGHAM, Joshua. w1869-79. Clock & watch M. Cockermouth

INGRAM, L. w1838-41. Clock & watch M. 239 High St, Lincoln

INTROFISI, P. e1810-30. London

INTROSS, A. e1820-40. Chatham

INTROSS, A. e1830-50. Rochester Bridge

INTROSS, A. & Co. e1840-60. Strood

INTROSS, A. & Co. w1858. e1840-60. 5 Sim's Terrace, Chatham

INTROSS, P. e1810-30. Rochester

INTROSS, P. e1815-50. Chatham

INTROSS, W. e1825-50. Rochester Bridge

INTROVINO, Gaspar. w1822-41. Carver & gilder. Manchester
43 Thomas St (1822-26) 88 St George Rd (1841)

INTROZI, D. e1810-30

INTROZZY, Joseph. e1800-20

IRELAND, Henry. w1832. e1815-35. Clock & watch M. Jersey

IRVIN, Thomas E. & Peter H. w1838-42. Math. & phil. IM. 11 Charles St, Hatton Garden, London

IRVINE, Elizabeth. w1837-45. Opt. IM. 32 Kirby St, Hatton Garden, London

IRVINE, John G. w1830-37. Opt. IM. 32 Kirby St, Hatton Garden, London

ISAACS, M. L. w1891-1901. Opt. IM. 40 Furnival St & 2 Dyers' Buildings, Holborn, London

ISSACHAR 1830-50. Cheltenham

IVES, T. w1866. e1840-66. Clock & watch M. Colchester

J

JACK, Arthur & Co. e1880-1900. Cheltenham
Barographs.

JACKSON, James. w1820-22. Opt. math. & phil. IM. 16 Knightsbridge, London

JACKSON, John. w1846-58. Clock & watch M. Scarborough

JACKSON, Richard. w1786-1827. Carver & gilder. 5 Essex Bridge, Dublin

JACKSON, Thomas. w1747-52. Glass seller. Essex Bridge, Dublin
A bill head dated 28 November 1747 included 'Pocket weather glasses'.

JACOB, Isaac. e1840-60. 33 Castle St, Swansea

JACOB, Isaac. w1866-68. w1880-86. 23 & 24 Brooke St, Holborn, London

JACOB & PENSO w1869-79. 23 & 24 Brooke St, Holborn, London

JACOBS, Wolff. w1830-38. Opt. math. & phil. IM. 36 Great Saffron Hill, London

JACOPI, C. e1820-40. Salop

JACQUEMIN Bros. w1879-1900+. Opt. math. & phil. IM. London
64 Hatton Garden (1879-80) 42 Hatton Garden (1881-87) 65 Hatton Garden (1888-1900+)

JAMES, Henry. w1862-78. e1850-80. Clock & watch M. Godalming

JAMES, John. w1874. Clock & watch M. Saffron Walden

JAMES, S. e1805-25. London

JAMIESON, George. w1786-1810. Clock & watch M. 36 Charing Cross, London. High St, Portsmouth

JANTROVINO. e1830-50. 49 Thomas St, Manchester

JEACOCK, James. w1836-77. Math. & phil. IM. Limehouse, London
32 Fore St (1836-43) 96 Fore St (1844-47) 32 Fore St (1848-53) 33 Fore St (1855-73)

JEFFREY, William. w1864. Clock & watch M. Scarborough

JEFFREY, W. R. e1850-70. Saffron Walden

JEFFREYS, James. w1830. Opt. math. & phil. IM. 132 St John St, Smithfield, London

JEFFREYS, William. w1830-47. Opt. math. & phil. IM. 26 Wilderness Row, Goswell St, London

JEFFREYS, William George. w1853-78. Math & opt. IM. London
26 Wilderness Row (1853-59) 20 Wilderness Row (1860-64) 24 Wilderness Row (1865-78)

JEFFS, John. w1877. Clock & watch M. Luton

JENKINS, Alexander. w1854-64. London
15 Garnault Place, Clerkenwell (1854-56) 19 Remington St (1857-64)

JENKINS Bros. w1865-1900+. 19 Remington St, City Road, London

JENKINS, Frederick. w1882. 63 & 64 Milton St, Fore St, London

JENKINS, Henry. w1757-78. Clock & watch M. London
46 Cheapside (1774) 68 Aldersgate St (1778)

JENKINS, S. e1850-70. 65 Red Lion St, London

JENNER & KNEWSTUB w1881. Clock & watch M. London
33 St James's St and 66 Jermyn St

JENNINGS, J. e1820-40. Ipswich

JENNINGS, T. e1810-30. Ipswich

JESTY, R. e1835-55. Bath

JEWITT & Co. e1860-80. 49 South John St, Liverpool

JEWITT, W. & Co. e1840-60. 39 South Castle St, Liverpool

JOHN, Peter. e1830-50. Lynn

JOHN, Peter. e1830-50. Wisbech

JOHNSON, Anne (Mrs). w1865-76. London
34 Hatton Garden (1865-68) 85 Hatton Garden (1869-76)

JOHNSON & BLACKBOURN w1847-48. 34 Hatton Garden, London
A partnership between William Johnson and Cuthbert Blackbourn.

JOHNSON, Samuel. w1724-72. Opt. IM. At the Sign of Sir Isaac Newton and Two Pair of Golden Spectacles, 23 Ludgate St, London
Apprenticed to James Mann and succeeded him on his death. His trade card shows his to be 'The Oldest Shop' and that he made and sold barometers and thermometers.

JOHNSON, William. w1830-67. London
19 Cross St, Hatton Garden (1830) 20 Cross St, Hatton Garden (1831-33) 29 Kirby St (1834-40) 34 Hatton Garden (1841-67)
In partnership with Cuthbert Blackbourn under the name of Johnson & Blackbourn 1847-48.

JOLLY, Charles A. E. e1870-90. Mansfield

JONES e1850-70. Opt. IM. 210 Strand, London

JONES, Charles. w1820-37. Opt. & math. IM. Liverpool
57 Stanley St. 25 Strand
Marine barometers.

JONES & Co. e1800-20. 241 Oxford St, London
Barometers signed 'JONES' with this address.

JONES, David. w1851-81. Clock & watch M. London

JONES, David. w1856-90. Clock & watch M. Newtown

JONES, David & Andrew. w1887. e1885-90. Clock & watch M. Pwllheli

JONES, Edward. w1830. Chronometer, clock & watch M. 1 Small St, Bristol

JONES, GRAY & KEEN e1865-85. Strand, Liverpool

JONES, Henry. w1654-d1695. Clock M. Inner Temple Lane, London
He was the first to be asked to make barometers for general sale around 1675. He made a few but was not particularly interested, as he preferred clockmaking; Henry Wynne was asked to take his place.

JONES, James William. w1838-79. Opt. math. & phil. IM. London
87 Goswell St (1838-62) 172 Goswell St (1863-79)

JONES, John. w1739-84. Opt. IM. 135 Holborn, Corner of the Bell and Crown Inn, London
A well-known maker who was called 'Jones of Holborn' to distinguish him from 'Jones of Charing Cross'. He took his son William into partnership in 1784 as JONES & Son.

JONES, John. w1840-60. Opt. IM. 28 & 29 Wellington Quay, Dublin

JONES, John E. e1865-85. Llandyssil

JONES, Mary (Mrs). w1828-41. Opt. math. & phil. IM. 241 Oxford St, London

JONES & Son. w1784-88. Opt. IM. 135 Holborn, London
A partnership between John Jones and his son William. The father died in 1788 and William formed a partnership with his brother Samuel.

JONES, Thomas. b1775-d1852. Opt. math. & phil. IM. London
120 Mount St, Berkeley Square (1806) 21 Oxenden St, Piccadilly (1811-14) 62 Charing Cross (1816-50) 13 Panton St, Haymarket. Cockspur St. 4 Arbour Terrace, Commercial Rd (1851-52) 4 Rupert St, Haymarket (1853-61)
Jones was apprenticed to Jesse Ramsden in 1789 and was in business on his own account by 1806. He worked from several addresses until 1850 when he appears to have taken a son into partnership. He was an authority on astronomical and meteorological instruments and made stick, marine and mountain barometers. He was instrument-maker to the Duke of Clarence and was elected a Fellow of the Royal Society in 1835. He was known as 'Jones of Charing Cross' to distinguish him from 'Jones of Holborn'. A son, who was in partnership with him from around 1850, continued to use his father's name, after he died in 1852, until 1861.

JONES, Thomas. w1822. Opt. & math. IM. 4 Harrington St, Liverpool

JONES, Thomas & Son. c1850-61. Opt. math. & phil. IM. London
62 Charing Cross (1850) 4 Arbour Terrace, Commercial Rd (1851-52) 4 Rupert St, Haymarket (1853-61)
A partnership between Thomas Jones (Jones of Charing Cross) and a son. The father died in 1852 but barometers were signed 'Thomas Jones & Son' or 'Thomas Jones' until 1861.

JONES, William. w1880-83. Opt. math. & phil. IM. 172 Goswell Rd, London

JONES, William & Samuel. w1788-c1860. Opt. math. & phil. IM. London

135 Holborn Hill (1793-98) 32 Holborn Hill (1801-05) 30 High Holborn (1798-1860)
(30 Lower Holborn is given as the address on some trade cards)
The sons of John Jones who was in partnership with William until John died in 1788. William was apprenticed to Benjamin Martin and also worked for George Adams (junior) before joining his father. The two brothers became important instrument-makers and advertised 'stick, wheel, diagonal and marine barometers' and, in 1843, 'a new stick barometer for ascertaining the heights of mountains, depths of valleys etc.' They also sold *A Concise Explanation of the Barometer, Thermometer and Hygrometer, with rules for predicting Changes in the Weather.*

JONES, W. T. e1880-1900. Glasgow
Barographs and thermographs.

JORDAN, Dominic. e1780-1800

JORDAN, James B. w1867-81. Engineer & inventor. London
Employed at the Mining Record Office and built large water barometers and glycerine barometers.

JOYCE, James. w1856-70. Clock & watch M. Whitchurch

JUDGE e1865-85. Chard

JUDSON, Thomas. w1830-38. Opt. math. & phil. IM. London
26 Waterloo Rd, Lambeth. 11 Alfred St, Newington Causeway

JUMP, Richard Thomas. e1830-50. Clock & watch M. London

K

KALABERGO, G. e1815-40. Banbury

KALABERGO, John. w1832-d1852. Clock & watch M. Banbury
Market Place (1832-52) Bridge St North (1832-52)
Born in Lombardy, Italy and mainly known for his numerous 'Sheraton shell' banjo-cased barometers. His nephew came over from Italy as his assistant in October 1851, but they fell out and John was shot by him in January 1852. The nephew was tried and executed in Oxford in March 1852. John traded as a licensed hawker no. 286 B.

KARRATT, S. e1820-40. Newcastle under Lyme

KEARY, Patrick J. w1886-90. Opt. & phil. IM. 17$^{1/2}$ Wellington Quay, Dublin

KEARY, P. J. w1892-1909. Opt. IM. 13 Wellington Quay, Dublin

KEELEY, J. e1845-65. Bolton

KEEN & FRODSHAM e1850-70. 17 South Castle St, Liverpool

KEEN, Robert John. w1834-40. Opt. math. & phil. IM. 8 Postern Row, Tower Hill and 4 Upper East Smithfield, London

KEIR, Peter. w1823. Clock & watch M. Falkirk

KEIZER, L. & Co. e1850-70. Liverpool

KELSO & Co. w1872-1900+. Opt. & phil. IM. Glasgow
67 Oswald St (1872-75) 133 Bothwell St (1876-78) 43 Union St (1881-86) 2 Commerce St (1887-94) 21 & 23 Clyde St (1895-96) 55 & 57 Oxford St (1897-1900+)

KELSO & TODD w1879-80. Opt. & phil. IM. 43 Union St, Glasgow

KELVIN & James WHITE Ltd. w1900. Opt. math. & phil. IM. Glasgow

KEMP & Co. w1835-87. Chemical & phil. IM. Edinburgh
7 South College St (1835-38) 53 South Bridge (1839-44) 12 & 13 Infirmary St (1845-87)

KEMP, John. e1830-40. Wakefield

KENDALL & DENT w1881-84. Clock & watch M. London

KENDALL, Samuel W. w1867-75. Clock & watch M. Portland

KENDRICK, Charles. w1842-50. Clock & watch M. Alcester

KEOHAN, Thomas. w1840-74. Math & opt. IM. London
2 Arbour Place, Commercial Rd (1840-53) 33 Upper East Smithfield (1857-74)

KERR, Alexander. w1796. Clock & watch M. Dumfries

KETTERER w1830. e1820-40. Clock & watch M. Queen St, Portsea

KETTERER & Co. w1839-48. Clock & watch M. Queen St, Portsea

KEWLEY, Thomas. w1816. Phil. IM. Aldersgate St, London

KEYZOR & BENDON w1857-78. Opt. math. & phil. IM. 50 High Holborn, London

KIDD, John. w1853-56. Naut. IM. 6 East Dock St, Dundee

KIESSLER, Theodore. w1869-91. Math. & opt. IM. London
18 Spencer St (1869-70) 361 City Rd (1871-91)

KIMBEL, Isaac. w1775-1817. Opt. IM. 21 Dean St, Fetter Lane, London

KIMBEL, John. w1817-25. Opt. math. & phil. IM. 21 Dean St, Fetter Lane, London

KILLICK, Charles. w1869. e1845-70. Clock & watch M. London

KING e1825-45. 45 Baldwins Gardens, Leather Lane, London
He made large wheel barometers with a fusée movement pendulum clock above the dial.

KING, Alfred. w1830-59. Clock & watch M. Chippenham

KING, Alfred. w1863. Engineer. Liverpool
Produced a self-registering barometer or barograph called a balance barograph.

KING, C. B. e1850-70. 41 College Green, Bristol

KING, J. e1865-85. Norwich

KING, John. w1780. Clock & phil. IM. Aberdeen

KING, John. w1830. Math. & phil. IM. 6 Cannon St, St George's End, London

KING, John. w1830. Math. & phil. IM. 13 Goswell St, London

KING, John. w1830. Opt. math. & phil. IM. 112 Leadenhall St, London

KING, John & Son. w1825-30. e1825-60. Opt. IM. 2 Clare St, Bristol

KING, Peter. e1810-30. Southwark

KING, Thomas D. w1848-51. 2 Clare St, Bristol

KIPPAX, John. w1849-76. Clock & watch M. East Retford

KIRBY, James. w1795. e1795-1820. Clock & watch M. St Neots, Hunts.

KIRKWOOD, John. e1720-40. Wooler, Scotland

KLEISER, Felix. w1850-79. Clock & watch M. 41 Commercial St, Hereford

KLEYSER & Co. w1828-57. Clock & watch M. Goswell St, London

KNEEBONE e1800-50. Jeweller. Redruth

KNIE, Balthazar. w1773 (Cork, Ireland) w1776-1816 (Edinburgh)
Cork (1773) Niddry's Wynd (1776) Opposite the Guard (1782-90) Opposite Forrester's Wynd Well (1793-98) Head Seller's Close (1800-03) Lawnmarket (1805-10) 405 Lawnmarket (1811-14) Borthwick's Close (1815) 204 High St (1816)
The most well-known and prolific maker of barometers in Scotland. He was born in Germany and spent several years travelling around Europe as an itinerant barometer maker giving exhibitions of glassblowing. He spent a year or so in Cork and arrived in Edinburgh in 1776 when he advertised his barometers and other activities which included: 'He blows and spins glass before company on the table, and forms many curiosities too tedious to mention. If any of the curious have in mind to see him work,

they are heartily welcome, from six to eight in the evening. His stay in the city will be short.' His stay in Edinburgh lasted for forty years. He intended to retire in 1814 and dispose of his stock by way of a lottery; he valued the stock at £309, which comprised some seventy instruments, but the lottery appears to have been abandoned through lack of support. He died in 1817.

KNIGHT e1820-40. Braintree

KNIGHT, George & Co. w1839-53. Opt. & phil. IM. 2, 41 & 42 Foster Lane, London

KNIGHT, George & Sons. w1864-77. Phil. IM. London
2 Foster Lane (1864-76) 5 St Bride St (1877)

KNOX, John. w1809-16. Clock & watch M & jeweller. Belfast

KRASA, F. & Co. w1898-1900+. 7 Wood St Square, London

L

LACKEN, John. e1795-1815. Maidstone

LACY, William. e1810-40. Frame M. West St, West Smithfield, London

LADD & OERTLING w1862-69. Phil. IM. London
192 Bishopsgate St Without (1862-63) 27 Moorgate St (1864-68)

LADD, William. w1846-72. Opt. math. & phil. IM. London
10 Cleaver St (1846) 7 Cleaver St (1847) 29 Penton St (1850-57) 31 Chancery Lane (1858-60) 11 & 12 Beak St (1861-72)

LADD, William & Co. w1873-83. Opt. math. & phil. IM. London
11 & 12 Beak St (1873-83) 199 Brompton Rd (1873-75) 1 Plough Yard, Shoreditch (1879)

LAFFRANCHO, J. e1815-50. Ludlow
Many of his wheel barometers had rectangular mirrors above the spirit level, with the main dial above the thermometer and below the hygrometer.

LAINTON, J. e1840-60. Halifax

LAINTON, Samuel. e1820-50. Halifax
Made many stick and angle barometers with paper plates. His angle barometers had one or two tubes and were identical to those made by Charles Howorth.

LAIRD, David W. w1834-51. Clock, watch & naut. IM. Leith
4 Bridge St (1834-42) 58 Bridge St (1843-51)

LAKE, F. & C. w1861-66. e1840-70. Clock & watch M. Taunton

Some barometers signed 'LAKE & Son' with this address.

LAMBERT, Michael. w1878-81. e1845-81. Opt. IM. 47 Rathmines, Dublin

LANCASTER, James & Son. w1874-80. Opt. & phil. IM. Birmingham
Compton House, 87 Ball St and 5 Colmore Row

LANG, Charles & Co. w1896-97. 3 Bradford Avenue, London

LANG & Co. w1863-72. London
26 Skinner St, Newgate and Green Arbour Court, Old Bailey (1863-68) 27 Houndsditch (1868-72)

LANGFORD, William. w1825-70. Clock & watch M. 52 Broad Quay, Bristol
Also William LANGFORD & Son at this address. w1870-79

LANGLEY, William. w1871-79. Opt. math. & phil. IM. London
20 Southwark (1871-73) 46 Tooley St (1875-79)
By appointment to H.M. Customs.

LANITI, Vincent. e1815-35. Manchester

LANOTA, B. e1800-20. Portsmouth

LAPPI & SOLCHA e1835-55. Hull
Also barometers signed 'S. LAPPI & Co.' at this address.

LARA, A. e1810-30. Glasgow

LARA, A. e1870-90. Edinburgh

LARGE, J. Jerome. e1865-85. Birmingham

LASHMORE, Edward. w1863-79. Clock & watch M. Oswestry

LASSETER, W. w1851-62. Clock & watch M. Arundel

LAST, William Robert. w1846-65. Clock & watch M. Acle, Great Yarmouth

LATCH, William. w1830-71. Clock & watch M. Newport, Mon.

LAURIE, James. c1800. Phil. IM. Glasgow

LAWRENCE & MAY w1894. e1880-1900. Opt. IM. 67 & 69 Chancery Lane, London

LAYBOURN e1800-20. Royston

LAZARS, Isaac. w1841-53. Opt. math. & phil. IS. 89 George St, Edinburgh
Also appears to have had a shop in Cupar which opened from time to time.

LEA, Philip. w1689-1700. Opt. & math. IM. The Sign of the Atlas and Hercules, against the Old Jewry, London

LEACH, George. w1830-48. Clock & watch M. Salisbury

LEAR, Anthony James. w1830. Math. & phil. IM. 36 St John's Lane, Clerkenwell, London

LEE, Albert. w1897-1900+. 59, 60 & 61 Hatton Garden, London

LEE, George & Son. e1880-1900. Math. opt. & naut. IM. Ordnance Row, The Hard, Portsea, and at 3 Palmerston Rd, Southsea
'Instrument-makers to the Honourable Corporation of Trinity House and the Admiralty'.

LEE, Joseph. w1835-68. Watch M, jeweller & optician. Belfast
24 High St (1839) 74 High St (1840-43) 57 High St (1846-68)

LEE & Son. w1850-70. Watch M, jeweller & optician. 57 High St, Belfast

LEFEVER, Charles. w1845-60. Math. & phil. IM. 14 Duncan Place, Hackney, London

LEFEVOR, Thomas. w1824. Math. & phil. IM. 1 College Place, Highbury Vale, London

LEGGET, David. w1820. Math. & phil. IM. 35 Tavistock St, Covent Garden, London

LEIGHTON, John. w1838. e1835-65. Clock & watch M. Lancaster

LEJEUNE & PERKIN w1857-87. Math. opt. & phil. IM. London
15 Wine Office Court (1857-65) 24 Hatton Garden (1866-84) 10 Hatton Garden (1883-86) 112 & 113 Hatton Garden (1885-87) 99 Hatton Garden (1887)

LELLI, S. e1820-40. Chester

LELLI, S. e1820-40. Chichester

LELLI, S. w1839-55. Clock & watch M. Newport, Isle of Wight

LENNIE, Eliza. w1857-1901. Opt. IM. 46 Princes St, Edinburgh
Widow of James Lennie. (See Fig. 18.)

LENNIE, James. w1840-57. Opt. IM. 14 Leith St, Edinburgh
Lennie died in 1854 and his widow Eliza carried on the business in his name until 1857 when she moved to 46 Princes St and then traded in her own name.

LENTON c1780. Congleton

LEONARD, Charles. w1828. Clock & watch M. Camberwell, London
Produced large wheel barometers with a clock above the dial.

Fig. 18 Cover of price list of E. Lennie *(Science Museum, London)*

LEONE e1840-60. Exeter

LEONE, John. e1830-50. Aylesbury

LEONI, Frederick. w1839-48. Clock & watch M. Andover

LERBONI, A. e1825-45. Sheffield

LERBONI, J. & Co. e1810-30. London

LE ROY, J. B. e1830-50. Jersey
Some barometers made by him have an ivory plate on which is inscribed 'Made from the wreck of the Royal George. Sunk, August 29th 1782'. The *Royal George* was a 100-gun flagship launched in 1757 which sank in Portsmouth harbour with the loss of around 900 lives. She was blown up in 1839 and the wood was used in a commercial way to commemorate the disaster.

LERRA, P. e1820-40. Leeds

LERRA, P. & Co. e1820-40. Sheffield

LERRA, V. & Co. e1810-30. 26 Church St, Sheffield

LESLIE, John. w1821. Clock & watch M. Kirkaldy

LETCHER, J. T. w1880. Opt. math. & phil. IM. Truro
Successor to Letcher Bros and Jeffrey.

LETTEY, P. & W. e1820-40. Dunster

LETTI & Co. e1790-1810. Leeds

LEVERTON, J. w1777. Opt. IM. Liverpool

LEVI, A. e1835-55. Hastings

LEVI, Jones & Co. Ltd. w1898-1900+. 29 Hoxton Square, London

LEVI, Joseph. w1860-61. Opt. math. & phil. IM. 40 Castle St, Holborn, London

LEVI, Joseph & Co. w1861-1900+. Opt. math. & phil. IM. London
40 Castle St, Holborn (1861-85) 2 Dyers Buildings, Holborn (1876-95) 10 Kirby St, Holborn (1881-86) 97 Hatton Garden (1896-1900+)

LEVI, Moses. e1830-50. Ipswich

LEVI, S. J. & Co. w1891-97. Opt. & phil. IM. Farringdon Rd, London

LEVIN, Alexander. w1847. e1830-55. Clock & watch M. Penzance

LEVIN, M. & E. e1830-50. London

LEVINE, Moses. w1875. e1840-75. Clock & watch M. Norwich

LEVY, J. e1840-60. Bristol

LEVY, Josiah. w1835. e1820-40. Clock & watch M. Gainsborough

LEVY, Moses. w1839-46. Clock & watch M. Ipswich
Carr St (1839) St Matthew's St (1844-46)

LEWIS & ROSS w1820. Math. & phil. IM. 96 Brick Lane, Spitalfields, London

LEWIS & Sons. w1862-70. Clock & watch M. Brighton

LEY, George. w1780. Upholsterer. 52 High St, Birmingham

LEYSER, K. & Son. e1865-85. Southwark, London

LIDDELL, J. J. w1840-58. Math. opt. & phil. IM. Edinburgh
3 Hanover St (1843-57) 91 South Bridge (1858)
Exhibited at the Great Exhibition at the Crystal Palace in 1851.

LIDDELL, William. w1819-22. e1819-45. Clock & watch M. Edinburgh

LIDDLE, William. w1823-33. Math. & opt. IM. Edinburgh

LIDSTONE, G. e1840-70. Sympiesometers. Dartmouth

LILLEY, John. w1827-45. Math. & opt. IM. 7 Jamaica Terrace, Limehouse, London

LILLEY, John & Son. w1846-1900+. Math. naut. & phil. IM. London
Commercial Place, Commercial Rd. 7 Jamaica Terrace, Limehouse (1846-65) 9 London St, Fenchurch St (1866-86) 10 London St, Fenchurch St (1887-1900+)

LILLY, L. e1780-1830. Edinburgh

LILLY & RIVOLTA w1844-45. Carver. Edinburgh

LILLY, Stephen. w1812-32. e1812-50. Looking glass M. Candlemaker Row, Edinburgh

LIMBACH e1840-60. Hull

LINCOLN, Charles. born c1744-d1807. Opt. & math. IM. London
11 Cornhill, Poultry (1763) 62 Leadenhall St (1791-1801)

LINGFORD, John. w1793-1835. Jeweller & watch M. Nottingham
Market Hill (1793-1814) Parliament St (1835) 5 Milton St (1835)

LINNELL, J. e1820-50. London

LINNELL, Joseph. w1763-75. Opt. math. & phil. IM. The Great Golden Spectacles

and Quadrant, 33 Ludgate St, London
Apprenticed to James Ayscough in 1754 and succeeded him in 1763. He used Ayscough's name and trade card until 1767 and this shows that he sold 'barometers, diagonal, standard, or portable'.

LIONE & Co. e1800-30. 81 Holborn, London

LIONE, D. e1835-55. Liverpool

LIONE, D. & Co. e1810-30. 81 High Holborn, London

LIONE, Dominick. w1805-36. London
125 Holborn Hill (1805-07) 14 Brooke St (1811-20) 16 Brooke St (1821-36)

LIONE & FARONI e1810-30. London

LIONE, J. e1835-55. Aylesbury

LIONE, James. e1810-30. 81 Holborn Hill, London

LIONE, SOMALVICO & Co. w1805-22. Opt. IM. London
125 Holborn Hill (1805-07) 14 Brooke St (1811-19) 16 Brooke St (1820-22)
Some barometers signed 'LIONE & Co.' and 'LIONE & SOMALVICO' with these addresses.

LIONE, TARONI & Co. e1800-20. London
Some barometers signed 'LIONE & TARONE'.

LISTER, John. e1810-30. Dean St, Holborn, London

LISTER, William. w1827-56. Clock & watch M. Newcastle upon Tyne

LITTLEJOHN, Wilson. w1846. Clock & watch M. Peterhead
Also at Turriff. w1860.

LITTLEWOOD & Co. e1865-90. 34 Dundas St, Glasgow
Marine barometers with sympiesometers.

LITTLEWOOD, Thomas. w1868-1900+. Opt. & phil. IM. Glasgow
45 Sauchiehall St (1868) 25 Howard St (1869-95) 54 St Enoch Square (1896-1900+)
Also branches in London and Manchester. Admiral Fitzroy barometers.

LITTLEWORT, George. w1838-43. Opt. IM. 11 Bull Alley, Lombard St, London

LITTLEWORT, William. w1826-46. Opt. & math. IM. 7 Bull Alley, Lombard St, London

LIZARS, John. w1858-1900+. Opt. & phil. IM. Glasgow
24 Glassford St (1858-74) 13 Wilson St (1876) 16 Glassford St (1877-87) 16 Glassford St and 260 Sauchiehall St (1888-90) 101-107 Buchanan St (1891-1900+)
Some barometers were made of oak from the Royal Exchange which was destroyed

by fire on the night of 10 January 1838.

LLOYD, John. w1850-56. Clock & watch M. Hereford

LLOYD, PAYNE & AMIEL e1875-95. Manchester

LOCK, Henry. w1802. Clock & watch M. Oxford

LOCKWOOD, J. J. e1850-90. Preston

LOFTUS, William Robert. w1858-1900+ Opt. IM. London
6 Beaufoy Terrace, Edgware Rd (1858-68) 146 Oxford St (1869-80) 320 Oxford St (1882-85) 321 Oxford St (1886-1900+) 2 & 3 Lancashire Court, New Bond St (1884-1900+)

LOGAN, Thomas. w1855. e1840-60. Clock & watch M. Dorchester

LOMAS, H. e1800-20. Adlington

LOMBARDINI, A. w1856. e1840-60. Looking glass M. 13 Lower Castle St, Bristol

LOMBARDINI & CASTELETTI e1810-30. Salop
Also LOMBARDINI, CASTELETTI & Co. e1810-30. Shrewsbury

LOMBARDINI, F. e1810-30. Totnes

LOMBARDINI, G. or S. e1815-45. Bristol

LOMBARDINI, J. B. e1840-60. Huddersfield

LONG, J. e1845-65. Tiverton

LONG, James. w1769-1811. Opt. math. & phil. IM. Royal Exchange, London

LONG, Joseph. w1820-1900+. Hydrometer & saccharometer M. London
20 Little Tower St (1820-84) 43 Eastcheap (1885-1900+)

LONG, Joseph. w1827-33. Opt. math. & phil. IM. 136 Goswell St, London

LONGDON, Rev. Alfred. e1875-1900. One-time vicar of St Denys Church, Sleaford, Lincs.
He made at least two double-angle barometers on a 'T'-shaped base with paper register plates. An aperture below gives expected weather conditions for barometer readings indicated.

LONGONI, F. e1810-30. London

LOOF, William (senior). w1823-55. Clock & watch M. Tunbridge Wells
Also William LOOF (junior). w1845-47

LOPRESTI, Antonie Joseph. w1875-81. Clock & watch M. London

LORDELLI, J. e1800-20. London

LORENZE & BRUGGER, A. w1843. 79 High Holborn, London

LORG, C. e1845-65. 16 Frederick Place, Old Kent Rd, London

LOSA, Joseph & Co. w1877-78. 5 Phipp St, Curtain Rd, London

LOVI, Angelo. w1772-1804. Specific gravity bead M. Edinburgh
Niddry St (1772) 83 South Bridge (1804) 16 South Bridge
He made stick, wheel and double barometers.

LOVI, Isabell. w1805-27. Spirit proof M. Edinburgh
82 South Bridge (1806) Geddes Close (1807-11) 79 High St (1812-13) Strichen's Close (1814-21) 113 High St (1822) 114 High St (1823-25) Strichen's Close (1826-27)

LOVI, J. & Son. w1820. Glassblower & chemical IM. 104 High St, Edinburgh

LOWDON, George. w1850-1900+ Opt. & phil. IM. Dundee
25 Union St (1850-61) 1 Union St (1864-74) 23 Nethergate (1876-80) 60 Reform St (1882-1900+)

LOWE, Alexander & Co. w1810-30. London and Madras

LOWRY, John. w1850-57. w1862-80. Clock, watch & chronometer M. Belfast
55 High St (1850) 19 High St (1852-57) 66 High St (1862-68) 46 High St (1870-77) 94 High St (1880)

LOWRY, J. & S. w1858-61. Jeweller & watch M. 66 High St, Belfast

LOWTHER, George. w1870. Naut. & math. IM. 62 Grainger St, Newcastle upon Tyne

LOZANO, Thomas. e1810-30. Clock & watch M. London

LUCIN, Francis. w1839-40. 142 Great Saffron Hill, London

LUCIONI, Guiseppi A. w1851-54. 36 Ray St, Clerkenwell, London

LUCKING, James & Co. e1870-90. 14 Broad St, Worcester

LUCKING, R. e1875-95. Aneroid barometers. 5 Corporation St, Birmingham

LUNAN, William. w1824-25. Watch, clock & phil. IM. 8 Castle St, Aberdeen

LUNATTI, P. e1810-30. Preston, Warminster

LUND, Hardaker. w1873-75. Phil. IM. 12 Brooke St, Holborn, London

LUND, W. e1840-60. 23 & 24 Fleet St, London

LUNN, J. e1800-50. Edinburgh

LUPPIE, Salvador. w1838-51. 17 Robinson Row, Hull

LUPPIE & SOLCHA w1840. e1835-50. 17 Robinson Row, Hull
Some barometers signed 'S. LUPPIE & Co.' and 'LUPPI & SOLCHA'.

LURAGHI, F. w1832-33. 9 City Rd, Finsbury, London

LURASCHI, Alex. w1884-93. 15 Cross St, Hatton Garden, London

LUSTIE, J. e1810-30. London

LUVATE, Dominic. w1828-34. e1820-45. Looking glass M. Preston
43 Friargate (1828) 27 Friargate (1834)

LYM, James. e1840-60. Glasgow

LYNCH & Co. w1841-42. Opt. IM. 36 Westmorland St, Dublin

LYNCH & Co. w1879-1900+. Surgical IM. London
171 Aldersgate St (1879-80) 192 Aldersgate St (1881-1900+)

LYNCH, James (1). w1767-72. Opt. IM. Dublin
Father of James Lynch (2) and grandfather of James Lynch (3).

LYNCH, James (2). w1784-1807. Opt. IM. 26 Capel St, Dublin

LYNCH, James (3) & Co. w1845-46. Opt. IM. 26 Capel St, Dublin

LYNCH, James (3) & George. w1840-44. Opt. math. & phil. IM. 26 Capel St, Dublin
Instrument-makers to the University and the Royal Dublin Society.

LYNCH, James (2) & James (3). w1826-39. Opt. math. & phil. IM. 26 Capel St, Dublin
James Lynch (2) died in 1833 and was succeeded by James (3).

LYNCH, James (2) & Son. w1808-25. Opt. IM. 26 Capel St, Dublin

LYON e1835-45. South Molton

LYON, Craven. w1822-68. Clock & watch M. Bridlington

LYON, David. w1872-78. Opt. IM. London
43 St John's Square (1872-76) 2 & 3 St John's Square (1878)

LYON, Henry. w1875. Clock & watch M. Trowbridge

LYON, James. e1805-35. 6 Dove Court, Swithen's Lane, Lombard St, London

LYON, Peter. w1780-99. Opt. IM. Edinburgh
At the Cross Well (1782) Near the Guard (1784) Head Old Assembly Close (1786) High St (1788-90) Bull Turnpike (1794) Castle Hill (1795) Calton Hill (1796-97) 10 Parliament Close (1799)

LYON, Peter. w1784-88. Math. naut. & phil. IM. On the Shore, Leith

M

McADAM, Robert. w1820-45. Clock & watch M. Dumfries
Also Robert McADAM (junior) w1840-67.

McALLISTER e1810-30. London

McCABE, James. e1830-50. Clock & watch M. Royal Exchange, London

McCARTHY, William Henry. w1875-1900+. Glassblower. London
4 Coldbath Square, Clerkenwell (1875-83) 9 Mount Pleasant (1883-1900+)

McDONALD, James. w1846. Clock & watch M. Aberdeen

McDONALD, James. w1847-52. Phil. IM. Edinburgh
56 Potterow (1847-48) 36 Lothian St (1849-50) 4 Hill Place (1852)

McDONALD, James. w1854-57. Phil. IM. Glasgow
37 Union St (1854) 192 Argyle St (1855-57)

MACDONALD, John. e1865-85. Edinburgh

McDOWALL e1835-55. Edinburgh

McELROY, F. e1860-80. Aneroid barometers. Manchester

McFARLANE, A. P. w1841. Clock & watch M. Glasgow

M'GILLIVRAY, John. w1876. Phil. IM. 17 West Nicolson St, Edinburgh

M'GILLIVRAY, John. w1877. w1881-83. Phil. IM. Glasgow
146 West Nile St (1877) 158 George St (1881-82) 73 John St (1883)

M'GILLIVRAY & SCOBIE w1878-80. Phil. IM. Glasgow
146 West Nile St (1878) 204 George St (1879-80)
Philosophical instrument-makers to Anderson's College.

McGREGOR, D. & Co. w1856-1900+. Naut. math. & opt. IM. Glasgow
38 Clyde Place (1856-57) 38-40 Clyde Place (1858-68) 44 & 45 Clyde Place (1869-90) 37 & 38 Clyde Place (1891-1900+)
Also branches in Greenock, Liverpool and London.

McGREGOR, Duncan. w1844-55. Naut. math. & opt. IM. Glasgow
24 Clyde Place (1844-54) 38 Clyde Place (1855)

MACHI, P. e1835-55. Liverpool

McHUGH, M. or H. e1830-50. Staleybridge

McINNES & CAIRNS w1889-93. Chronometer & naut. IM. 41 & 42 Clyde Place, Glasgow

McINNES, Thomas S. w1885-89. Chronometer & naut. IM. 41 & 42 Clyde Place, Glasgow

McINNES, T. S. & Co. Ltd. w1893-1903. Chronometer & naut. IM. 41 & 42 Clyde Place, Glasgow

MACKENZIE, Alexander. w1816-22. Math. IM. 15 Cheapside, London

MACKEY, P. D. w1820. e1820-50. Carver & gilder. 3 Skinner Row, Dublin

MACKIE, James. w1828-81. Clock & watch M. London

MACKINTOSH, Thomas. w1780-82. e1780-1830. Opt. & math. IM. London Archimedes and Globe, Long Acre. 7 Great Queen St, Lincoln's Inn Fields

M'KNIGHT, Andrew. w1895-1900+. Opt. & phil. IM. 24 Argyle Arcade, Glasgow

MACKROW, I. e1850-70. 14 Upper Smithfield, London

McMILLS, I. e1780-1800. Bury

MACNEIL w1790-1801. e1790-1820. Opt. IM. London
He was apprenticed to Jesse Ramsden and some marine barometers are signed 'Macneil, London. App.tice of the late Mr Ramsden'.

McNEILAGE, John. w1868-72. Opt. & naut. IM. 14 Cathcart St, Greenock

McPHERSON, Robert. e1820-40. Dumfries

McQUEEN, H. & Co. e1840-60. Glasgow
Marine barometers with sympiesometer.

McQUEEN, Hugh. w1880-86. Chronometer M. 63 Clyde Place, Glasgow

McQUINN, John. w1841. Market Drayton

MacRAE e1830-60. 29 Royal Exchange, London

MacRAE, Henry. w1833-85. Opt. IM. London
34 Aldgate (1833-84) 29 Royal Exchange (1861-76)

MAFFIA, A. e1835-55. London

MAFFIA, Angelo. w1851-74. Clock & watch M. Hertford

MAFFIA, C. e1830-50. Monmouth

MAFFIA, Dominic. w1868-71. e1845-71. Clock & watch M. Monmouth
Also Dominic MAFFIA & Son. w1871-80

MAFFIA, Edward. w1880. Clock & watch M. Monmouth

MAFFIA, Peter. w1841-71. Clock & watch M. Monmouth

MAFFIA, Peter & Dominic. w1868. Clock & watch M. Monmouth
Also P. MAFFIA & Co. e1810-30

MAGATTI & KELLY w1864-68. 8 Leather Lane, London

MAGGI, I. e1810-30. 15 Union Court, Holborn Hill, London

MAGGI, M. e1825-50. Exeter
Barometers also signed 'M. MAGGY'.

MAGGI, Michael & Co. e1820-40. London

MAGGI & ORTELLI e1810-30. London

MAGGIO, Michael. e1815-35. London

MAIN, Peter. e1850-70. Edinburgh

MAINWARING, R. e1845-65. Maidstone

MAKEPEACE, George. w1857-63. e1840-63. Clock & watch M. London

MAKINSON e1840-60. Manchester

MALACRIDA e1810-30. 237 Holborn, London

MALACRIDA e1840-60. 4 Withy Grove, Manchester

MALACRIDA, Charles & Co. w1805-22. London
Some barometers have the address as 'Dublin' and others 'Dublin & London'.

MALI, Charles. w1875. Clock & watch M. Wisbech

MALLETT, Henry. w1839. Clock & watch M & silversmith. Woodbridge

MALLUGANI, Mark. w1830-35. Umbrella S. New St, Dudley

MALT, James. w1858-75. e1845-75. Clock & watch M. Wisbech

MALTWOOD, Richard Austen. w1829-59. London
19 Charles St, Hatton Garden (1829-44) 22 Charles St, Hatton Garden (1845) 129 Great Saffron Hill (1845-48) 5 Cross St (1854-59) 3 Shoe Lane, Fleet St (1847)

MAMINI, Girolomo. w1861. 90 Hatton Garden, London

MANDER, George. w1833-70. Math & phil. IM. London
21 Great Crown Court, Soho (1833-53) 25 Old Compton St, Soho (1845-70)

MANGACAVALI, John. w1836. 5 Greville St, London

MANGACAVALLI, J. e1790-1810. 22 Baldwins Gardens, Holborn, London

MANGIACAVALLI, G. or J. e1825-50. London
22 Charles St, Hatton Garden. 17 Leather Lane, Holborn

MANGIACAVALO, J. e1810-30. Leeds

MANLEY, Thomas Christian. w1876-82. Phil. IM. 18 Sekforde St, Clerkenwell, London

MANN, James (senior). c1693-1717. Opt. IM. Archimedes and Two Pairs of Golden Spectacles, Fleet St, London

MANN, James (junior). c1717-43. Opt. IM. Archimedes and Two Pairs of Golden Spectacles, Fleet St, London
His trade card advertised barometers and thermometers and that his shop was the oldest.

MANN, James & James AYSCOUGH. w1743-49. Opt. IM. At the Sign of Sir Isaac Newton and Two Pair of Golden Spectacles, near the West-End of St Paul's, London

MANN, John. w1694-1709. Mathematician & math. IM. Edinburgh and Leith
At the Sign of the Globe, Cross-staff and Quadrant, Castle Hill, Edinburgh (1694-98)
At the Sign of the Globe, Cross-staff and Quadrant, on the Shore, Leith (1699-1709)

MANN, Peter. w1788. Math. IM. Castlebank, Edinburgh

MANNING & Co. w1876. Clock & watch M. Worcester

MANNING, Frederick. w1868-72. Clock & watch M. Worcester

MANNING, J. e1840-60. Barnstaple

MANNING & MANNING w1860. Clock & watch M. Great Malvern. Also at Worcester

MANOLLA, A. e1795-1815. 39 Leather Lane, London

MANSELL, Thomas. w1865-75. Clock & watch M. Fakenham

MANSFIELD, J. w1848-67. Clock & watch M. Shaftesbury

MANSFORD e1840-50. London
Some of his barometers have a small circular ivory plate inscribed 'Made from the wreck of the Royal George. Sunk, August 29th 1782'. This was the 100-gun flagship launched in 1757 which sank in Portsmouth harbour, when about 900 lives were lost. Her hulk became a shipping hazard and she was blown up in 1839. Using the old wood was a commercial way of commemorating the disaster.

MANSON, F. e1830-50. London

MANTEGANI, Antonio. w1851-58. e1825-60. Clock & watch M. High St, Wisbech

MANTEGANI, J. w1858. Clock & watch M. Wisbech

MANTEGANI, John. w1875. Clock & watch M. Wisbech

MANTICHA e1790-1810. 281 Holborn, London

MANTICHA, A. e1810-30. London

MANTICHA, B. e1800-20. Greenock

MANTICHA & Co. e1790-1810. London

MANTICHA, Dominick. w1781-1805. 11 Ely Court, Holborn, London
One of the many Italians who migrated to England, some via Holland and France, during the last quarter of the eighteenth century. He made high-quality stick and wheel barometers, with many of his stick instruments having printed paper plates and square hinged cistern covers. He also made double or multiple-tube barometers.

MANTICHA, G. e1790-1810. Greenock

MANTICHA, G. & G. e1810-30. Paisley

MANTICHA, Peter. e1790-1820. Crown Feathers Court, Holborn, London

MANTOVA, P. e1840-60. Luton
Wheel barometers elegantly inlaid with variegated pearl and brass depicting birds, flowers, buds and trailing foliage.

MANTUA, Peter. w1839. Clock & watch M. Luton
Also P. & J. MANTUA. w1875

MANZOCHI, Girolano. w1838. Looking glass M. 22 Brook St, Hull

MAPLE & Co. Ltd. e1900. London

MAPPIN e1840-60. 61 Newhall St, Birmingham

MAPPIN & WEBB Ltd. e1900. London
Barometers also signed 'MAPPIN'.

MAPSON, William. w1863-79. Clock & watch M. Tetbury

MARGAS, John. w1761-67. Opt. IM. Capel St, Dublin

MARGOSCHIS, D. S. w1860-68. Clock & watch M. Leamington

MARIA, G. de e1810-30. Taunton

MARINONE, C. e1810-30. Bedford

MARIOT, James. w1742. Sign of the Crown, Gallowgate, Glasgow
Advertised 'all sorts of Barometers and Thermometers at the lowest prices. He mends any Old Ones, and exchanges new Ones for Old Ones.'

MARK, C. e1825-45. Plymouth

MARK, J. & Co. w1864. e1835-65. Clock & watch M. Peterborough
Also J. & A. MARK. w1854. J. & L. MARK. w1864

MARK, J. & Co. w1892-1900. Opt. math. & phil. IM. 76 Fann St, London

MARKS, A. J. w1856. e1850-70. Clock & watch M. High St, Sunderland

MARKS, L. e1790-1810. York

MARKS, Solomon & Co. w1822-75. Clock & watch M. Broad St, Cardiff

MARKWICK, James. w1692-1720. Clock & watch M. Royal Exchange, London

MARLOW, Harry. w1891-96. 5 Mount Pleasant, London

MARLOW, Harry Frederick. w1897-1900+. 28 Aylesbury St, London

MARLOW, P. H. e1875-95. Harrogate

MARNONI, Anthoni. w1844-49. Spirit proof & math. IM. 34 Brunswick Place, Glasgow

MARR & ANDERSON w1859. Chronometer & phil. IM. 14 Renfield St, Glasgow

MARR, David. w1876-77. Opt. & phil. IM. 35 South Bridge St, Edinburgh

MARR, J. & A. w1860. Clock & watch M. Falkirk

MARR, John. w1842-45. Chronometer & phil. IM. Glasgow
35 Montrose St (1842-44) 17 Canon St (1845)

MARR, J. & R. & Co. w1849-58. Chronometer & phil. IM. 27 North Albion St, Glasgow

MARR, Robert & Co. w1860-61. Phil. IM. 27 North Albion St, Glasgow

MARRATT & ELLIS w1874-1900+. Opt. IM. 63 King William St, London

MARRATT, John Symonds. w1829-77. Opt. math. & phil. IM. London
54 Shoe Lane (1833) 15 Great Winchester St (1832-54) 63 King William St (1845-77)
Exhibited at the Great Exhibition at the Crystal Palace in 1851.

MARRATT & SHORT w1847-67. Opt. math. & phil. IM. 63 King William St, London

MARSH, B. w1858. 83 Coleshill, Birmingham

MARSH, I. e1820-40. 22 Tysoe St, London

MARSHALL e1830-50. Alnwick

MARSHALL, John. w1690-1722. Opt. IM. The Archimedes and Two Golden Spectacles, Ludgate St, London

MARSHALL, Peter. w1830-60. Clock & watch M. South Queensferry, Scotland

MARSON, Francis. w1868-70. 1 Hatton Garden, London

MARSON, Francis. w1879-1900+. 32 Clerkenwell Green, London

MARTELLA, B. e1840-60. Swansea

MARTIN, Benjamin. b1704-d1782. Phil. opt. & math. IM. London
Near Crane Court in Fleet St (1756) Hadleys Quadrant and Visual Glasses, near Crane Court, 171 Fleet St (1759-82)
The son of a farmer, he was born at Worplesdon, Surrey and was a teacher before moving to London in 1740 to work as an assistant to the scientist J. T. Desaguliers. Whilst a teacher, he made microscopes and other optical instruments, and appears to have set up in business in Fleet Street in 1756. He was an enterprising instrument-maker who lectured and wrote copiously about his instruments. He held courses, public demonstrations, wrote over thirty popular scientific works and in 1755 launched a monthly *General Magazine of the Arts and Sciences* which ran until 1765; these were subsequently published in book form. Martin made a distinctive stick barometer called a triple weather-glass, because it had three aids to weather forecasting: a barometer, thermometer and hygrometer. He appears to have been the first to add a hygrometer to the barometer and preferred the gut rather than the oat-beard. Martin took his son Joshua into partnership in 1780, just two years before he died; within those two years the partnership went bankrupt.

MARTIN & Co. w1863-70. Clock & watch M. Cheltenham

MARTIN, Felix. e1850-70. Clock & watch M. Swansea

MARTIN, John. w1832-47. Clock & watch M. Maidstone

MARTINELLI, A. e1825-35. 36 Charlotte St, Blackfriars Rd, London

MARTINELLI, Alfred. w1839-d1851. London
43 Union St, Borough (1839) 96 Vauxhall St, Lambeth (1843-44) 18 Vauxhall St, Lambeth (1845-51)
Succeeded by his widow Mrs. E. Martinelli.

MARTINELLI, A. & William DAY & Co. e1835-55. 70 Union St, Borough, London

MARTINELLI, D. w1802. 34 Grays Inn Lane, London

MARTINELLI, D. e1810-30. 19 Leather Lane, London

MARTINELLI, E. (Mrs). w1852-53. 18 Vauxhall St, Lambeth, London
Widow of Alfred Martinelli.

MARTINELLI, Lewis. w1802-11. Carver & gilder. 82 Leather Lane, Holborn, London

MARTINELLI, Lewis. w1834-46. 62 King St, Borough, London
An address of 102 London Rd, Brighton has been recorded.

MARTINELLI, Lewis & Son. w1837-40. Opt. IM. 62 King St, Borough, London
A partnership between Lewis Martinelli, of the same address, and his son.

MARTINELLI, N. e1835-55. 2 King St, Borough, London
Also N. MARTINELLI & Sons.

MARTINELLI, P. e1820-40. Edinburgh

MARTINELLI, P. L. D. & Co. w1799. 82 Leather Lane, London

MARTINELLI, P., RONCHETTI & Co. e1810-30. Coventry

MARTINELLI & RONKETTI e1805-25. 34 Gray's Inn Rd, London

MARTINELLI, W. e1830-50. 62 King St, Borough, London

MARTINELLI, W. e1835-45. 2 King St, Borough, London
Barometers signed 'W. MARTINELLI & Son' and 'W. MARTINELLI & Sons' with this address.

MARTINELLI, William. w1839-80. Opt. math. & phil. IM. London
21 Wells Rd, Oxford St (1840) 5 Friars St, Blackfriars (1841) 120 Snow Fields (1853-59)

MARTINELLI, W. & Sons. e1840-60. 54 Snow Fields, Borough, London

MARTINOIA, G. & Co. e1820-40. York

MARZORATI, E. e1815-35. Edinburgh

MARZORATI & RIVOLTA e1810-30. Edinburgh

MASEFIELD, Robert. c1750-d1773. Cabinet M. 13 New St, Birmingham
Produced stick and angle barometers and used enamel, silvered brass or paper plates.

MASON & Co. w1876. Opt. IM. 11 Essex Bridge, Dublin
Opticians to the Lord Lieutenant. Successors to Mason & Son.

MASON, George. w1837-66. Math. & phil. IM. 52 Squirrus St, Bethnal Green Rd, London

MASON, George & Co. w1869-98. Opt. IM. Glasgow
39 Union St (1869) Sauchiehall St (1890) Buchanan St (1891-98)

MASON, Jonathan. w1805-49. Opt. IM. Dublin
8 Arran Quay (1809) 9 Ormond Quay (1810-12) 14 Chapel St (1818-22) 6 Patrick St, Limerick (1846-49)

MASON, Seacome (1). w1780-1804. Opt. IM. 8 Arran Quay, Dublin
The Mason family originated from Seacombe in Cheshire and moved to Dublin in the early 1700s as part of a government incentive scheme. In 1787 an advertisement included 'Barometers, Thermometers, Celestial and Terrestrial Globes of all sizes'.

MASON, Seacome (2). w1838-78. Opt. IM. Dublin
6 Essex Bridge (1838-44) 11 Essex Bridge (1845-77)
11 Upper Ormond Quay (1878)
'Optician to His Excellency the Lord Lieutenant'.

MASON, Seacome (3). w1877-79. Opt. IM. Dublin
11 Nassau St (1877) 24 Wellington Quay (1879)

MASON & Son. w1865-75. Opt. IM. 11 Essex Bridge, Dublin
Opticians to the Lord Lieutenant.

MASON, Thomas (1). w1805-37. Opt. IM. Dublin
4 Essex Bridge (1809) 3 Essex Bridge (1810-19) 3, 4 or 6 Essex Bridge (1820-38)

MASON, Thomas (2). w1866-99. Opt. math. & phil. IM. Dublin
9 Nassau St (1866-68) 11 Essex St (1869-83) 21 Parliament St (1884-95) 4, 5 & 6 Dame St (1896-99)
'Instrument-makers to His Excellency the Lord Lieutenant and the Irish Court'.

MASON, Thomas & Jonathan. w1805-17. Opt. IM. Dublin
8 Arran Quay (1805-08) 3 Essex Bridge (1813-17)
Two sons of Seacome Mason (1). They carried on his business until 1838 when Seacome Mason (2) took control. The two brothers traded separately from time to time during the overall period of the partnership.

MASPERO, C. e1850-70. Manchester
Made wheel barometers elegantly inlaid with variegated pearl and brass depicting birds, flowers, buds and leaves.

MASPERO, William Angelo. w1878. Clock & watch M. Leatherhead

MASPOLI, Augustus. w1826-55. Opt. math. & phil. IM. Hull
49 Salthouse Lane (1826-31) 79 Lowgate (1835-55)

MASPOLI, Augustus & James. w1831-35. Opt. math. & phil. IM. Hull
49 Salthouse Lane (1831) 79 Lowgate (1835)
Some barometers signed 'A. MASPOLI & Co. Hull'.

MASPOLI, G. e1835-55. Hull

MASPOLI, James. w1831-59. Watch & looking glass M. Hull
49 Salthouse Lane (1831) 79 Lowgate (1835) 17 Robinson Row (1839-48) 9 Robinson Row (1851-59)

MASPOLI, MONTI & Co. w1838-40. Clock & watch M. Sandwich

MASPOLI, P. e1840-60. 13 John St, Westagate, Bradford

MASPOLI, Peter. w1845-47. Clock & watch M. Sandwich

MASPOLI, P. & V. e1820-50. Canterbury

MASPOLI, Vittore. c1810-41. Clock & watch M. Sandwich

MASPOLLI, C. e1830-50. Manchester

MASSI, Charles. w1838. Math. & phil. IM. 38 Steward St, Goswell St, London

MASSINO, Peter. w1808-15. Edinburgh
Canongate (1808) West College St (1809-11) Fountain Close (1812-14) North College St (1815)

MASTAGLIO, FORNELLI & MOLTENI w1837-38. Grainger St, Newcastle upon Tyne

MASTAGLIO & MOLTENI w1841-47. 24-5 Grainger St, Newcastle upon Tyne

MASTAGLIO, V. w1851-60. Newcastle upon Tyne
24 Grainger St (1851-53) 45 Grainger St (1855-60) 4 Carliol Square (1857-60)

MASTALLIO, A. e1810-30. Oxford

MASTALLIO, A. & TOIA e1800. Oxford

MATHERS, Thomas. w1848. Math & opt. IM. 88 Glassford St, Glasgow

MATHEW, Peter. w1839-70. Clock & watch M. Uckfield

MATHEWS, J. H. w1856. Clock & watch M. Oswestry

MATHEWS, Robert. w1830-46. Clock & watch M. Ely

MATTER e1835-55. Worcester

MATTERI, C. e1840-60. Tenbury

MATTHEWS, Alfred. w1847-77. Clock & watch M. Leighton Buzzard

MATTHEWS, T. B. w1840-47. e1830-50. Opt. IM. 9 Athol Place, Pentonville, London

MATTHEWS, William. w1834-58. Clock & watch M. Penrith

MATTHEWS, William L. w1867-75. Clock & watch M. Bridport

MATTHEWS, W. & J. e1835-45. Penrith and Kendal

MAUER, J. e1810-30. Brooke St, Holborn, London

MAUGHAM, J. e1850-70. Beverley

MAUL, S. E. w1838. Rule M. 13 Little Compton St, Soho, London

MAVER, J. e1815-35. 281 Holborn, London

MAVER, J. e1830-50. 1 Beauchamp Place and Brooks Market, London

MAVER, John. w1832-34. 46 Baldwins Gardens, London

MAVER, John. e1835-55. 4 Beauchamp St, Leather Lane, London

MAVERO, J. e1820-40. 11 Brooke St, Holborn, London

MAW, S. & Son. w1894-1900+. Surgical IM. 7-12 Aldersgate, London
Made Admiral Fitzroy barometers.

MAW, W. & Son. e1875-95. London
Admiral Fitzroy barometers.

MAYERS, M. e1830-50. Holborn, London

MAZZUCHI, B. & Co. e1820-45. Gloucester

MAZZUCHI, Innocento. e1800-50. Aylesbury

MEARS, R. e1840-60. Boston

MEDCALF, S. e1820-40. Steeple Bumstead

MEDECI, G. & Co. e1810-30. 14 St Michael's Square, Southampton

MEDICI, Mark. w1866. Clock & watch M. Middlesbrough

MEDICI, Peter. e1810-30. Newcastle

MEDICI, Peter. e1835-55. Shotley Bridge

MEDLAND, John Brandon. w1876-98. Opt. math. & phil. IM. London
10a Borough High St (1876-81) 12 Borough High St (1882-89) 53 Borough High St (1890-91) 141 Borough High St (1892) 70 Borough High St (1896-97) 13 York St, Walworth (1898)

MELLER, Joseph. w1825-26. 28 Princes St, Birmingham

MELLING, Edward & Co. w1848-51. Chronometer & opt. IM. Liverpool

MELLING, John. w1672-1704. Opt. IM. Abchurch Lane, off Lombard St, London

MERCER, Joseph H. w1869-79. Clock & watch M. Appleby

MERGA, A. e1850-70. Nantwich

MERITO, William. w1847. Clock & watch M. Canterbury

MERLINE, Paolo. w1858. 72 Hatton Garden, London

MERONE, Joseph. w1816-41. Looking glass M. Manchester
98 Market St (1816-22) 28 Market St (1822-41)

MESSER, J. e1830-50. Harmer St, Gravesend

MESSER, John James. w1849-84. Opt. math. & phil. IM. London
19 & 20 Upper King St, Commercial Rd (1849-60) 78 & 80 Christian St, Commercial Rd (1861-84)

MEYER e1830-50. Abingdon

MEYER, George. e1810-30. London

MILESIO, D. e1810-30. Kendal

MILESSIO, Dominick. w1812-25. Carver & gilder. Looking glass M. Dublin
25 High St (1812) 35 Skinner Row (1813-19) 6 Skinner Row (1820-24) 11 Skinner Row (1825)

MILL & PRICE e1850-70. Opt. IM. Bristol

MILLAR, Adam. w1868-73. Math. & phil. IM. London
93 Castle St, Holborn (1868) 1a High Holborn (1869-73)

MILLARD, Joseph. w1825-38. Opt. math. & phil. IM. 24 Coppice Row, Clerkenwell, London

MILLARD, Joseph & Son. w1838-43. Opt. IM. 24 Coppice Row, London

MILLARD, Thomas & Son. e1840-1895. Opt. IM. 245, 334 & 354 Oxford St, London

MILLER & ADIE w1804-22. Math. opt. & phil. IM. Edinburgh
94 Nicolson St (1804-06) 96 Nicolson St (1807-09) 8 Nicolson St (1810) 15 Nicolson St (1811-22)
A partnership between John Miller and his nephew Alexander Adie who was his apprentice.
Back of the Fountain Well (1774) Parliament Close (1775-94) 38 South Bridge (1795-

MILLER, John. w1771-1804. Math. opt. & phil. IM. Edinburgh

Back of the Fountain Well (1774) Parliament Close (1775-94) 38 South Bridge (1795-1801) 86 South Bridge (1803-04)
Miller served an apprenticeship in the workshops in London of George Adams senior; he returned to Edinburgh in 1771 and set up in business on his own. He took his nephew, Alexander Adie, as an apprentice in 1789 and made him a partner in 1804. Miller died in 1815.

MILLER, Thomas. w1881-86. Phil. IM. Edinburgh
51 Cockburn St (1881-82) 46 Cockburn St (1883-86)

MILLESIO, D. e1810-30. Kendal

MILLS, George. w1825-46. Math. & phil. IM. 82 Parsons St, Ratcliff, London

MILLS, Henry. w1851-69. Clock & watch M. London

MILLS, William. w1799-1824. Clock & watch M. London

MILNE, Alexander. b1806-d1896. Scientist and inventor. London
He designed a self-recording mercurial barometer in 1857 which is in the Science Museum, London. By 1864 a few meteorological instrument-makers were making a modification of the Milne barograph for sale to the public.

MINOLLA, G. e1820-40. 39 Leather Lane, London

MINOLLA, James. e1795-1830. London

MINORETTI e1840-60. Leicester

MITCHELL, F. e1800-50. Opt. IM. Market Harborough

MITZKO, Henry Thomas. w1838. Math. & phil. IM. 36 St John's Lane, Clerkenwell, London

MODD, James. w1849-68. Clock & watch M. Donnington, Nr Spalding

MOGINIE, C. w1857-69. Clock & watch M. Finchley, London

MOIANA, B. e1810-30. London

MOLINARI, Antonio. w1830. e1815-50. Halesworth

MOLINARI, D. e1825-50. Halesworth

MOLINER, Charles. w1784-1801. Phil. IM. Edinburgh
Baillie Grant's Close (1784) Netherbow (1786-90) High St (1794) Baron Grant's Close (1799-1801)
Also known as Molinari. He came from Como, Italy in 1752. Made stick, angle and double-angle barometers similar to those made by Balthazar Knie and William Robb.

MOLLINI, C. e1825-45. London

MOLLISON, Alexander. w1825. Math. & phil. IM. 17 Chapman St, Islington, London

MOLTENI, A. e1835-55. Wigan

MOLTENI, A. w1851-58. Newcastle upon Tyne
185 Pilgrim St (1851-53) 154 Pilgrim St (1855) 152 Pilgrim St (1857-58) 91 Clayton St (1857-58)

MOLTENI, Alexander. w1826-30. 13 Baldwins Gardens, Leather Lane, London
An invoice dated 1826 shows that he was a 'Looking-glass, barometer, thermometer, picture-frame, waistcoat and brace manufacturer' and that he had a Sheffield and a Birmingham warehouse.

MOLTENI, C. e1810-30. Clock & watch M. London

MOLTENI, C. w1851-60. Newcastle upon Tyne
25 Grainger St (1851-53) Collingwood St (1851-53) 47 Grainger St (1855-60)

MOLTENI, ZERBONI & Co. w1833-38. Carvers & gilders. 9 Carlton St, Edinburgh

MOLTON, Francis. w1822-30. Dove Lane and St Lawrence Steps, Norwich
He made stick and wheel barometers with some wheel instruments having the dial at the top of the case. On some cases he favoured a cogged spindle to adjust the set hand.

MOLTON, Francis & Co. e1790-1810. London

MONAGHAN, James. w1760-62. Weatherglass M. Winetavern, Dublin

MONASTERI, Louis. e1800-20. Darlington
Also L. MONASTERI & Co. e1835-55

MONTI, Anthony. w1845-65. Clock & watch M. Palace St, Canterbury

MONTI, Antonio. w1874. Clock & watch M. Ramsgate

MONTI, G. e1800-20. Leeds
Also G. MONTI & MOIANA e1810-30.

MONTI, John. w1847. Clock & watch M. 82 Northgate St, Canterbury

MONTI, Joseph. w1838. Clock & watch M. 33 Northgate St, Canterbury

MONTI, MASPOLI & Co. w1838-40. Clock & watch M. Sandwich

MONTI, P. & Co. e1810-30. Lewes

MONTI, Peter. w1849-95. Clock & watch M. Sandwich

MONTONA, e1820-40. Luton

MOON & FLEMING w1843. Opt. IM. 76 Minories, London

MOON, John. w1830-65. Opt. math. & phil. IM. London
3 Lucas Rd, Commercial Rd (1830) 28 Green St, Stepney (1838) 76 Minories (1844-50) 31 & 32 Limekiln Hill, Limehouse (1848-59) 213-15 Upper St, Islington (1860-65)

MOON, William (senior). w1820-51. Opt. IM. Minories and West India Dock Rd, Limehouse, London

MOON, William (junior). e1850-70. Opt. IM. West India Dock Rd, London

MOONEY & KLOEPFFER w1880-1900. 12 Cullum St, Fenchurch St, London

MOORE, F. M. w1854-1898. Watch & chronometer M & opt. IM. Belfast
114 High St (1854-68) 102 High St (1870-87) 100 High St (1890-98) Also in Dublin

MOORE, F. M. w1864-1900. Watch, opt. & naut. IM. 23 Eden Quay, Dublin. Also in Belfast

MOORE, John Curtis. w1828-39. Clock & watch M. Worthing

MOORE, Jonas. b1627-d1679. Lecturer in Mathematical Sciences. Tower of London
He made the Tower of London a centre of scientific observation and supplied his pupils with books and instruments.

MORE, James & Co. w1891-98. Opt. IM. 77 Renfield St, Glasgow

MORELEY & Sons. e1840-60. Guildford

MORELLI, F. e1815-35. London

MORETTI, C. e1840-60. Paulton

MORETTI, G. e1835-55. Bath

MORETTI, J. C. e1840-60. Lynn

MORETTI, P. e1810-30. Lynn

MORETTI, Rocco. w1865-87. Clock & watch M. Cardiff

MORGAN, Francis. w1770-1840. Opt. math. & phil. IM. At the Sign of Archimedes and Three Spectacles, 27 Ludgate St, London
His trade card was written in English and French and he worked in St Petersburg for some considerable time.

MORGAN, John Thomas. w1838. Math. & phil. IM. 7 Crown St, Hucton Square, London

MORGANTI, John Baptist. w1823-39. Jeweller & watch M. 31 George St, Brighton

MORISON, Thomas. e1800-20. Watch M. London

MORLAND, Samuel. b1625-d1696. Engineer. London
He is credited with the invention of the angle barometer in the late 1670s; also the balance barometer of which only a very few were made. (See Fig. 19.)

MORLEY, H. e1830-50. London

MORRELL, John. w1823-34. Clock & watch M. Whitby

MORRIS, E. H. w1865. e1865-75. Clock & watch M. Ipswich

MORRIS, J. e1820-40. Opt. IM. Kendal

MORRIS, John. w1835-49. Clock & watch M. Market Deeping

MORRIS, John B. w1825. Math. & phil. IM. 14 New Walnut Tree Walk, London

MORRIS, S. e1835-55. Windsor

MORRIS, William. w1887-99. Clock & watch M. Cardiff

MORTINCIA, G. & Co. e1810-30. York

MORTON, Alexander. w1832-46. Phil. IM. Edinburgh
29 Richmond Place (1832-33) 2 Roxburgh Place (1834-37) 9 Drummond Place (1838) 11 Hill Square (1839) 71 Adam Square (1840-42) 7 South College St (1843-46)

MORTON & Co. w1847-51. Opt. & phil. IM. 7 South College St, Edinburgh

MOSS, Benjamin. w1830. Opt. math. & phil. IM. 7 Catherine St, Commercial Rd, London

MOSS & WINDRED w1838. Math. & phil. IM. 8 Crescent St, Southwark, London

MOTHERWELL & Co. w1890. Phil. IM. 101 West Nile St, Glasgow

MOTHERWELL, John. w1863-88. Phil. IM. Glasgow
24 Jamaica St (1863-64) 32 Union St (1865-68) 73 Union St (1869-74) 295 Argyle St (1875-78) 275 Argyle St (1879-80) 67 & 69$^{1/2}$ Oswald St (1881-84) 77 Renfield St (1885-87) 114 West Nile St (1888)

MOTTERSHEAD & Co. w1888. e1870-90. Barographs. Market Place, Manchester

MOULDER & WALL e1850-70. Ross-on-Wye

MULLALLY, Luke. w1751. At the Blue Window in Caple St, near Mary's St, Dublin
He advertised 'all sorts of Jet Necklaces, Pendants, Buttons, Bugles, Glass Toys, Barometers and mercurial Thermometers. As he manufactured the above Goods, and exceeds any imported, will sell by Wholesale or Retail on the most reasonable Terms.'

Fig. 19 Sir Samuel Morland (1625-96)

MUMMERY, Thomas. e1865-85. Clock & watch M. Dover

MUNEAUX, VIDEPIED, OKERMANS & Co. w1877-81. Opt. math. & phil. IM. 13 Hatton Garden, London

MUNRO, James. w1823-56. Opt. math. & phil. IM. Lambeth, London
72 Oakley St (1823-28) 27 North St (1826-28) 4-5 North St (1830-56) 4 High St (1843) 12 York Place (c1850)

MURDOCH, Laurie. w1852-82. Opt. IM. Edinburgh
45 Rose St (1858) 44 Rose St (1859-65) 1 Young St (1866-69) 3 Young St (1870-73) 108 Rose St (1874-82)

MURDOCK, John G. & Co. Ltd. e1875-95. London and Melbourne
Produced Admiral Fitzroy barometers, often with a clock in the pediment.

MURPHY, W. e1840-60. 5 Meeting House Alley, Green Bank, London

MURRAY & CALLIEU w1866-77. Math. & phil. IM. 22 St John's Square, London
The name was changed to 'MURRAY & Co.' in 1877.

MURRAY & Co. w1877-92. Opt. & math. IM. London
22 St John's Square (1878-86) 141 Oxford St (1891-92)
Formerly 'MURRAY & CALLIEU'.

MURRAY & HEATH w1857-83. Opt. phil. & math. IM. London
43 Piccadilly (1857-66) 69 Jermyn St (1867-83)

MURRAY, James. w1815-40. Watch & chronometer M. 30 Cornhill, London

MURRAY, Robert Charles. w1871-90. Opt. math. & phil. IM. London
69 Jermyn St (1871-83) 113 Pentonville Rd (1884-90)

MYERS e1830-50. Yarmouth

MYERS, George. w1810-20. Looking glass M. 104 High St, Belfast

MYERS, Philip. w1825-35. e1825-45. Opt. & math. IM. Nottingham
Smithy Row (1825) Pelham St (1834-35)

N

NAFTEL, Paul. e1800-45. Guernsey

NAGELE, J. B. w1868-76. Clock & watch M. Wolverhampton

NAGELE, P. & J. w1860. Clock & watch M. Wolverhampton

NAIRNE & BLUNT w1774-93. Opt. math. & phil. IM. 20 & 22 Cornhill, London
A partnership between Edward Nairne and his apprentice Thomas Blunt. It would appear to have been a very loose arrangement as both Nairne and Blunt continued their own individual businesses using their sole names during the partnership. This was probably because they were neighbours; Nairne traded from 20 Cornhill and Blunt from 22 Cornhill. Very many good-quality stick barometers are still extant.

NAIRNE, Edward. b1726-d1806. Opt. math. & phil. IM. 20 Cornhill, London
Apprenticed to Matthew Loft in 1741. He published various booklets on his navigational, astronomical and pneumatic instruments and was elected a Fellow of the Royal Society in 1776. In 1773 Nairne invented an improved marine barometer with a partly constricted tube to contain the violent oscillations of the mercury; this principle was used for upwards of a hundred years. He advertised 'barometers, marine, diagonal, standard or portable'. (See Fig. 20.)

NANNY e1865-85. Shrewsbury

NARRIEU, John. w1805-25. e1780-1825. Opt. & math. IM. 70 St James's St, London

NAYLOR w1722. Black Lion, Longacre, London

NAYLOR e1810-30. Halifax

NEALE & BAILEY e1810-30. 8 St Paul's Churchyard, London

NEALE, John. w1744-58. Math. IM. Leadenhall St, London

NEEVES, Richard William. w1857-88. Phil. IM. London
3 Regent Place East, Grays Inn Rd (1857-67) 55 Sidmouth St, Grays Inn Rd (1868-73) 87 Long Acre (1874-76) 55 Sidmouth St, Grays Inn Rd (1877-88)

NEEVES, William. w1830-56. Math. & phil. IM. London
17 Great St, Andrew St (1830-42) 67 High St, St Giles's (1843-56)

NEGRATTI, H. w1839. 2 Dorrington St, London

NEGRETTI w1810-30. 36 Redcliffe St, Bristol

NEGRETTI & Co. e1790-1810. 55 Pike St, Plymouth

NEGRETTI, Enrico Angelo Ludovico. w1840-50. Phil. IM. London
20 Greville St, Hatton Garden (1840-41) 19 Leather Lane (1845-49) 9 Hatton Garden (1849-50)
Known as Henry NEGRETTI. Some barometers signed 'H. NEGRETTI & Co.' with the 19 Leather Lane address. Negretti came to England from Italy in 1830 at the age of twelve and was apprenticed to F. A. Pizzala. In 1840 Pizzala died and Negretti assisted his widow Ann, for a time, to run the business. He formed a partnership with J. W. Zambra in 1850 named Negretti & Zambra.

NEGRETTI, G. e1835-50. Liverpool

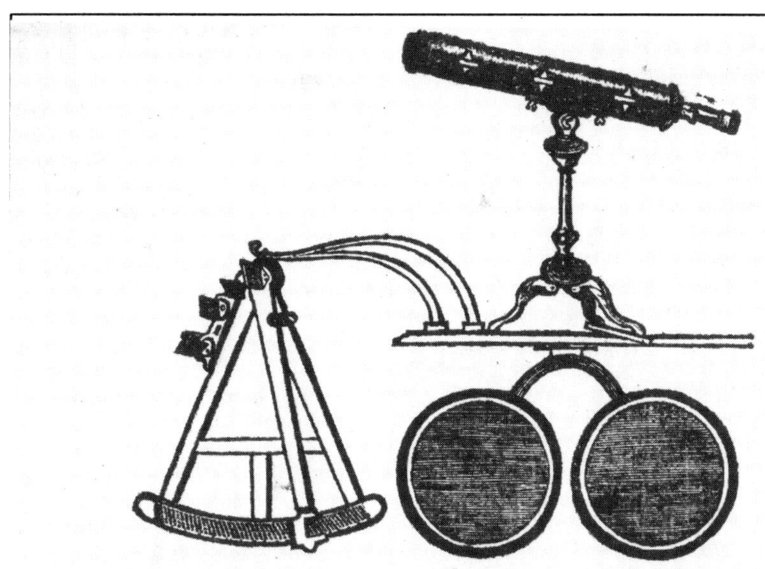

EDWARD NAIRNE,

Optical, Philoſophical, *and* Mathematical Inſtrument-Maker,

At the GOLDEN SPECTACLES, REFLECTING TELESCOPE *and* HADLEY'S QUADRANT, *in* Cornhill, *oppoſite the* Royal Exchange, LONDON;

MAKES and Sells Spectacles, either of GLASS or BRAZIL PEBBLE, ſet in neat and commodious Frames, ſome of which neither preſs the Noſe nor Temples.

CONCAVES for Short-Sighted Perſons; READING, BURNING and MAGNIFYING-GLASSES.

Newtonian and *Gregorian* REFLECTING TELESCOPES; alſo EQUATORIAL TELESCOPES, or PORTABLE OBSERVATORIES.

REFRACTING TELESCOPES of all Sorts; particularly one of a new CONSTRUCTIŌN (which may be uſed either at Land or Sea) that will ſtand all Kinds of Weather without warping, and is allowed by thoſe eſteemed the beſt JUDGES, who have made ſeveral late Trials of them at Sea, to exceed all others yet made in *England*; alſo a peculiar Sort to be uſed at Sea in the Night.

MICROSCOPES, either DOUBLE, SINGLE, AQUATICK, SOLAR, or OPAKE; likewiſe a new-invented POCKET MICROSCOPE, that may be uſed with the SOLAR, and anſwers the Purpoſes of all the other Sorts.

CAMERA OBSCURAS for delineating Landſkips and Proſpects (and which ſerve to view Perſpective Prints) made with truly Parallel Planes; SKY-OPTIC BALLS; PRISMS for demonſtrating the Theory of Light and Colours; CONCAVE, CONVEX, and CYLINDRICAL SPECULUMS; MAGICK LANTERNS; OPERA GLASSES; OPTICAL MACHINES for Perſpective Prints; CYLINDERS and CYLINDRICAL PICTURES.

AIR PUMPS, particularly a ſmall Sort that ſerves for Condenſing; AIR FOUNTAINS of various Kinds; GLASS PUMPS; WIND GUNS; PAPIN'S DIGESTORS; alſo a PORTABLE APPARATUS for ELECTRICAL EXPERIMENTS, which is allowed by the CURIOUS to exceed any of the Kind.

BAROMETERS, DIAGONAL, STANDARD, or PORTABLE.

THERMOMETERS, whoſe Scales are adjuſted to the Bores of their reſpective Tubes; HYGROMETERS; HYDROSTATICAL BALANCES, and HYDROMETERS.

HADLEY'S QUADRANTS, after the moſt exact Method, with Glaſſes, whoſe Planes are truly parellel; DAVIS'S QUADRANTS; GLOBES of all Sizes; AZIMUTH and other Sea Compaſſes; LOAD-STONES; NOCTURNALS; SUN-DIALS of all Sorts; Caſes of DRAWING INSTRUMENTS; SCALES; PARALLEL RULERS; PROPORTIONAL COMPASSES and DRAWING PENS.

THEODOLITES, SEMICIRCLES, CIRCUMFERENTERS, PLAIN TABLES, DRAWING BOARDS, MEASURING WHEELS, SPIRIT LEVELS, RULES, PENCILS, and all other Sorts of OPTICAL, PHILOSOPHICAL, and MATHEMATICAL INSTRUMENTS, of the neweſt and moſt approved Inventions, are made and ſold by the abovesaid *E D W A R D N A I R N E.*

Fig. 20 Trade card of Edward Nairne *(Science Museum, London)*

NEGRETTI, Gaeton. w1841. 4 Thomas St, Manchester

NEGRETTI, J. e1800-40. 52 Cardiff St, Bristol

NEGRETTI, L. & Co. e1830-55. Liverpool

NEGRETTI, L. & Son. e1820-40. Portsmouth

NEGRETTI & ZAMBRA w1850-1900+. Opt. math. & phil. IM. London
11 Hatton Garden (1850-59) Ceramic Court, Crystal Palace, Sydenham (1854-99) 68 Cornhill (1857-59) 1 Hatton Garden (1859-67) 107 Holborn Hill (1859-67) 59 Cornhill (1860-72) 122 Regent St (1862-1900+) 153 Fleet St (1865-73) 103 Hatton Garden (1867-69) 38 Holborn Viaduct (1869-1900+) 45 Cornhill (1872-1900+)
The most prolific and leading makers of all types of barometers during the second half of the nineteenth century. The partnership was formed by Enrico (Henry) Negretti and Joseph Warren Zambra as makers of scientific instruments. They expanded rapidly and took over the business of John Frederick Newman, a leading barometer maker, of 122 Regent St in 1862. The partnership exhibited at the Great Exhibition at the Crystal Palace in 1851 and won a Prize Medal. They held the appointment of instrument-makers to the Queen and the Prince Consort. The firm still trades today under the name of Negretti Automation.

NEGRETTY & Co. e1820-40. London

NEGRINI, C. e1820-40. Tenterden

NEILL Bros. w1850-63. Watch M, jewellers & opt. IM. 23 High St, Belfast

NEILL, James. w1854-61. Watch M, jeweller & opt. IM. 6 Donegall Place, Belfast

NEILL, James & Co. w1865-80. Watch M, jewellers, opt. IM & silversmith. Belfast
8 Donegall Place (1865-68) 14 Donegall Place (1870-77) 33 Castle Lane (1878) 14 Donegall Place (1880)

NEILL, John R. w1865-80. Watch M, jeweller & silversmith. Belfast
23 High St (1865-68) 21 High St (1870-80)

NEILL, Robert. w1805-40. Clock & watch M & jeweller. 25 High St, Belfast

NEILL, Robert & Sons. w1842-46. Watch & clock M & opt. IM. 25 High St, Belfast

NEILL, Robert & Sons. w1843-46. Watch & clock M & opt. & naut. IM. Londonderry
6 Diamond (1843-46) 27 Shipquay St (1846)

NEILL & MINNIECE. w1852-61. Watch M, jeweller & opt. IM. Shipquay St, Londonderry

NEILL, Sharman D. w1884-1900+. Watch & clock M & jeweller. 12 Donegall, Belfast

NELSON, William. w1830-62. Opt. & math. IM & jeweller. Dublin
21 Essex Quay (1830-31) 20 Essex Quay (1832) 24 Essex Quay (1833) 37 Lower Ormond Quay (1834-51) 42 Lower Ormond Quay (1845-51) 66 Dame St (1852-62)
Optical and mathematical instrument-maker to the Lord Lieutenant.

NERGA, A. e1835-55. Nantwich

NERORETTY & Co. e1790-1810. Gloucester

NESTLER, Albert Lahr. w1896-98. Math. IM. 31 Snow Hill, London

NEWBERY, F. & Sons. w1877-79. Aneroid barometers. 37 Newgate St, London

NEWBY, James. w1770-97. Clock & watch M. Kendal

NEWCOMBE, F. & Co. w1874-81. Opt. & math. IM. 62 Hatton Garden, London

NEWCOMBE, Frederick. w1855-57. Opt. & math. IM. 8 Hatton Garden, London

NEWCOMBE, Frederick & Co. w1858-70. Opt. & math. IM. London
8 Hatton Garden (1858-61) 82 Hatton Garden (1867-70)

NEWCOMBE & SYMONS w1862-67. Opt. & math. IM. 82 Hatton Garden, London

NEWCOMBE & TACCHI w1871-73. Opt. math. & phil. IM. 62 Hatton Garden, London

NEWMAN, James. w1793-1827. Phil. & math. IM. Exeter Exchange, Strand, London
He was apprenticed to T. Newman, probably his father, and succeeded him at Exeter Exchange around 1800.

NEWMAN, John Frederick. w1816-62. Opt. math. & phil. IM. London
7 & 8 Lisle St (1816-25) 122 Regent St (1827-62)
He made standard and portable barometers for the Ross Antarctic expedition and his meteorological station barometers were installed throughout the British Empire. He was also responsible for the Newman mountain barometer with a two-compartment iron cistern. He exhibited at the Great Exhibition at the Crystal Palace in 1851 and was, without doubt, the leading scientific barometer maker of his day. The business was taken over by Negretti & Zambra in 1862.

NEWMAN, John & Son. w1857-62. Opt. math. & phil. IM. 122 Regent St, London

NEWMAN, T. w1758-1800. Math. & phil. IM. Exeter Exchange, Strand, London
He took over the business of Heath & Wing in 1773 and was joined by his apprentice, James Newman, who was probably his son, in 1793. His trade card shows that he made and sold all sorts of instruments and 'the best Black lead Pencils and Books of the Use of Instruments'.

NEWTON Bros. e1850-70. Hull

NEWTON, E. T. & Son. w1847-e1870. Opt. math. & chemical IM. Cross St, Camborne

NEWTON, F. M. e1845-65. Opt. IM. Leicester

NEWTON, F. M. e1850-70. Halifax

NEWTON, Frederic & Co. w1858-1900+ Opt. math. & phil. IM. 3 Fleet St, London
Instrument-makers to the Queen. Barometers usually signed 'Newton & Co.'.

NEWTON, John. w1810-68. Globe M. 97 (later 66) Chancery Lane, London

NEWTON, William, Edward & Fred. w1851-58. Opt. math. & phil. IM. 3 Fleet St, Temple Bar, London

NEWTON, William & Son. w1841-83. Opt. math. & phil. IM. London
66 Chancery Lane (1844-83) 3 Fleet St (1853-58)

NICHO, P. e1835-55. Liverpool

NICHOLLS, Arthur. w1877-82. Hydrometer M. London
129 Cloudesley Rd (1877) 6 College St (1878-80) 57 College St (1881-82)

NICHOLSON, I. e1840-60. Kirkcudbright

NICOLA, P. e1810-30. Liverpool

NICOLL, William. e1790-1810. Great Portland St, London
Made at least one wheel barometer with a round top symmetrical case with the dial in the centre of the case.

NINORETTI, J. e1835-55. Leicester

NITSCHE & Co. w1881-84. Opt. IM. 41 Holborn Viaduct, London

NITSCHE & GUNTHER w1894-1900+ Opt. IM. London
41 Holborn Viaduct (1884-87) 64 Hatton Garden (1888) 66 Hatton Garden (1889-1900+)

NOAKES, John. w1833-70. Clock & watch M. Burwash

NODEN, John. w1826-28. 10 Charles St, Hatton Garden, London

NOLCINI, Joseph. w1865-68. Clock & watch M. Cardiff

NOLFI & BIANCHI e1800-20. Salisbury

NOLFI, P. e1820-40. Manchester

NOLFI, Peter. 1810-30. Yeovil

NOLFI, Peter. e1820-45. Taunton

NOLLI, I. COMOLI & Co. e1830-50. Edinburgh

NOLLI, J.B. & Co. e 1810-40. Perth

NORETTI & ABATTI e1815-35. Peterborough

NORIE & Co. e1810-30. London

NORRIS & CAMPBELL w1848-51. e1848-70. Clock, watch & chronometer M. Liverpool

NORTHEN, Richard. w1790-1841. Jeweller, watch & opt. IM. Hull

NORTHEN, Richard & Son. e1805-25. Watch M & opt. IM. 46 Lowgate, Hull

NORTHWOOD, James. w1850-70. Clock & watch M. Newport, Salop

NORTON, Eardley B. e1875-95. Manchester

NORTON, Robert. w1841-70. Watch M & silversmith. Stamford

NOSEDA, John. w1774-79. Weatherglass & philosophical bubble M. Belfast
Made at least one wheel barometer in a straight-sided symmetrical case with a paper scale dial in the centre.

NOSEDA, J. & P. w1779. Walsall

NOVATI, BORDESSA & EATON w1853-54. 54 Exmouth St, London

NOWACKI, Ignatius. w1862. Clock & watch M. 207 Bright St, Sheffield

NOYES, John. e1810-30. Math. IM. Grocers Hall, Poultry, London

O

OAKES, E. G. e1830-50. Bath

OAKESHOTT, William. w1844-45. Phil. IM. 29 St John St, Clerkenwell, London

OATES, John. e1820-40. Pump, nr Halifax
Angle barometers with paper plates.

OGILVIE, Robert A. w1845. 19 Upper Wharton St, London

OKERMANS, PORCUITTE, ALEPEE & Co. w1886-91. Opt. math. & phil. IM. 56 Hatton Garden, London

OLIVER, Daniel. w1861-83. Clock & watch M. Wellington

OMER, John. w1857-88. Opt. math. & phil. IM. 99 Minories, London

ORCHARD, John. w1853-89. Opt. math. & phil. IM. London
28 Hornton St, Kensington (1853-57) 2 Lower Phillimore Place, Kensington Rd, (1857-71) 100 Kensington High St (1872-89)

OREGGIA, L. e1805-25. Nottingham

ORIGONI, John. w1837. 34 Dean St, Newcastle upon Tyne

ORME, Charles. b1688-d1747. Ashby de la Zouch, Leics
The son of Thomas Orme, the vicar of Garesden in Wiltshire, who moved to Ashby de la Zouch before he died in 1715. Little is known of Charles except that he distinguished himself by making very attractive angle barometers with one, two or three tubes using boxwood cisterns. He was the first to distil mercury and to boil it in the tube, stipulating a time of four hours as being necessary to boil the mercury in an angle tube forty-nine inches long.

O'RONZO, Sombarto. w1862-81. 3 Kirby St, Hatton Garden, London

ORREGGIO, S. e1815-50. Nottingham

ORTELLI, A. w1790-1846. Clock & watch M. High St, Oxford

ORTELLI, A. e1810-35. Buckingham

ORTELLI, A. e1820-40. Birmingham

ORTELLI, A. & D. w1790-1846. Clock & watch M. Oxford

ORTELLI, A. & D. & PRIMAVESI w1846. Opt. IM & jewellers. 114 High St, Oxford

ORTELLI, Andrew Matthew. w1839-66. Clock & watch M. Godalming

ORTELLI & Co. e1815-35. Carmarthen

ORTELLI & Co. e1835-55. Oxford

ORTELLI, D. e1825-50. Marlborough

ORTELLI, D. & Co. e1810-30. Bath
Some barometers signed 'D. ORTELLY & Co.'.

ORTELLI, Defendent. w1852-54. Looking glass M. 49 Hatton Garden, London

ORTELLI, Defendent & John. w1854-62. Looking glass M. 49 Hatton Garden, London

ORTELLI, J. e1810-30. Bath

ORTELLI, John. w1862-64. Looking glass M. 48 & 49 Hatton Garden, London

ORTELLI, Joseph. e1835-55. Reading

ORTELLI, Joseph & Co. w1809-18. 20 Cross St, Hatton Garden, London
Some barometers signed 'ORTELLI & Co.' with this address. e1825-35.

ORTELLI, N. e1810-30. Macclesfield
Some barometers signed 'N. ORTELLI & Co.'.

ORTELLI, P. e1810-30. Buckingham

ORTELLI, P. & Co. w1805. e1800-30. Macclesfield
Also 'ORTELLY & Co.'.

ORTELLI, Peter. w1835-56. Looking glass M. London
3 Leather Lane (1835-51) 49 Hatton Garden (1848-51) 15 Leather Lane (1852-56)

ORTELLI & PIZZA w1830. Clock & watch M. Buckingham

ORTELLI & PRIMAVESI w1848-49. Looking glass M. 49 Hatton Garden, London

ORTELLY & Co. e1810-30. 94 Holborn Hill, London

OSBORN, D. e1830-50. 18 Park Lane, Liverpool

OSBORNE, Benjamin. w1838-71. Math. & phil. IM. London
9 Northampton Square (1838-41) 11 Guildford St (1841-65) 47 St John St Rd (1866-67) 102 St John St Rd (1868-71)

OSMAN & Co. w1888-91. 132 Commercial St, London

OTLEY, Jonathan. w1828-34. Clock & watch M. Keswick

OTTWAY, John. w1826-70. Opt. math. & phil. IM. London
87 St Johns Rd (1826-33) 5 York St, Covent Garden (1830-39) 10 King St, Holborn (1840-41) 11 Devonshire St, Queen Square (1842-48) 33 Upper King St (1849-70) 21 Packenham St (1853-58) 83 St John St Rd (1859-67) 178 St John St Rd (1868-70)

OTTWAY, John & Son. w1870-1900+. Opt. IM. 178 St John St Rd, London

OWEN, John. w1760-75. Clock & watch M. Llanrwst

OWEN, William. w1841-67. Clock & watch M. The Cross, Oswestry

OWEN, William & Thomas. w1868-75. Opt. IM & cutlers. The Cross, Oswestry
A partnership between the two sons of William Owen.

OWENS, Owen. w1851. e1850-65. Clock & watch M. South Castle St, Liverpool

OWERS & WILLSON w1892-95. Hydrometer & saccharometer M. 51 East Rd, London

P

PACKER, John. w1837-77. Clock & watch M. Newbury

PAGANI, A. e1815-45. Gainsborough, Nottingham

PAGANI, Anthony. w1818-25. e1815-45. Opt. IM. Goose Gate, Nottingham

PAGE KEEN & PAGE e1860-80. Clock & watch M. Plymouth

PAGE, Thomas. w1735-d1784. Watch & clock M & IM. Norwich

PAIGE, Walter. w1874. e1855-75. Clock & watch M. Southborough, Tunbridge Wells

PAKEMAN, John E. w1866-68. Hydrometer M. 32 Kirby St, Hatton Garden, London

PALLANT, Charles Nathan. w1881. e1880-1900. Clock & watch M. 51 Strand, London

PALMER, Edward. w1834-46. Phil. IM. 123 Newgate St, London

PALRONI, B. e1835-55. Exeter

PAPIN w1678-92. Phil. IM. near the Bell Inn, Friday St, London
A nephew of Denis Papin FRS who had assisted Robert Boyle with his experiments. He arranged for his nephew to work in Boyle's laboratory making baroscopes and other instruments. His baroscopes were recommended to travellers.

PARACHINI, F. e1810-30

PARACHINI, G. e1810-30

PARIS SPECTACLEMAKERS' SOCIETY w1869-72. Opt. IM. 36 Brooke St, Holborn, London

PARK, Robert. w1853-63. Opt. & naut. IM & chronometer M. Greenock
17 William St (1853-60) 14 Cathcart St (1861-63)

PARKER e1835-55. Wisbech

PARKER, James. w1806-25. Opt. IM. London
53 Princes St, Leicester Square (1806-17) 22 Little Queen St, Holborn (1818-25)

PARKER, James. w1843. Opt. IM. 39 Theobald's St, London

PARKES, James & Son. w1848-1900+. Opt. math. & phil. IM. 5 St Mary's Row, Birmingham

PARKINSON & FRODSHAM w1801-1900+. Clock, watch & chronometer M. London
4 Change Alley, Royal Exchange. 15B Royal Exchange. Also in Liverpool.

PARKINSON & FRODSHAM w1834. Watch, clock & chronometer M. 54 Castle St, Liverpool

PARNELL, Thomas. w1815-51. Opt. & math. IM. At the Mariner and Quadrant, 94 (later 2) Lower East Smithfield, London

PARNELL, William. w1814-46. Math. IM. 2 Lower East Smithfield, London

PARRISH, H. w1860. 61/2 Wood St, Bath Row, Birmingham

PARSONS, James. w1838. Math. & phil. IM. 22 Bull and Mouth St, London

PARSONS, William. w1822-38. Math. & phil. IM. London
9 Kirby St, Hatton Garden. 8 St Paul's Alley, St Paul's Churchyard

PASINI, G. e1815-35. Dorchester

PASINI, John. e1835-45. Dorchester

PASTORELLI, A. & F. w1847-49. 4 Cross St, Hatton Garden, London
A partnership between Anthony Pastorelli and his son Francis. Some barometers signed 'A. PASTORELLI & Son'.

PASTORELLI, Alfred. w1884-94. Hydrometer M. London
5 Mount Pleasant (1884-87) 13 Featherstone Buildings (1891-94)
He joined Pastorelli & Rapkin.

PASTORELLI, Anthony. w1829-46. Chronometers. London
4 Cross St, Hatton Garden (1829-40 & 1842-46) 19 Upper Wharton St (1841-42)
Succeeded Fortunato Pastorelli and was succeeded by his son Francis.

PASTORELLI, C. w1821-38. Chronometers. 4 Cross St, Hatton Garden, London

PASTORELLI & CETTI w1853. 11 Brooke St, London

PASTORELLI & Co. e1805-25. 180 High Holborn, London

PASTORELLI & Co. e1825-45. 4 Cross St, Hatton Garden, London

PASTORELLI, F. & J. w1816-18. 4 Cross St, Hatton Garden, London

PASTORELLI, Fortunato. w1805-30. Glassblower. London
252 High Holborn (1805) 156 High Holborn (1811) 4 Cross St, Hatton Garden (1815-30)

PASTORELLI, Francis. w1849-80. Opt. math. & phil. IM. London
4 Cross St, Hatton Garden (1849-69) 208 Piccadilly (1856-78) 10 New Bond St (1879-80)

PASTORELLI, Francis & Co. w1855-80. Opt. math. & phil. IM. London
4 Cross St, Hatton Garden (1855-69) 208 Piccadilly (1857-78) 10 New Bond St (1879-80) 7 Great Warner St (1870-71)
Made wheel barometers elaborately inlaid with brass and mother-of-pearl.

PASTORELLI, Frank & Co. w1881-97. Math. opt. & phil. IM. 10 New Bond St, London

PASTORELLI, J. e1790-1820. Bowling St, Westminster, London

PASTORELLI, J. e1810-30. 180 High Holborn, London

PASTORELLI, J. e1815-35. 93 Regent St, London

PASTORELLI, John. w1837-57. Opt. IM. Liverpool
28 Cable St (1837) 55 Cable St (1841-47) 61 Cable St (1851) 10 South Castle St (1857)

PASTORELLI, Joseph. e1800-20. 47 Atheron St, Liverpool

PASTORELLI, Joseph. w1820-28. Leopard's Court, Leather Lane, London

PASTORELLI, Joseph. e1820-40. 54 Leather Lane, Holborn, London

PASTORELLI, Joseph. w1852. 67 Hatton Garden, London

PASTORELLI, Peter Caparani. w1827. 5 Leopard's Court, Baldwins Gardens, London

PASTORELLI & RAPKIN w1872-1900+. Opt. math. & phil. IM. London
61 Hatton Garden & 7 Great Warner St (1872) 46 Hatton Garden (1873-1900+)
A prolific maker of all types of barometers during the last quarter of the nineteenth century.

PATERSON, James. w1681-93. Math. IM. Sign of the Sea Cross-Staff and Quadrant, Cowgate, Edinburgh
He compiled almanacks, wrote textbooks and made and sold mathematical instruments which included 'weather glasses of all sorts and sizes'.

PATRICK, John. w1686-1722. Over against Bull Head Court in Jewin St, near Cripplegate Church, and in Ship Court in the Old Baily, London
By far the most prolific and interesting of the early domestic barometer makers. He was apprenticed to a joiner, William Thompson, in 1686 for seven years and appears to have specialised in making barometers from the time he completed his apprenticeship in 1693. From his own research and observations, he published *Rules and Observations on the Various Rising and Falling of the Mercury to foreknow the Weather by the Barometer*. When repeating these rules in his Lexicon Technicum in 1704, John Harris described Patrick as the 'Torricellian Operator' and added: 'I think myself obliged in justice to tell the world that I have never seen better Weather Glasses of all kinds made any where than by Mr Patrick; who doth really deserve all possible encouragement for the many experiments he hath made in order to improve the Barometer, and which he is always willing to shew to all ingenious and curious

persons.' As well as selling barometers direct to the public, Patrick sold them to other instrument-makers and retailers. Many of his barometers are unsigned and records show that some were sold to John Marshall, John Yarwell, George Graham and Daniel Quare. He became a member of the Clockmakers' Company in 1712. He made all types of stick barometer, including pendant, pillar and angle. (See Fig. 21.)

PATTRICK, Thomas. w1800-03. Opt. math. & phil. IM. 29 King St, Covent Garden, London

PATTRICK, Thomas. e1815-35. Clock & watch M. Wisbech

PATTRICK, T. M. & Son. w1865. Clock & watch M. Wisbech

PAVOLVEI, B. e1810-30. Newcastle upon Tyne

PAYNE, George. w1846-79. Clock & watch M. Hadleigh

PAYNE, G. P. e1830-50. Marine barometers. South Castle St, Liverpool

PAYNE, J. e1820-40. Banbury

PAYNE, John. w1795-1820. Clock & watch M. Hadleigh

PAYNE, William. c1770-1812. Clock & watch M. Hadleigh

PEACE, Philip. w1842-57. Opt. IM. Edinburgh
61 Broughton St (1842-45) 71 South Frederick St (1846) 99 Princes St (1847-57)

PEACOCK, James. e1835-55. Opt. IM. 36/42 New Oxford St, London

PEACOCK, William. w1789-1832. Watch M. York

PEACOCK, William. w1854-64. e1830-65. Clock & watch M. Kimbolton

PEARCE, George Edward. w1890-1900+. Math. & phil. IM. 22A New Church St, Strand, London

PEARCE, Stanley. w1894. Opt. IM. 161 Wardour St, Soho, London

PEARCE, Thomas. w1856. e1840-60. Silversmith. Cricklade St, Cirencester

PEARSON e1840-60. Tunbridge Wells

PEARSON, Charles. w1841-54. Clock M. Towcester

PECK, William. w1839-54. Clock & watch M. Sharnbrook

PEDRAGLI, M. & Co. e1810-30. Rochdale

PEDRAGLIO e1810-30. Rochester

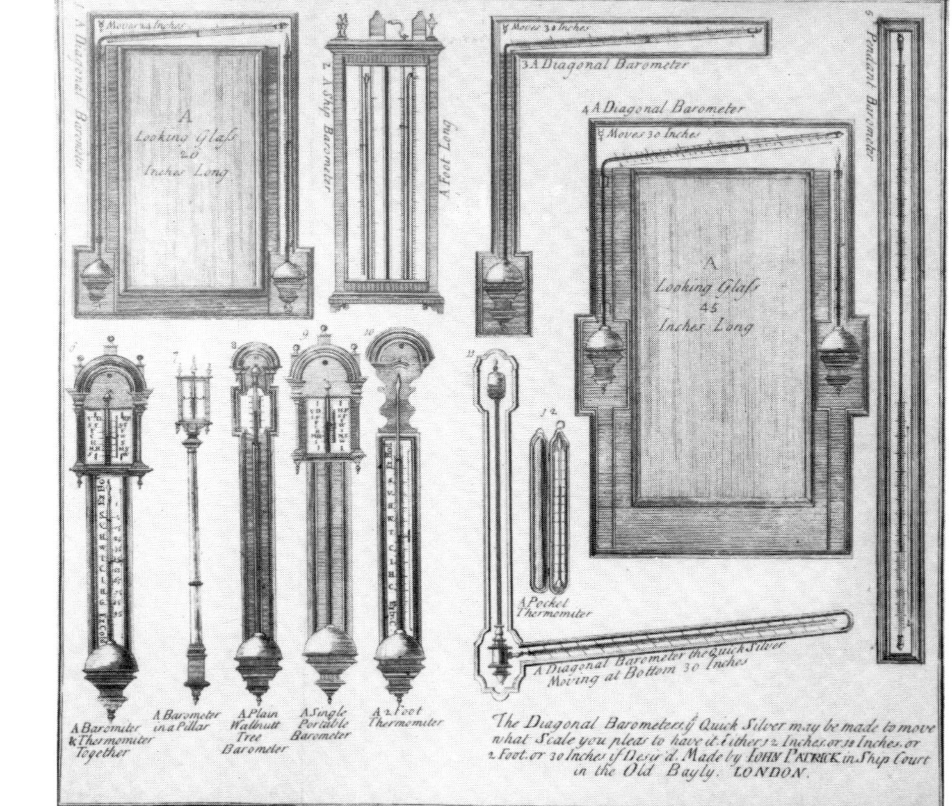

Fig. 21 Advertisement of John Patrick *(Trustees of the British Museum)*

PEDRAGLIO, M. & C. e1810-30. London

PEDRALIO, Baptista. e1790-1820. Angle barometers. Norwich

PEDRAZZINI. e1840-60. Cardiff

PEDRENE, P. e1835-55. Bristol

PEDRETTI, C. e1835-55. Birmingham

PEDRETTI, Peter. w1831-51. Carver & gilder. London
Great Bath St, Clerkenwell (1831-44) 13 Dorrington St (1844-51)

PEDRONCELLI, G. e1810-30. Truro

PEDRONCELLI, Joan. e1840-60. Bodmin

PEDRONCELLI, John. e1810-30. Bodmin

PEDRONE Bros. e1825-50. Carlisle
Barometers also signed 'PEDRONE Bros & Co.'.

PEDRONE, J. B. e1810-30. Glasgow

PEDRONE, L. e1830-50. Looking glass M. 74 Market Place, Carlisle

PEDRONE, L. w1834. Opt. IM. English St, Carlisle

PEDRONE, Louis. w1848-51. Clock & watch M. 57 Lord St, Liverpool

PEDRONE, P. e1830-50. Bristol

PEDRONE, S. & G. e1810-30. Carlisle

PEDRONE, Simone. e1835-55. Carlisle

PEDRONI, J. B. e1830-50. Bridge St, Shrewsbury

PEDUZZI, Anthony. w1825-41. Manchester
23 Piccadilly (1834) 31 Oldham St (1841)

PEDUZZI, J. e1810-30. Newbury St, Manchester

PEDUZZI, James. w1825-41. Manchester
49 Oldham St (1825-41) 97 Oldham St (1834-41)

PEDUZZI, M. e1815-35. 74 Leather Lane, London

PEDUZZY, Joseph & Co. e1820-40. Manchester

PELASCENO, P. e1835-55. 11 Vine St, Hatton Garden, London

PELEGRINO, Francis. e1790-1820. London
Also 'Francis PELLEGRINO'.

PELLAI, Antonio. w1869-81. Clock & watch M. London

PENCOTTI, I. e1810-30. High St, Dudley

PENDER & Co. e1810-30. Norwich

PENI, J. e1830-50. 13 Baldwins Gardens, Leather Lane, London

PENNACK, William. w1895-96. 35 Gunter Grove, London

PENNINGTON, Robert. w1780-1824. Watch & chronometer M. London

PENSA, J. e1835-55. 2 Charles St, Hatton Garden, London

PENSA, John. w1830-40. London
39 Charles St, Hatton Garden (1830-34) 5 Greville St (1835-40)

PENSA, J. & Son. w1835. e1830-45. London
39 Charles St, Hatton Garden (1830-34) 5 Greville St, Hatton Garden (1835-40)
A partnership between John Pensa and a son.

PENSA, Margaret (Mrs). w1840-48. 25 Charles St, Hatton Garden, London

PENSO, Victor. w1878-96. 55 Hatton Garden and 8 & 13 Hatton Yard, London

PENSOTTI & COMOLLI e1810-30. Dudley

PENSOTTI, J. w1855. Clock & watch M. Gravesend

PENSOTTI, Joseph. w1816-41. Umbrella M. High St, Dudley

PENSOTTI, Santino. e1820-40. Dudley

PEOTE, James. w1792. Boston, Lincs.

PEPPER, G. w1847-69. Clock & watch M. Biggleswade

PEPPER, John. w1830-47. Clock & watch M. Biggleswade

PERCIVAL, Gerald. w1881-83. Electrical & phil. IM. 8 Robert St, Cork

PERKEN, Son & RAYMENT w1888-1900+. Opt. math. & phil. IM. London
99 Hatton Garden (1888-95) 141 Oxford St (1895)
Trade mark 'OPTIMUS'.

PERKINS, Francis Joseph. w1875-83. Clock & watch M. Frome

PERRETT, William Edward. w1875-83. Clock & watch M. Weston-super-Mare

PERRY e1855-75. Cork

PERSE, J. w1859. Clock & watch M. Winchester

PETERS, Bernard. w1862-70. Clock & watch M. 12 Grand Parade, St Leonards. Also at Hastings

PETERS, James. e1820-40. Sherbourne

PETERS, James. w1858-65. Clock & watch M. Cambridge
He used pewter instead of mother-of-pearl to decorate his wheel barometers.

PETERS, William. w1880-96. Phil. IM. London
18 Gloucester St (1880) 11 Spencer St, Goswell Rd (1882-96)

PEVERELLE, John B. w1849-54. 16 Pershore St, Birmingham

PFAFF, S. e1820-40. Oxford

PHELPS, Thomas. w1799-1830. Opt. math. & phil. IM. London
Fetter Lane (1799) 30 Red Lion St, Holborn (1802-05) 33 Monkwell St, Cripplegate (1817-18) 28 Holywell Lane, Shoreditch. 19 Jewin St, Cripplegate (1819-22) 17 Jewin St, Cripplegate (1822-23)

PHILLIPS e1850-70. Northampton

PHILLIPS, A. e1820-40. Nottingham

PHILLIPS, James. w1830. Clock & watch M. Salisbury

PHILLIPS, Michael. w1853. Clock & watch M. Banbury

PHILLIPS, Thomas. w1875-77. 1 Oldham Place, Farringdon Rd, London

PHILLIPS, Thomas Jackson. w1860. Frame M. London

PHILPOT, James. w1839. e1820-40. Clock & watch M. Bardfield. Also at Thaxted

PIAMAS e1820-40. 15 Great Ancat St, Manchester

PIANTA & Co. e1810-30. Birmingham

PICKERING, Thomas. w1838. Math. & phil. IM. 30 Regent St, Kensington, London

PICKERING, Thomas. w1844-47. Math. IM. 36 Regent St, Lambeth, London

PICKETT, George. w1832. e1830-50. Clock & watch M. 265 Oxford St, London

PIDDUCK, Henry. w1842-68. Clock & watch M. Hanley
Also Henry PIDDUCK & Sons. w1868-76.

PIERS, Charles. w1848. Clock, watch & chronometer M. 34 Strand, Liverpool

PIFFARETTI e1820-40. 21 Argyle St, New Rd, London

PIFFARETTI e1825-45. 48 Judd St, Euston Rd, London

PIGGOTT, Peter William. w1838-46. Math. & phil. IM. 4 Penton St, Walworth, London

PIGGOTT, William Peter & Co. w1857-63. Opt. math. & phil. IM. 523 Oxford St, London
Barometers signed 'PIGGOTT & Co.' with this address.

PIGOT, John. w1836. 7 Noble St, Wilmington Square, London

PILATTO, A. e1820-40. Nottingham

PILFSON, J. c1770. Terril

PILKINGTON, George. w1838-49. Opt. math. & phil. IM. London
48 St James's St, Clerkenwell and 14 Clarence Place, Pentonville

PILKINGTON, John. w1850-52. Opt. math. & phil. IM. 14 Clarence Place, Pentonville, London

PILKINGTON, Mary A. (Mrs). w1853-59. Opt. math. & phil. IM. 14 Clarence Place, Pentonville, London

PILLISCHER, Jacob. w1888-1900+. Opt. math. & phil. IM. 88 New Bond St, London
The son of Moritz Pillischer. In 1894 he advertised that the family had won medals in 1851, 1855, 1862, 1873, 1878, the decoration of the Imperial Francis Joseph Order; gold medal, Paris, 1889.

PILLISCHER, Moritz. w1850-88. Opt. math. & phil. IM. London
398 Oxford St (1850-53) 88 New Bond St (1854-88)
Exhibited at the Great Exhibition at the Crystal Palace in 1851 and won a medal (see above).

PINCKETTI, A. & Co. e1800-20. London
Barometers also signed 'A. PINCHETTI & Co.'.

PINI, J. e1810-30. 13 Baldwins Gardens, Leather Lane, Holborn, London

PINI, Joseph. w1835-48. Carver & gilder. London
1 Princes St, Red Lion Square (1835) 3 Princes St, Red Lion Square (1836) 23 Brooke St (1838-48)

PINI, Joseph & Luigi & Co. w1848-62. Carvers & gilders. 23 Brooke St, Holborn London
Some barometers signed 'J. PINI & Co.' with this address.

PINI, Joseph & RONCORONI Bros. w1863-66. Carvers & gilders. London
23 Brooke St, Holborn (1863-65) 2 College Hill (1866)

PINNEY, Francis. w1844-68. Clock & watch M. Stamford

PINNEY, Francis & Son. w1876. Clock & watch M. Uppingham and Stamford

PINNEY, Richard Matthew. w1830-57. Watch M. Stamford

PINNI, Francis. e1800-20. 81 Holborn, London

PIOTI, James. e1810-30. Boston

PIOTTE w1806-23. Carver, gilder & opt. IM. Queen St, Hull

PIOTTY, J. e1820-40. Lincoln

PIOTY e1820-40. Boston

PIPER e1890-1900. Exeter

PIRELLI, D. e1835-55

PISSARETTI e1835-55. 48 Tudd St, Custom Rd, London

PITKIN, Henry Thomas. w1871-77. Phil. IM. 54 Red Lion St, Clerkenwell, London

PITKIN, James. w1858-1900+. Opt. & phil. IM. London
3 Church St, Mile End (1858-59) 52 Red Lion St, Clerkenwell (1860-64) 56 Red Lion St, Clerkenwell (1865-77) 53 & 56 Red Lion St, Clerkenwell (1878-1900+)
Manufacturers of pocket watch and other aneroid barometers, hydrometers, electrical and philosophical instruments. In 1861 Pitkin provided jewels for the bearings of his aneroid barometers and was granted a patent.

PITKIN & SHORT w1868-71. Opt. & phil. IM. 56 Red Lion St, Clerkenwell, London
This was a brief partnership between James Pitkin and T. W. Short after which both men traded separately.

PITSALLA, Charles. w1805. e1800-20. 221 High Holborn, London
Barometers also signed 'C. PITSALLA & Co.' with this address.

PITZOLI, Anthony. w1831-35. Weatherglass M. 86 Pill Lane, Dublin

PIZZALA, A. w1840-53. Opt. math. & phil. IM. London
7 Charles St, Hatton Garden (1840-46) 19 Hatton Garden (1847-53)
He took over the business of F. A. Pizzala (1).

PIZZALA, A. w1868-83. London
20 Charles St, Hatton Garden (1868-75) 26 Charles St, Hatton Garden (1876-83)

PIZZALA, Charles. w1879-92. 90 Hatton Garden, London

PIZZALA, Charles F. w1893-1900+. Phil. IM. London
26 Charles St, Hatton Garden (1893-99) 175 St John St Rd (1900+)

PIZZALA, Francis A. w1885-86. 26 Charles St, Hatton Garden, London

PIZZALA, Francis Augustus (1). w1838-40. Opt. math. & phil. IM. 7 Charles St, Hatton Garden, London
Succeeded by A. Pizzala.

PIZZALA, Francis Augustus (2). w1854-66. Opt. math. & phil. IM. London
19 Hatton Garden (1854-66) 25a Hatton Garden (1862-66)
He took over the business of A. Pizzala at 19 Hatton Garden.

PIZZALA & GREENE e1860-70. Phil. IM. 19 Hatton Garden, London
A partnership between F. A. Pizzala (2) and Greene.

PIZZALA, Walter. w1887-89. 9 Cross St, Hatton Garden, London

PIZZALLA, Joseph. w1809-30. Looking glass M. 84 Leather Lane, Holborn, London

PIZZALOTE, A. e1830-40. Opt. IM. 9 Hatton Garden, London

PIZZI & CETTI w1830-42. Clock & watch M. Buckingham

PIZZI, Jane. w1840-c1845. 19 Leather Lane, London

PIZZI & NEGRETTI w1840-c1845. 19 Leather Lane, London

PIZZI & ORTELLI w1830. Clock & watch M. Buckingham

PIZZI, Valentine. w1835-d1840. 27 Cross St, Hatton Garden, London

PLACE, J. e1890-1900. Birmingham

PLASKETT e1840-60. Marine barometers. Bute Dock St, Cardiff.

PLATNAUER Bros. w1879-80. Clock & watch M. Bristol

PLAYER, John. w1830-77. Clock & watch M. Reading

PLIMPTON, George. w1830. Opt. math. & phil. IM. London
5 Tysol St and Lincoln's Inn Passage.

POCHAINE, John. w1811. e1800-20. Dean St, Newcastle upon Tyne

POCHAINE & Son. e1810-30. Newcastle

POITTI, James. e1810-30. Lincoln

POLLI, Angelo. w1866-71. 39 Briggate, Leeds

POLLOCK & STEWART w1898-1900+. Scientific apparatus M. 41 Renfield St, Glasgow

POLLOCK, William. w1893-97. Scientific apparatus M. Glasgow
8 Gordon St (1893-94) 12 Gordon St (1895-97)

POLTI, B. e1820-40. Hull

POLTI, C. e1780-1810. Exon

POLTI, G. e1810-30

POLTI, I. e1780-1800. Hull

POLTI, Joseph. w1822-34. Looking glass M. Leeds
7 Kirkgate (1822) Coxon's Yard, 72 Kirkgate (1834)

POLTI, L. e1820-40. Bristol

POLTI, T. L. e1780-1800. Leeds

PONCIA, A. e1810-30. Norwich
Also 'A. PONCIA & Co.' e1815-35.

PONCIA, A. e1810-30. Peterborough

PONCIA, Dominick. e1820-50. Aylesbury

PONCIA, J. w1822. Hardware S. Union St, Hereford

PONCIONE, J. COLOMBA & Co. e1800-30. 180 High Holborn, London

PONCIONE, John. e1800-20. Holborn

PONCIONE, John & Co. e1790-1820. Robinhood, 281 High Holborn, London

POND, James. w1822-30. Umbrella M. Lynn
High St (1822) 35 Broad St (1830)

PONISSO, J. e1820-40. Edinburgh
Also 'J. PONISSO & Co.'.

POOLE, John. w1832-81. Clock & watch M. Upper East Smithfield, London
Marine barometers and sympiesometers.

POOLE, Samuel & Son. w1871-76. 23 Charles St, Hatton Garden, London

POOLE, Thomas. w1814-18. e1814-40. Opt. & phil. IM. Upper North Place, Gray's Inn Lane, London

POOLER, R. T. w1796-1810. Math. IM. 6 Great Tower St, London

PORRI, Benjamin. w1834-41. Jeweller. Skipton
Caroline Square (1834) New Market Square (1841)

PORRI & Co. e1820-40. Aberdeen

PORRI, Domenico. e1820-40. London

PORRI, F. e1835-55. Dublin

PORRI, G. B. e1810-30. Leicester

PORRI, VECCHIO & Co. e1810-30. 17 Great Queen St, Lincoln's Inn Fields, London
Barometers signed 'PORRI' and 'PORRI & Co.' with this address.

PORTA e1810-30. Newcastle

PORTA, Peter. w1868. Clock & watch M. Cardiff

PORTELLO, William Forester. e1820-40. Clock & watch M. London

PORTER, George. w1830. Math. & phil. IM. 14 St James's Buildings, London

PORTER, Henry. w1881-96. Opt. & math. IM. London
181 Strand (1881-94) 7 Pall Mall (1895-96)
Apprentice and successor to W. Cary. Instrument-makers to the Admiralty, War Office, Geographical Society and Trinity House.

PORTER, Samuel. w1837-64. Clock & watch M. Wokingham

POSCHA, P. e1810-30. Bedford

POTHS, Hermann & Co. w1881-93. Phil. IM. London
4 Sugar Loaf Court, Leadenhall St (1881-86) 4 Creechchurch Lane (1887-93)

POTTER, J. D. w1850-84. w1893-1900+. Math. opt. & phil. IM. London
31 Poultry (1850-85, 1893-1900+) 11 King St, Tower Hill (1855-85, 1893-1900+)
Successor to R. B. Bate. Appointed maker to the Lords Commissioners of the Admiralty.

POTTER, S. C. w1885-92. Opt. math. & phil. IM. 31 Poultry and 11 King St, Tower Hill, London

POTTI, F. e1810-30. Pontefract

POTTS, James. w1876-90. 85 Hatton Garden, London

POTTS, Thomas. w1805-14. Opt. IM. London
371 Strand (1805) 18 St Martin's Court, St Martin's Lane (1807-14)

POUCHAINE e1820-40. Newcastle

POWELL & BARSTOW Ltd. w1900+. 58 Blackfriars Rd, London

POWELL, John. Apprenticed 1739-63. Clock & watch M. London

POWELL & LEALAND w1844-1900+. Opt. math. & phil. IM. London
24 Clarendon St (1844) 4 Seymour Place, Euston Square (1847-57) 170 Euston Rd (1859-1900+)

POWELL, Thomas. e1830-50. Clock & watch M. Ravensthorpe, Yorks

POZOLY, A. e1800-30

POZZAI e1860-80. Liverpool

POZZI e1810-30. Aberdeen

POZZI, A. e1820-40. Glasgow

POZZI, A. e1830-50. Wooton Bassett

POZZI, C. e1830-50

POZZI & Co. e1810-30

POZZI, J. e1815-35. Oswestry

POZZI, J. e1820-40. Rochdale

POZZI & MAFFIA e1810-30

POZZI, O. or C. e1835-55. Liverpool

POZZI, Peter. w1822-50. Looking glass M. Willow St, Oswestry
It is said that he taught Italian in one lesson, for one guinea, in Watkin's, Oswestry.

POZZIE, Joseph. w1820. Elgin

POZZOLI, Francis. e1825-45. Brittlewell

POZZOLY, A. & Co. e1820-40. London

POZZY, I. e1820-40. Glasgow

PRADA, Casmro. e1815-35. High Wycombe and Chesham
Also 'C. & F. PRADA'.

PRADA, F. e1810-30. Chester

PRADA, F. & Co. w1822. Carver & gilder. 26 Church St, Sheffield

PRADA, Francis. w1825-28. Carver & gilder. 32 Church St, Sheffield

PREDARI, J. e1820-40. Manchester

PREDARY, Charles. w1841. Carver & gilder. 17 Oak St, Thomas St, Manchester

PREDARY, J. e1850-70. Manchester

PREMOLI, P. & Co. e1810-40. Looking glass M. Postern, Newcastle

PRESCOTT, George. w1895-1901. Phil. IM. 9 Merrion Row, Dublin

PRESCOTT, George & Co. w1879-82. Watch M, opt. & phil. IM. 8 South King St, Dublin

PRESCOTT, George & Co. Ltd. w1883-84. Phil. IM. 9 Merrion Row, Dublin

PRESCOTT, George Ltd. w1896. Opt. IM. 1 Duke St, Dublin and Edinburgh

PREVOSTA, e1810-30. Gray's Inn Lane, Holborn, London

PRICE e1810-30. Wiveliscombe

PRICE, Charles W. e1885-1900+. Barographs. 1 Broad Quay, Bristol

PRICE & Co. w1892. Opt. math. & phil. IM. 26 Ludgate Hill, London

PRICE, E. W. e1860-80. Aneroid barometers. Liverpool

PRICE, Talbot & Co. Ltd. w1891. Opt. math. & phil. IM. 26 Ludgate Hill, London

PRICE Thomas. w1840-75. Clock & watch M. Newbridge-on-Wye

PRICE, William. w1830-43. Opt. math. & phil. IM. 115 Fetter Lane, London

PRIEST & ASHMORE w1894. Opt. IM. Newton Works, Earl St, Sheffield

PRIEST, John & James. w1835-76. Clock & watch M. Middlegate, Newark

PRIMAVESI e1835-55. Wellington

PRIMAVESI, A. C. w1870. Clock & watch M. Haywards Heath

PRIMAVESI, A. C. w1878. Clock & watch M. Shirley, Hants

PRIMAVESI Bros. e1870-90. Clock & watch M & opt. IM. Bournemouth

PRIMAVESI Bros & Co. w1867. e1850-70. Clock & watch M. Poole

PRIMAVESI Bros & Co. w1867-75. e1855-75. Clock & watch M. Wareham

PRIMAVESI, F. w1887. Clock & watch M. Cardiff

PRIMAVESI, F. w1887. Clock & watch M. Swansea

PRIMAVESI, J. w1855. Clock & watch M. Poole

PRIMAVESI, J. & Co. w1842-48. Clock & watch M. Warminster

PRIMAVESI, Peter. e1810-30. 7 Grevil St, Holborn, London

PRIMAVESI & Sons. e1870-90. Clock & watch M. Swansea and Cardiff

PRIOR, John. w1870-78. Clock & watch M. Hastings

PRITCHARD, Andrew. w1804-58. Opt. math. & phil. IM. London
312 Strand (1830) 18 Picket St (1834) 263 Strand (1837) 162 Fleet St (1840-58)
Before taking out a patent for his aneroid barometer, Lucien Vidie arranged in 1844 for Pritchard to make and test the barometer. Pritchard carried out various tests, including taking the instrument up to the dome of St Paul's Cathedral to test its accuracy in measuring heights.

PRITCHARD, W. & R. & Co. w1889-90. 66 Hatton Garden, London

PROFAZI, Constantine. w1869-81. Clock & watch M. London

PULHAM, S. e1730-50. Weybread, Nr Harlston, Suffolk

PULMAN, P. e1835-55. Clock & watch M. Axminster

PULSFORD, George. w1848. 36 Charles St, Hatton Garden, London

PURCHEON, George. e1820-40. Glass House, Leeds
He made a number of stick barometers with printed paper, painted and enamelled plates.

PUSTERLA, Anthony. w1820. Mirror M. 143 Chapel St, Dublin

PYE, William. w1841-65. Opt. math. & phil. IM. 20 Albion Buildings, Bartholomew Close, London

PYEFINCH, Henry. w1763-90. Opt. math. & phil. IM. At the Golden Quadrant, Sun and Spectacles, 67 Cornhill, London
Pyefinch was apprenticed to Francis Watkins in 1753 and became a member of the Spectaclemakers' Company in 1763. In 1765, in conjunction with J. H. de Magellan, a Portuguese scientist, he patented an instrument to measure the effect of the weight of the atmosphere and the variations caused by heat and cold. A catalogue lists five different barometers with prices ranging from £1 11s 6d to £4 4s.

PYOTT, J. e1865-85. 74 West India Dock Rd, London

Q

QUARE, Daniel. b1649-d1724. Clock, watch & math. IM. Kings Arms, Exchange Alley, London
A Quaker who became one of the outstanding watch, clock and barometer makers of all time. He invented the repeating watch around 1680 and became a Master of the Clockmakers' Company in 1708. He made, essentially, two types of portable barometer: one was a pillar portable barometer, designed to be free standing, and the other was a pendant portable designed only to hang on a wall. In 1695 he was granted a patent giving protection to 'A portable weather glass or barometer, which may be removed and carried to any place though turned upside-down without spilling one drop of quicksilver or letting any air into the tube, and that nevertheless the air shall have the same liberty to operate upon it as on those common ones now in use with respect to atmosphere.'

QUIN, Thomas. w1839. e1820-40. Clock & watch M. London

QUINSEY, G. e1800-20. Keighley

R

RABALIO, COSSA & Co. e1800-20

RABALIO, Peter. w1787-d1791. London (probably)

RABALIO, Peter. e1810-30. Birmingham

RABONE, John. w1825-60. Rule M. Birmingham
Ludgate Hill (1829) 61 St Paul's Square (1839-60)

RABONE, Kirtoni. e1830-50. Birmingham

RABONE & MASON w1834-47. 61 St Paul's Square, Birmingham

RABONE, T. e1840-60. London

RABONE, Thomas. w1829-62. Rule M & math. IM. Birmingham
8 Court Water St (1829) 12 Court Broad St (1835) Hockley Hill (1847) 172 Hockley Hill (1849-54) 63 Gt Hampton St (1858) 61 Gt Hampton St (1860-62)

RADEMACHER, A. w1858. Beccles

RADFORD & Co. w1881. 16 Newcastle St, Farringdon Rd, London

RAE Bros. w1898-1900. Opt. IM. 77 Renfield St, Glasgow

RAILINI, C. e1835-55. Manchester

RAMAGE & Co. w1837-38. Opt. IM. Aberdeen
41 St Nicholas St (1837) 6 St Nicholas St (1838)

RAMAGE, John. w1806-d1835. Opt. IM. Aberdeen
85 Broad St (1824) 39 Union St (1831-35)

RAMAGE, John (junior). w1835-36. Opt. IM. Aberdeen
39 Union St (1835) 104 Union St (1836)

RAMAS, Peter. e1815-35. Manchester

RAMOS, P. e1810-30. 281 Holborn, London

RAMPOLDI & Co. e1825-50. Huntingdon

RAMPOLDI, J. w1851-53. 22 Grey St, Newcastle upon Tyne

RAMSDEN, Jesse. b1731-d1800. Math. opt. & phil. IM. London
Near the Little Theatre in the Haymarket, St James's (1768-71) 199 Piccadilly (1772-1800)
Ramsden was probably the greatest instrument-maker of all time. He was born in Halifax, the son of a linen draper, and worked for his father for a time, but by 1758 he was apprenticed to an optician in London. He made instruments for Jonathan Sisson, George Adams, George Dollond and Edward Nairne before setting up in business in the Haymarket around 1768. His outstanding invention was a dividing machine for accurate scale division, but he is also credited with adapting the tripod as a carrying case for the mountain barometer, by hollowing out the legs sufficiently to contain the tube and the cistern. He wrote various booklets on scientific instruments, and the scientific literature towards the end of the eighteenth century was full of his praise. In 1787 J. D. Cassini, who bought instruments for the Paris Observatory, wrote of Ramsden: 'I have been able to give you a very inadequate picture of the admiration which the sight of the splendid instruments made in England by the famous Ramsden roused in us. The richness of this artist's creative genius, the perfection of his execution, and his wide experience, force me to recognize that it will be a long time before anyone is able, I do not say to surpass, but even to equal his achievement.' Although Ramsden employed more than fifty workmen, he appears to have undertaken himself the construction of the most delicate instruments. He had only just retired when he died in 1800; his workshop manager, Matthew Berge, having taken over the business. (See Fig. 22.)

RANKETH, T. (junior). w1814. 8 High St, Bloomsbury, London

RANKIN, George. w1844-71. Opt. IM. Edinburgh
112 Rose St (1844-66) 79 Rose St (1867) 108 Rose St (1869-71)

RAPHAEL, J. & Co. w1886-1903. Opt. IM. London
3 Oxford St (1886) 13 Oxford St (1886-97) 51 Clerkenwell St (1898-1903)

RAPKIN, Alfred Thomas. w1864-71. 61 Hatton Garden, London

Fig. 22 Portrait of Jesse Ramsden (1731-1800)

RASTRICK & Son. e1840-60. Southsea

RATCLIFF, Hughes. e1810-30. London

RAWLINGS, William. w1891-98. London
85 Hatton Garden (1891-94) 90 Hatton Garden (1895-98)

RAY, William. e1825-40. Clock & watch M. Battle

RAYMENT, Henry. w1857-62. Opt. math. & phil. IM. 8 Postern Row, Tower Hill, London

REA & Co. w1784. Clock & watch M. Walton-upon-Trent
Also 'REA'. e1810-30. Clock & watch M. Walton. Angle barometer.

REALINI, C. e1810-30. Manchester

REALINI, Charles. e1810-50. Preston
Also 'Charles REALINO'.

REALINI, L. e1830-50. Newcastle

REDPATH, Henry. w1787-1820. Clock & watch M. Sterling

REED, Jonathan. w1858-79. Clock & watch M & silversmith. Brampton

REEVER, P. e1830-50. Alnwick

REEVES, Caleb. w1862-70. Clock & watch M. Crawley

REEVES, W. e1880-1900+. 146 Minories, London

REFFELL, J. e1810-30. London

REHE, Samuel. w1770-92. Math. IM. Shoe Lane, London

REID, Adam. w1847. Clock & watch M. Woolwich

REID, Alexander. w1855-1901. Opt. IM. Edinburgh
6 Nicolson St (1855-67) 31 Castle St (1868-1901)

REID, William. w1874-77. Phil. IM. 2 St Giles St, Edinburgh

RENNOLDSON, Isaac. w1822-48. Opt. & math. IM. 5 Cambridge Place, Hackney Rd, London

RENNOLDSON, J. w1817-22. Math. IM. 23 Camden Row, Bethnal Green Rd, London

RENWICK, James. w1844-47. 2 Booths Place, Turnmill St, London

REY, Gustave. w1882-84. London
63 & 64 Milton St, Fore St (1882) 32 & 34 Clerkenwell Rd (1884)

REY, Gustave & Son. w1885-86. 32 & 34 Clerkenwell Rd, London

REYNOLDS & BRANSON e1890-1900+. Barographs. Leeds

REYNOLDS, J. w1851-56. Clock & watch M. St Austell, Wadebridge and St Columb Minor

REYNOLDS & Son. w1877-1900+. Opt. & naut. IM. London
22 John St, Crutchedfriars (1877-80) 32 Crutchedfriars (1881-99) 7 Dionis Yard (1892-95)

REYNOLDS, T. A. & Co. w1894-1900+. Phil. IM. London
15 Sekforde St (1894-96) 130 & 132 Clerkenwell Rd (1897-1900+)

REYNOLDS & WIGGINS w1870-72. Opt. IM. 125 Patrick St, Cork

REYNOLDSON, Thomas. w1846-58. Clock & watch M. 7 Queen St, Hull

RHODES, Manoah. w1837-66. Clock & watch M & silversmith. 138 Westgate, Bradford

RIALINI, C. e1835-55. Manchester

RIBOLDI, Joseph. w1824. Carver & gilder. 122 George's St, Limerick

RIBRIGHT, Thomas. w1768-c1810. Opt. & math. IM. 40 The Poultry, London

RICHARD & Co. w1872-1900+. Importer. 24 Cannon St, London and Paris
Importer of aneroid barometers.

RICHARDS, James. w1816. Clock & watch M. Birmingham

RICHARDSON, John. w1801-27. Opt. IM. 16 Somerset St, Aldgate High St, London

RICHARDSON, Matthew. w1716-40. Opt. IM. At Sir Isaac Newton's Head and Golden Spectacles, against York Buildings in the Strand, London
His trade card shows that he was apprenticed to Mr Edward Scarlett and that he sold barometers and thermometers wholesale or retail. Like Scarlett, he was 'Optician to His Majesty'.

RICHARDSON, Sidney & Co. Ltd. w1897-1900+. Opt. math. & phil. IM. 19 Cross St, Hatton Garden, London

RICKARD, S. e1835-55. Stroud

RIDER, Job. w1791-1805. Clock M & opt. IM. The Reflecting Telescope, Shambles St, Belfast
In 1792 he made a barometric clock.

RIDER, William. w1827. Opt. math. & phil. IM. 22 Ashton St, Poplar, London

RIELLA e1810-30. York

RIMMINGTON, G. & Son. w1849-64. Clock & watch M. Lubenham

RIMONDI, Charles. w1837-66. Clock & watch M, jeweller & opt. IM. Halifax
1 Union St (1837) 8 Waterhouse St (1838-50) 9 Waterhouse St (1850-66)

RIPLEY, James. w1807-43. Opt. & math. IM. London
335 Hermitage Bridge Rd, Wapping (1828) Mill Place, Commercial Rd, Limehouse
15 Warkworth Terrace, Commercial Rd, Limehouse (1843)

RIPLEY & Son. w1797-1807. Opt. & math. IM. London
364 Hermitage Bridge Rd (1797-1807) 335 Hermitage Bridge Rd (1800-07)

RIPLEY, Thomas. w1773-97. Math. IM. 364 Hermitage Bridge Rd, Wapping, London

RISSO, John. w1783. Saltmarket, Glasgow

RITTSON, John. e1750-70. Clock & watch M. Tekrill
Made stick barometers with the silvered brass register plates headed 'The Great Barometer'.

RIVA e1810-30. Uxbridge

RIVA, A. e1823. Glasgow

RIVA, A. e1835-55. Silver St, Marlborough

RIVA, A. & Co. w1823-25. Carvers & gilders. 70 High St, Glasgow
Also 'RIVA & Co.'.

RIVA, C. e1820-40. Glasgow

RIVA, F. e1810-30. Reading

RIVA, Ferdinando. w1830-34. Opt. IM. 7 Watson Walk, Sheffield

RIVA, H. e1825-45. Llangefni

RIVA, J. e1820-40. Bridport

RIVA, J. & M. w1825-61. Carvers, gilders & looking glass M. Glasgow
143 High St (1825-49) 147 High St (1849-57) 63 John St (1857-61) 249 Argyle St (1844-46)

RIVA, M. w1826. Carver & gilder. 143 High St, Glasgow

RIVA, P. e1825-45. Edinburgh

RIVA, P. & Co. w1832. Edinburgh

RIVERS, John. w1822-35. Swansea
Wind St (1822) Goat St (1830) High St (1835)

RIVOLTA, A. e1815-45. Chester

RIVOLTA, Anthony. w1820-51. Looking glass M. London
32 Brooke St, Holborn (1822-45) 21 Lower Calthorpe St (1846-51)

RIVOLTA & Co. e1810-30

RIVOLTA, D. e1810-30

RIVOLTA, D. e1835-45. Edinburgh

RIVOLTA & DEL VECCHIO w1863. Clock & watch M. Wellington, Salop

RIVOLTA, F. e1800-20. Reading

RIVOLTA, F. e1810-30. Macclesfield

RIVOLTA, Francis. w1870-79. Clock & watch M. Wellington, Salop

RIVOLTA, J. & Co. e1820-40. Macclesfield

RIVOLTA, L. e1820-40

RIZZI, A. e1830-50. Lowerhead Row, Leeds

ROBB, William. w1776-1816. Clock M. Montrose
He made stick barometers but is particularly noted for his double-angle barometers which were similar to those made by Balthazar Knie and Charles Moliner.

ROBELOU, Isaac. w1719. London
Known only for his bulb cistern barometer with a gold and black japanned case which is in the Science Museum, London.

ROBERTO, William. w1879. Clock & watch M. Oswestry

ROBERTS e1860-80. Stonehouse

ROBERTS, Henry. w1746-56. Clock & watch M. London

ROBERTS, Henry. w1877. 9 Oldham Place, Farringdon Rd, London

ROBERTS, Mary Ann (Mrs). w1871. Clock & watch M. Selby

ROBINSON, Edward Henry & Co. w1894. e1870-1900+. Opt. IM. 52 Bishopsgate, London

ROBINSON, Henry. w1870. Clock & watch M. High St, Shrewsbury

ROBINSON, Thomas Charles. w1821-42. Opt. math. & phil. IM. 38 Devonshire St, Portland Place, Marylebone, London
He made a portable mountain barometer in 1831 which was exhibited at the Royal Institution.

ROBSON, F. e1855-75. Opt. IM. 46 Dean St, Newcastle upon Tyne

ROBSON, F. & Co. e1875-95. Opt. IM. Newcastle upon Tyne

ROBSON, William. w1860. e1845-65. Clock & watch M. Banff

RODGERSON, William. w1835-90. Opt. & math. IM. Liverpool
Chatham Buildings (1837) 10 St James St
Marine barometers and sympiesometers.

RODWELL e1865-85. Oxford

ROE e1840-50. Godalming

ROE, Joseph Adolphus. w1853-65. Clock & watch M. Tacket St, Ipswich

ROE, William. w1828-62. Clock & watch M. Midhurst

ROGERS, George. w1799-1805. Math. IM. Mile End, Grove, London

ROLANDO, Joseph. e1810-30. Braintree

RONCATI, P. w1848. Clock & watch M. Southampton

RONCHETI, Bap. & LOMAS e1785-1800. Manchester

RONCHETI & GATTY e1790-1810. London
Probably a partnership between John Merry Ronketti and James Gatty.

RONCHETI, T. e1810-40. Bristol

RONCHETI, Thomas. e1805-25. Dukes Head, Bow St, Bloomsbury, London

RONCHETTI, Baptista. w1785-e1810. Opt. & phil. IM. 15 High St, Manchester
Arrived in Manchester in 1785 from Tavernerio, near Lake Como in Italy, and worked in Spear St before setting up in business at 15 High St. After a while he sent for his son Charles Joshua and his nephew Lewis Casartelli from Italy and Dominic Bolongaro accompanied them. The three worked for him for a time and then went their separate ways. Baptista was a prolific producer of high-quality instruments which included stick, wheel, angle and double barometers.

RONCHETTI Bros. e1860-80. 172 Strand, London

RONCHETTI, Charles Joshua. w1817-52. Opt. & phil. IM. Manchester

29 Balloon St (1817-28) Stock St (1829) 4 St Ann's Parade (1830) 4 Cateaton St (1830-31) 43 Market St (1832-52)
Came to Manchester from Tavernerio, near Lake Como, Italy to join his father Baptista Ronchetti around 1787. He worked for his father for a time and then travelled around the country selling barometers at town markets. He lived in Shrewsbury, Carlisle and Liverpool before settling in Manchester and working for Vincent Zanetti. In 1817 he set up on his own at 29 Balloon St. His two sons, John Baptist and Joshua, joined him in the business at St Ann's Parade and the name was changed to John B. and Joshua Ronchetti, although some barometers were still signed Joshua Ronchetti until the partnership ceased in 1852.

RONCHETTI, Edmund. w1850. Waterbeer St, Exeter

RONCHETTI, John. w1836-38. 25 Hatton Garden, London
Appears to have been connected with a new self-registering barometer or hydrometer.

RONCHETTI, John B. & Joshua. w1830-52. Opt. & phil. IM. Manchester
4 Cateaton St (1830-31) 43 Market St (1832-52)
A partnership between Charles Joshua and his two sons John Baptist and Joshua. The two brothers provided weekly weather forecasts in the Manchester press from 1830 to at least 1845. Their brother-in-law, Joseph Casartelli, took over the business in 1852.

RONCHETTI, Joseph. w1837-66. Watch M. 11 Parliament St, York

RONCHETTI, Joseph. w1858-66. Watch M. Scarborough
27 St Nicholas Cliff (1858) 34 St Nicholas Cliff (1866)

RONCHETTI & Son. w1836-39. 2 Hatton Garden, London

RONCHETTI, Thomas. w1822-56. Opt. IM. Exeter
New Bridge St (1822) 4 Mount Pleasant, Black Boy Rd (1830) Black Boy Rd (1850-56)

RONCHETY, I. & M. e1790-1810. London

RONCI e1835-55. London

RONCORONE, Francis. e1815-35. 2 Holborn and 81 Holborn, London

RONCORONE, S. e1820-40. 2 Holborn, London

RONCORINI, G. e1810-30. Salisbury

RONCORINI, P. e1839. Clock & watch M. Basingstoke

RONKETTI, J. G. H. w1843-47. Opt. math. & phil. IM. London
102 St Martin's Lane (1843-5) 116 Gt Russell St (1843-45) 19 Leather Lane (1846) 6 Mary's Terrace, Camden Town (1847)

RONKETTI, John. w1820-44. Hydrometer & saccharometer M. 15 Museum St, London

Some barometers signed 'I. G. M. RONKETTI' with this address.

RONKETTI, John George. w1820-21. Math. & phil. IM. 8 Back Hill, Hatton Garden, London

RONKETTI, John Merry. w1787-1819. Artificial flower & feather M. London
180 Holborn (1787-97) 6 Peter St, Bloomsbury (1800-19)
An Italian immigrant who settled in London. He made a very large number of very fine stick and wheel barometers, often favouring paper plates and bulb cisterns for his stick instruments. The engravers appear to have had difficulty in spelling Ronketti and the name has several variations on barometers: Ronkite, Roncketi, Ronchetti, Roncheti and Ronkitte are common. Some barometers are signed 'RONKETTI & Co.' and 'J. & A. RONKETTI' with the 6 Peter St address.

RONKETTI, Joseph. w1820. 8 Back Hill, Hatton Garden, London

RONKETTI, Joseph. w1854-97. Hydrometer M. London
31 Northampton Rd (1854-1870) 25 Northampton Rd (1870-97)

ROOKE, John. w1856-79. Clock & watch M. Dyer St, Cirencester

ROOKER, John. w1815-46. Math & phil. IM. London
1 Little Queen St, Holborn (1815-44) 26 East St, Lamb's Conduit St (1845-46)

ROOKER, John & Son. w1847-60. Math. & phil. IM. London
26 East St, Lamb's Conduit St (1847-48) 26 East St, Red Lion Square (1849-60)

ROSASPINI, P. e1835-55. Ticehurst

ROSATA, F. & Co. e1810-30. Edinburgh

ROSATTE, J. e1800-20. Leeds

ROSE, James H. w1866-74. e1855-75. Clock & watch M. Ramsgate

ROSENTALL, I. e1830-50. Burton-on-Trent

ROSS, A. H. e1830-50. Marine barometers. Sunderland

ROSS, Andrew. w1830-59. Opt. math. & phil. IM. Clerkenwell, London
15 St John's Square (1830) 21 Featherstone Buildings (1840-47) 2 Featherstone Buildings (1848-59)
Exhibited at the Great Exhibition at the Crystal Palace in 1851 and won a Gold Medal.

ROSS, Andrew & Co. w1837-42. Math. & phil. IM. 33 Regent St, Piccadilly, London

ROSS & Co. w1874-1897. Opt. math. & phil. IM. London
7 Wigmore St (1874-77) 164 New Bond St (1876-81) 112 New Bond St (1822-92) 111 New Bond St (1893-97)
This was the continuation of the business of Thomas Ross which was noted for its high-quality instruments. It claimed to have won gold medals in London, 1851 and 1862;

Paris 1867; Philadelphia 1876; Paris 1878; Inventions Exhibition 1885; Grand prix and gold medal in Paris 1889; Kingston, Jamaica 1891 and Chicago 1893. Barometers also signed 'ROSS' with the 111 New Bond St address.

ROSS, Joseph. e1825-50. Liskeard

ROSS Ltd. w1897-1900+. Opt. math. & phil. IM. London
111 New Bond St (1897-99) 31 Cockspur St (1900+)

ROSS & Son. e1865-90. Clock & watch M. Winchester
Also 'Ross & Sons'.

ROSS, Thomas. w1860-72. Math. opt. & phil. IM. London
2 & 3 Featherstone Buildings (1860-67) 53 Wigmore St (1868-69) 7 Wigmore St (1870-72)
Only son and successor of Andrew Ross.

ROSS,Thomas & Co. w1873. Math. opt. & phil. IM. 7 Wigmore St, London

ROSSI, George. w1822-46. Looking glass M. Exchange St, Norwich

ROSSI, Joseph. w1860-62. Clock & looking glass M. Shrewsbury

ROSSI, P. e1810-30

ROSSI, Theodore. w1875. Clock & watch M. Norwich

ROSSITER, George. w1861-66. e1850-66. Clock & watch M. Bridgwater

ROSSITER, George. w1875-83. Clock & watch M. Weston-super-Mare

ROTHWELL e1820-40. Manchester

ROUND, G. w1862-66. Clock & watch M. Carshalton

ROUND GLASS HOUSE w1754. Dublin
An advertisement included 'Weather Glasses, Receivers for Air Pumps, and all sorts of Philosophical Experiments'.

ROUND, John. w1870-75. Math. & phil. IM. London
263 Camberwell Rd (1870) 196 Camberwell Rd (1871-75)

ROUTLEDGE, Adam. w1828-58. Clock & watch M. 32 English St, Carlisle
He often used printed paper plates and hemispherical cistern covers for his stick barometers.

ROWE e1815-35. Cambridge

ROWELL, George. b1770-d1834. Clock & watch M. Oxford

ROWELL, Richard Rouse. w1834-65. Clock & watch M. Oxford
Son of George Rowell.

ROWLAND, Edward. w1848-51. Watch M & silversmith. 50 Broad Quay, Bristol

ROWLAND, Richard. w1792-1810. Math. IM. 50 Broad Quay, Bristol
There are two known 'upside-down' wheel barometers with the dial at the top of the case above a hygrometer and a thermometer.

ROWLAND, Thomas & Edward. w1825-30. Opt. & math. IM. 50 Broad Quay, Bristol

ROWLEY, T. e1840-60. Opt.IM. 128 St James St, Brighton

ROWLEY, T. & Son. e1860-80. Opt. IM. 128 St James St, Brighton
Some barometers signed 'ROWLEY & Son' with this address.

RUBERGALL, Thomas. w1802-54. Opt. math. & phil. IM. London
Princes St, Soho (1802) 27 Coventry St (1805-23) 24 Coventry St (1826-54)
He was optician and mathematical instrument-maker to the Duke of Clarence and optician to King George III.

RUMBALL, Samuel. w1838. Math. & phil. IM. 5 Crane Court, St Peter's Hill, London

RUMBOLD, John. w1859-75. Clock & watch M. Salisbury

RUSHMER e1845-65. Great Yarmouth

RUSSELL, Alexander & Co. w1834. Clock, watch & sundial M. Kirkcaldy

RUSSELL, John. born c1745-d1817. Clock & watch M. Falkirk
The son of a blacksmith, he opened a shop at the top of Kirk Wynd, Falkirk around 1770, where he became renowned for his clocks, watches, musical boxes and barometers. An advertisement in the *Edinburgh Evening Courant* in 1783 stated that he 'makes and repairs musical clocks, organs, etc.; also makes portable jacks of a new construction, barometers, thermometers, and every kind of machinery in the watch and clock branch'. It appears that he concentrated on only two types of barometer. One was a large stick instrument with a distinctive silvered Corinthian column, with a brass base and capital, to protect the tube and a typical Scottish oval-shaped cistern cover. The other type was a large wheel barometer with gilt brass rope-twist mouldings and glass panels of black and gilt *verre églomisé* above and below the dial, which had two subsidiary dials, one to allow readings to one-hundredth of an inch and the other for recording purposes. Russell was appointed watchmaker to the Prince of Wales and became watchmaker to the Prince Regent when the Regency was established in 1811.

RUSSELL, Thomas & Son. w1848-1902. Clock & watch M. Liverpool

RUST & EYRE w1740. Math. IM. The Minories, London

RUST, Richard. w1753-82. Naut. IM. Corner of St Catherine's Stairs, Near the Tower of London, London

RUSTON e1730-50. Birmingham

S

SABATIER, James. w1876-77. 39 Hatton Garden, London

SALA, Dominico. e1780-1810. London
He made double barometers; some had printed paper plates and others had the weather indications stamped directly on to a boxwood base.

SALAMSOM e1865-85. Bristol

SALDERINI, Joseph. w1830-41. Opt. IM. Long Causeway, Peterborough

SALERI, F. e1810-30. Nottingham

SALKIND, Solomon. w1858-75. Clock & watch M. Walsham and Norwich

SALLA, A. e1810-30. 20 Cross St, Hatton Garden, London

SALLA, Anthony. w1832-40. London
65 Paradise Row, Chelsea (1832-33) 66 Paradise Row, Chelsea (1836-40)

SALLA, Antonio. e1780-1800
Double barometer.

SALLA, J. Bapt. e1790-1820

SALLA, Mark. e1810-30 Preston
Barometers signed 'M. SALA' with this address.

SALLA, P. B. e1820-40. London

SALMON, William John. w1840-81. Opt. IM. London
105 Fenchurch St (1840-45) 254 Whitechapel Rd (1846-53) 100 Fenchurch St (1855-61) 48 Lombard St (1860-61) 11 Fenchurch St (1862) 1 Aldgate (1863-64) 85 Fenchurch St (1865-77) 2 Aldgate (1878-81)
Some barometers signed 'W. J. SALMON & Co.' with the 48 Lombard St address.

SALMONI, Mark. w1830-38. e1810-40. St Clements, Oxford
He described himself as a dealer in barometers. Instruments signed 'M. SALAMON', 'M. SALEMONE' and 'M. SALAMONI' with this address.

SALMONI, Peter Paul. w1829-41. Optician. Bath
4 Milsom St (1829-30) 24 Union St (1833-41)
Barometers signed 'P. SALMON' with these addresses.

SALOM & Co. w1867-82. Opt. math. & phil. IM. London and Edinburgh
137 Regent St London (1867-82) 98 Princes St, Edinburgh

SALT, William. w1892-1900+. Opt. math. & phil. IM. 65 Hatton Garden, London

SALTERI, A. e1800-30. 17 Great Queens St, London

SALTERI, F. and SALTERI, F. & Co. e1810-35. Nottingham

SALTERY, Francis. e1800-30. 94 Holborn Hill, London
Also 'Francis SALTERY & Co.'.

SALTERY, F. VECHIO & Co. e1800-30. 94 Holborn Hill, London

SALVADE, P. e1810-45. Liverpool

SALVANI, V. & Co. e1830-50. Brighton

SANDFORD, Patrick. w1820-22. Mirror M. 45 Henry St, Dublin

SANDRINI, B. e1820-40. Liverpool

SANGSTER, William. e1815-35. Math. IM. Kings Arms, Butcher Row, Temple Bar, London

SANKEY, J. e1810-30. Coalbrookdale, Salop

SARGENT, Thomas C. w1800-20. Opt. & math. IM. 2 Thames St, Rotherhithe, London

SARGENT, Thomas Cornelius. w1854-1900+. Opt. math. & naut. IM. London
29 Cannon St (1854-55) 4 Thames St (1856-59) 2 Thames St (1860-92) 10 Russell St (1866-67) 37 Odessa St (1893-1900+)

SARGENT, Thomas Cornelius & Co. w1860-61. Opt. math. & phil. IM. 2 Thames St, London

SATORELLI, A. e1830-50. Aylesbury

SATORELLI, A. & MAZZUCHI e1810-30. Aylesbury

SAUNDERS, E. e1865-85. 100 High St, Oxford

SAUNDERS & JACOB w1875. Clock & watch M. Dorchester

SAUNDERS, Richard. w1681-1715. Math. IM. Leicestershire
Ouston (1683-95) Leesthorp, near Melton Mowbray (1696-1711)
His work included 'the making and adjusting of weather glasses, and the construction of every variety of dial'.

SAUNDERS, Thomas. w1793-1819. Math. & opt. IM. Dublin
7 George's St (1793-94) 35 College Green (1796-99) 6 Church Lane (1800-18) Eden Quay (1819)

SAVAGE e1890-1900. Gravesend

SAVAGE & Son. e1825-45. London

SAX, Julius. w1858-64. Math & phil. IM. London
63 Gray's Inn Rd (1858-59) 64 Gray's Inn Rd (1860) 477 Oxford St (1861) 29 Hart St (1862) 8 Hatton Garden (1863) 455 Oxford St (1864)

SCACHI, F. e1820-40. 81 High Holborn, London

SCANTLEBURY, John B. w1817. Campo Lane, Sheffield

SCARLETT, Edward. born c1688-d1743. Opt. IM. Archimedes and Globe, near St Ann's Church, Soho, London
A leading instrument-maker who was apprenticed to Christopher Cock in 1691 and started on his own around 1700. His son of the same name was apprenticed to him in 1716 and carried on the business after his father's death. His trade card shows him to have been 'Optician to His Majesty King George the Second'; the wording is also in French and Dutch which suggests that he must have carried on a significant trade with the Continent. He sold straight tube and angle barometers. (See Fig. 23.)

SCATLIFF, Daniel. w1796-1830. Math. & phil. IM. 6 Wapping Wall, Shadwell, London

SCHAFFERD BUNDENBERG Ltd. w1875-95. Manchester

SCHALFINO, C. e1810-30. White Lion Court, Taunton

SCHALFINO, John. w1840-43. e1820-45. East St, Taunton

SCHALFINO, L. S. e1850-70. Taunton

SCHALLER, Andrew Francis. w1869. Clock & watch M & barometer repairer. Lambeth, London

SCHARASNELLA, P. J. e1835-55. Kingswood

SCHIAVI, Antonio. w1821-32. Carver, gilder & looking glass M. Liverpool
14 Standish St (1821-23) 67 Stanley St (1824-32)

SCHIAVI, N. e1810-30. Chesham

SCHIERWATER & LLOYD w1897-1900+. Watch M & jeweller. Liverpool
A partnership between Amandus Schierwater and William Lloyd.

SCHMALCALDER, Charles Augustus. w1806-40. Opt. & math. IM. 82 Strand and 399 Strand, London

SCHMALCALDER, John. w1841-45. Opt. math. & phil. IM. 400 Strand and 2 Fairfax Court, London

SCHMIDT, George. w1889-92. 27 Milton St, London

SCHOCK, W. C. e1860-80. 8 Ashby St, Clerkenwell, London

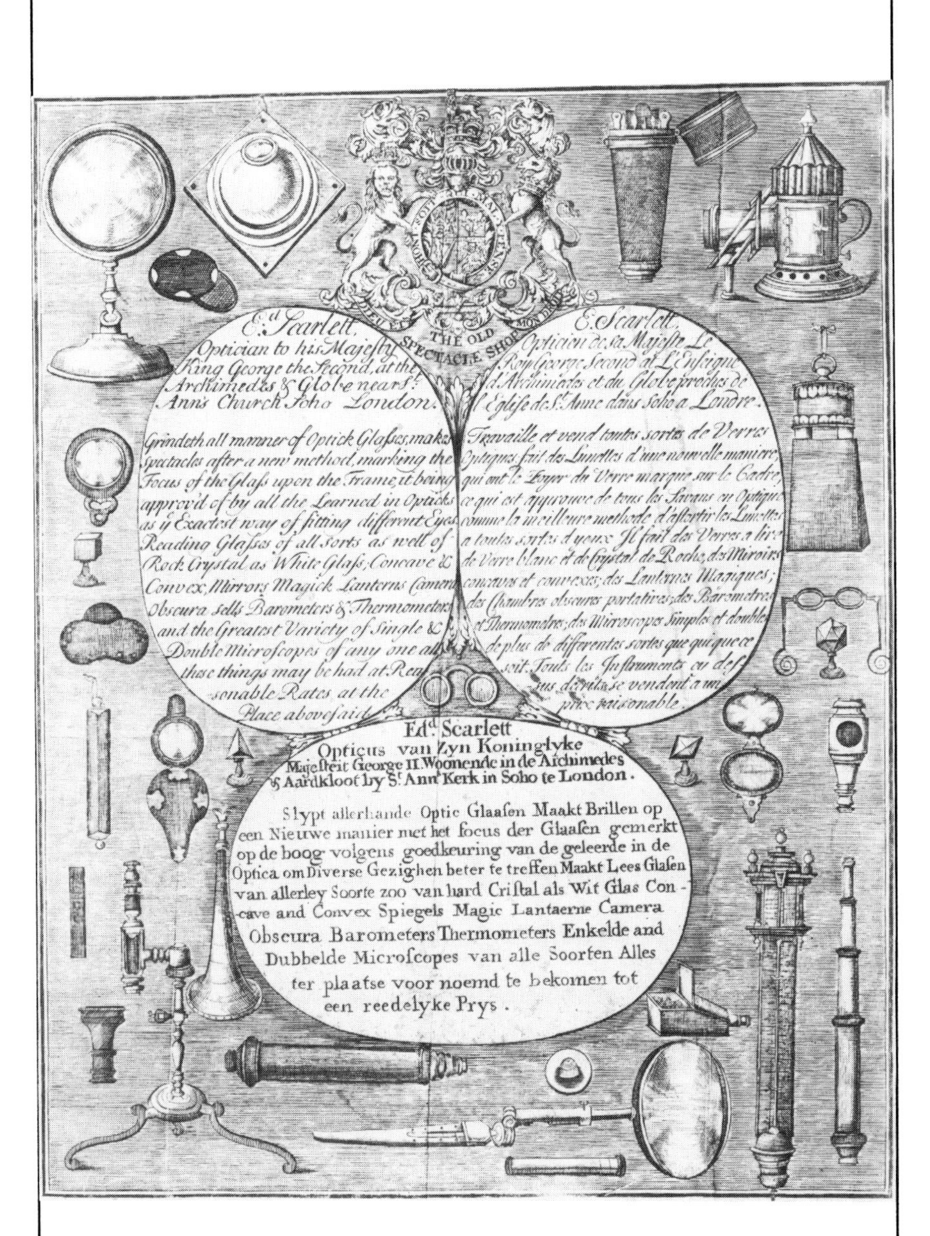

Fig. 23 Trade card of Edward Scarlett *(Science Museum, London)*

SCHULER, Philip. w1863. e1840-65. Clock & watch M. 16 City Rd, London

SCHWARCK, D. w1860-68. Clock & watch M. Leamington

SCHWARTZ, Anthony. w1868-90. Clock & watch M. Whitford St, Holywell

SCHWARTZ, Anthony. w1887-90. Clock & watch M. Chester Rd, Flint

SCHWER & KETTERER e1820-40. Southampton

SCHWERER, Charles. w1871-87. e1850-87. Clock & watch M. Aberdare

SCHWERER, J. w1856. e1840-60. Clock & watch M. Truro
Also 'SCHWERER & Co.'.

SCHWERER, J. & HOFFMEYER w1863-69. Clock & watch M. London

SCIOPTICAN Co. w1877. 157 Great Portland St, London

SCOBBIE, Andrew. w1884-1900+. Phil. IM. 204 George St, Glasgow

SCOLA, Lewis. e1830-50. Guildford

SCOTT e1840-60. Henley

SCOTT, Benjamin. w1712-33. Math. IM. Mariner and Globe, Exeter Exchange, Strand, London
He advertised 'all sorts of Mathematical Instruments in Silver, Brass, Ivory and Wood etc. performed according to the latest Improvements of Philosophers and Practicers of the several Mathematical Arts ... Globes, Spheres, Weather-Glasses ...'. In 1733 he went to St Petersburg as part of Peter the Great's endeavour to establish modern science in Russia. He died there in 1751.

SCOTT, J. e1865-85. Taunton

SCOTT, James. w1832-71. Clock & watch M. Kendall

SCOTT, James George. w1840-83. Math. IM. 17 Bermondsey Wall, London

SCOTT, James Wilson. w1871-79. Clock & watch M. Kendall
Son of James Scott.

SEARCH, James. w1780. e1760-80. Math. IM. Crown Court, Soho and Pultney St, Golden Square, London

SEARLE e1840-60. Plymouth

SELF, Charles. w1861-62. London
85 Pentonville Rd (1861) 17 New Charles St (1862)

SELVA, John. e1815-35. Plymouth

SELVEA, George. w1826. Jeweller. 25 Grimsby Lane, Hull

SELVEA, John. w1831. Jeweller. 25 Grimsby Lane, Hull

SEMMENS, Herman. w1834-44. Clock & watch M. Truro

SESINO, S. e1820-40. Norwich

SEWILL, J. e1830-50. Liverpool and London
Also 'SEWILL & Co.'.

SEWILL, John. w1875-81. Clock & watch M. London

SEWILL, Joseph. w1848-51. Clock, watch & chronometer M. Liverpool
Maker to the Queen of Spain.

SEWILL, Joseph. w1881. Clock, watch & chronometer M. London
Maker to the Queen of Spain.

SEXTON, W. w1846-65. e1830-65. Clock & watch M. Holt

SHARP, John Bunyea. w1823-32. Clock & watch M. Faversham

SHARP, Joseph. e1810-30. Coventry

SHARP, Robert. w1774. Long Formacus

SHARP, Samuel. w1825. Opt. math. & phil. IM. 29 Brownlow St, Drury Lane, London

SHAW, J. e1820-40. Gosberton

SHAW, John. w1672-1715. Clock M. At the Dyall in Holborn, London

SHAW, Thomas. e1820-40. Websey Low Moor

SHENFIELD, John. w1848-51. Clock & watch M. Manchester

SHEPHARD, J. H. w1860. Clock & watch M. Congleton and Hanley

SHEPHERD, Charles. w1832-63. Clock & watch M. 53 Leadenhall St, London

SHEPHERD, Charles & Son. w1869-81. Clock & watch M. 53 Leadenhall St, London

SHETRINO, J. e1835-55. Worcester

SHOOLBRED e1865-85. London

SHOOLBRED & RENWICK w1843. Surgical IM. 34 Jermyn St, London

SHORT & MASON w1873-1900+. Compass & naut. IM. London
62 Hatton Garden (1873-75) 40 Hatton Garden (1876-1900+)
The firm made a very large number of barographs.

SHORT, T. W. w1872-73. Compass & naut. IM. 62 Hatton Garden, London
Became Short & Mason in 1873.

SHORTGRAVE, Richard. w1658-d1676. Surveyor & instrument M. Gresham College, London
He made various instruments for the Royal Society, including thermometers and weather glasses, some of which were from designs suggested by Robert Hooke. He 'died poor' in 1676.

SHUTTLEWORTH, Henry Raines. w1746-1811. Opt. IM. 23 Ludgate St, London
He was apprenticed to John Cuff and was succeeded by his son of the same name.

SHUTTLEWORTH, T. e1830-50. Lewisham, London

SIDERY, Charles. w1848-68. Clock & watch M. Kingsclere

SIEBERT, John Martin. w1883. 81 Queen Victoria St, London

SIGRAY, Richard. w1790-92. Opt. IM. 80 Tottenham Court Rd, London

SILBERRAD, Charles. w1801-33. Opt. & math. IM. 34 Aldgate St, London

SILBERRAD, S. I. B. w1805. Clock, watch & sundial M. London

SILLO & Co. e1820-40. Leeds

SILLO, John. e1810-30. Manchester

SILO, J. e1800-50. Glasgow

SILO, Modesto. w1843-46. Carver, gilder & looking glass M. 21 Cornmarket, Londonderry

SILO, R. e1850-70. London Bridge, London

SILVA, G. e1810-30. Boston

SILVA, L. e1810-30

SILVANI & Co. e1825-45. Brighton
Produced large wheel barometers with a pendulum clock above the dial.

SILVANI, G. & B. e1820-40. Brighton

SILVANI, Vincent. w1850. Leamington

SILVANO, V. e1825-45. Brighton

SILVE, J. e1820-40. 9 East St, Plymouth

SILVER & JAMES & Co. w1828-32. Clock & watch M. London

SIMINS, Thomas. e1780-1800. London

SIMMONS & FREDERICKS w1886-98. Opt. IM. London
21 Red Lion Square (1886-89) 19 Charterhouse Buildings (1890-96) 10a Featherstone Buildings (1897-98)

SIMMONS, George Alexander. w1873-97. Phil. IM. London
57 Great Saffron Hill (1873) 21 St James's Walk (1874-75) 12 Sekforde St (1876-77) 16 Woodbridge St (1878-85) 25 Hatton Wall (1886-90) 90 Hatton Garden (1891-97)

SIMMS, Frederick. w1816-94. Clock & watch M. Chipping Norton

SIMMS, James & George. w1822-46. Math. & phil. IM. London
4 Broadway, Blackfriars and 9 Grenville St, Hatton Garden

SIMMS, William. w1763-1820. Math. IM. Bowmans Buildings, Aldersgate St, London

SIMMS, William. w1785-1844. Clock & watch M. Chipping Norton

SIMON, James. e1800-20. London

SIMONS, D. e1835-55. Trowbridge

SIMONS, George. w1839-44. e1820-45. Clock & watch M. London

SIMONS, James. w1773-91. Math. phil. & opt. IM. London
Sir Isaac Newton's Head, the corner of Marylebone St opposite Glasshouse St (1773-85) 17 Marylebone St (1791) (See Fig. 24.)

SIMPSON, George. w1850. e1830-60. Chemical & phil. IM. 1 & 2 Kennington Rd, London

SIMSON, Stephen. w1830-39. Clock & watch M. Southampton

SINCLAR, George. w1654-96. Teacher. St Andrews (1654-55) Glasgow (1655-66) Edinburgh (1666-89) Glasgow (1689-96)
He was originally a schoolmaster at St Andrews and was appointed to a Chair of Philosophy at Glasgow. From there he went to Edinburgh to teach mathematics and philosophy and later returned to Glasgow to become professor of mathematics.He wrote *The Explanation of the Weather Glass* in 1683 and this was updated in 1688. This created a demand for the instruments and he made and sold them himself.His weather glasses cost '£2.8s.4d. for the enclosed variety and £1.10s. for the open variety'.

SINGLETON e1835-45. Ipswich

SIOLI, L. w1807. Richmond

SIOLI, L. e1810-30. Norwich
Also spelt 'SIOLLI'.

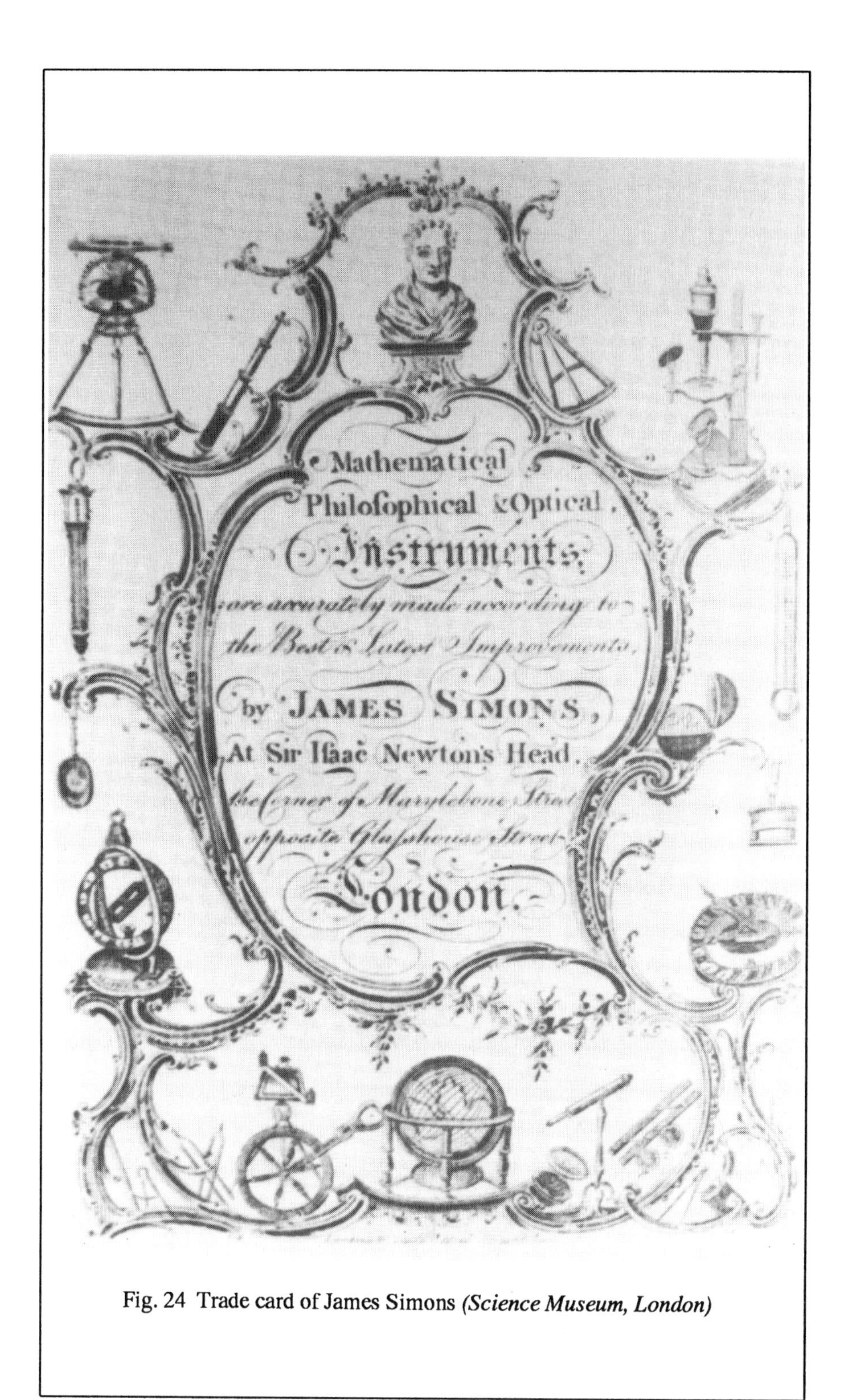

Fig. 24 Trade card of James Simons *(Science Museum, London)*

SISSON, Jeremiah. w1747-88. Math. & phil. IM. Corner of Beaufort Buildings, Strand, London
Succeeded his father Jonathan Sisson in 1747 and was active until at least 1788 when he was instrument-maker to the Prince of Wales. He was basically a mathematical instrument-maker and at least maintained the eminence of his father. Both father and son signed their barometers 'J. SISSON' so it is often difficult to be sure which man made them.

SISSON, Jonathan. b1690-d1747. Corner of Beaufort Buildings, Strand, London
Born in Lincolnshire and had established a workshop in the Strand by 1722. He made optical and mathematical instruments of distinction and in 1729 was appointed instrument-maker to the Prince of Wales. He was considered specially adept at the precise division of scales but very few of his barometers appear to have survived. Both father and son signed their barometers 'J. SISSON' so it is often difficult to decide which man made them.

SKIRROW, James. w1783-1834. Clock & watch M. Wigan.

SMEDLEY, William. w1868-69. London
17 Cross St, Hatton Garden (1868) 15 Cross St, Hatton Garden (1869)

SMITH e1810-30. Reading

SMITH, Addison. w1750-89. Math. IM. London
St Martin's Lane, Charing Cross. 5 Charing Cross (1763-74) 481 Strand (1779) Charlotte St, Rathbone Place (1783)
Smith was apprenticed to Francis Watkins and became his partner in 1763 under the name of Watkins & Smith at 5 Charing Cross. The partnership lasted for eleven years when they traded on their own, but Smith himself does not appear to have made any barometers.

SMITH, B. e1780-1800. Bath

SMITH & BECK w1848-58. Opt. IM. 6 Coleman St, London

SMITH, BECK & BECK w1859-67. Opt. IM. London
6 Coleman St (1859-63) 31 Cornhill (1864-67)
The chief proprietor in the 1860s was Richard Beck and the name was changed to R. & J. Beck in 1867. Conrad Beck wrote standard textbooks on lenses, published by the firm.

SMITH, Edward. w1845-84. Opt. math. & naut. IM. London
11 Exmouth St (1845-67) 69 Fenchurch St (1868) 11 Gould Square (1869-71) 11 America Square (1874-80) 14 America Square (1881-82) 4 Vine St (1883-84)

SMITH, Egerton. w1766-d1788. Math. IM. Newton's Head, 17 Pool Lane, Liverpool

SMITH, Egerton (junior). w1803. Math. IM. 18 Pool Lane, Liverpool
Some barometers signed 'EGERTON SMITH & Co.'. This was probably a partnership between father and son of the same name.

SMITH, F. & Son. e1890-1900+. Southampton
Barographs

SMITH, J. e1810-30. 15 Palace Row, New Rd, London

SMITH, James. w1815-28. Opt. IM. North Gate, Royal Exchange, London

SMITH, James. w1822-38. Opt. IM. 17 Bath Place, New Rd, Fitzroy Square, London

SMITH, John. w1678-94. Clock & instrument M. London
He made and wrote about barometers and in 1688 published *A Complete Discourse of the Nature, Use and Right Management of that Wonderful Instrument the Baroscope or Quicksilver Weather Glass.* In 1694 he wrote *Horological Disquisitions* which included 'Rules for the Use of the quicksilver or spirit Weather Glass'.

SMITH, Joseph. w1817-46. Opt. math. & phil. IM. London
42 Threadneedle St (1817) Northgate, Royal Exchange (1822) 17 Bath Place (later 15 Palace Row), New Rd, Fitzroy Square

SMITH, R. w1804. Accrington
A surviving stick barometer is in a mahogany, boxwood and Tunbridge marquetry rectangular case of Gothic influence with two thermometers.

SMITH & RAMAGE w1852-61. Naut. & opt. IM. 45 Regents Quay, Aberdeen

SMITH, Samuel. w1857-81. Clock & watch M. Clerkenwell, London

SMITH, Thomas S. w1838. Math. & phil. IM. 11 Goldsmith St, Hackney Rd, London

SMITH, William. w1828-50. Clock & watch M. North St, Crowland

SMITH, William & Andrew. w1838. Math. & phil. IM. 46 Lisle St, Leicester Square, London

SMYTH e1810-30. London

SNART, John. w1802-31. Opt. math. & phil. IM. 215 Tooley St, London

SNART, Neariah (Miss). w1831-47. Math. IM. 35 King St, Borough, London

SNELLING, James. w1793-1830. Clock & watch M & silversmith. High St, Alton

SNOW, Richard R. w1866-71. e1850-71. Clock & watch M. Ripon

SOCIÉTÉ des LUNETIERS w1873-1900+. Opt. math. & phil. IM. London
36 Brooke St, Holborn (1873) 13 Hatton Garden (1875-81) 56 Hatton Garden and Paris (1882-1900+)

SOLARI, Giovanni. w1887-99. Clock & watch M. Cardiff

SOLCA, A. e1840-60. Tunbridge Wells

SOLCA, J. & J. e1835-55. Hull

SOLCA, Joseph. e1835-55. Manchester

SOLCHA, A. e1835-55. Kettering

SOLCHA, Joseph. e1830-60. Hull

SOLCHA, L. & D. e1810-30. Hull

SOLCHA, Lewis. w1851-59. Carver, gilder & looking glass M. Hull
1 Dagger Lane (1851) 17 Robinson Row (1855-50)

SOLDANO, Joseph. w1851. Clock & watch M. London

SOLDANO, Louis & Son. w1857. Clock & watch M. London

SOLDINI, G. w1830. e1810-30. Jeweller. High St, Wincanton

SOLDINI, P. w1855. e1835-55. 9 Robinson Row, Hull

SOLDINI, P. & MASPOLI w1860. 9 Robinson Row, Hull

SOLOMAN, Alfred. w1883-85. 51 Lever St, St Luke's, London

SOLOMAN, Charles. e1865-85. Clock & watch M. King's Lynn

SOLOMON, John. w1848. Opt. IM. 17 Cathay, Bristol

SOLOMON, Samuel. e1835-55. Devizes

SOLOMON, Samuel. w1839-70. Clock & watch M. Lewes

SOLOMONS, Abraham. w1838. Opt. math. & phil. IM. 6 New Rd, St George's East, London

SOLOMONS, Elias. w1832-64. Opt. math. & phil. IM. London
36 Old Bond St (1832-47) 27 Old Bond St (1857-64)

SOLOMONS, G. M. w1838. Opt. math. & phil. IM. 9 East Bedford Square, Commercial Rd, London

SOLOMONS, M. E. w1856-1905. Opt. IM. 19 Nassau St, Dublin
Opticians to the Royal Family.

SOLOMONS, Samuel & Benjamin. w1838-79. Opt. IM. London
5 New Rd, St George's East (1838) 39 Albemarle St, Piccadilly (1839-79) 76 King William St, City (1841-43)

SOMALVICO, C. e1805-35. 41 Kirby St, Hatton Garden, London

SOMALVICO, C. e1815-45. 11 Brooke St, London
Probably Charles Somalvico, the brother of James Somalvico.

SOMALVICO, C. e1820-40. 4 Leather Lane, Holborn, London

SOMALVICO, I. e1820-40. 11 Brooke St, London

SOMALVICO, J. e1810-30. 12 Leather Lane, Holborn, London

SOMALVICO, J. e1810-60. Hatton Garden, London
41 Kirby St (1810-30) 42 Kirby St (1820-40) 44 Kirby St (1835-60)

SOMALVICO, J. & Son. e1820-40. 91 Hatton Garden, Holborn, London

SOMALVICO, James. e1800-20. 8 Charles St, Hatton Garden, London

SOMALVICO, James. e1820-40. 22 Kirby St, Hatton Garden, London
The son of Joseph Somalvico (1) and brother of Charles Somalvico.

SOMALVICO, Joseph. e1800-45. 67 Leather Lane, Holborn, London

SOMALVICO, Joseph (1). w1805-19. London
125 Holborn Hill (1805-07) 14 Brooke St (1811-18)
The father of James and Charles Somalvico.

SOMALVICO, Joseph (2). w1833-43. Opt. & phil. IM. London
37 Charles St, Hatton Garden (1833-41) 2 Hatton Garden (1839-43)
Son of James Somalvico and brother of Vincent Somalvico.

SOMALVICO, Joseph & Co. e1795-1825. 81 Holborn, London

SOMALVICO, Joseph & Co. e1800-30. 256 Holborn, London

SOMALVICO, Joseph & Co. w1840-1900+. Opt. & phil. IM. London
2 Hatton Garden (1840-67) 16 Charles St (1868-99) 18 Charles St (1900+)

SOMALVICO, Joseph & Co. Barometers with this signature are extant with the following London addresses: 17/18 Charles St. 25 Holborn. 125 Holborn.

SOMALVICO, Joseph & Son. e1820-40. Chronometer M. 37 Charles St, Hatton Garden, London

SOMALVICO, LIONE & Co. e1810-30. 125 Holborn Hill, London

SOMALVICO, V. & Co. e1810-30. London

SOMALVICO, Vincent. w1856-58. Phil. IM. 14 Charles St, Hatton Garden, London
Barometers signed 'V. SOMALVICO & Son' and 'V. SOMALVICO & Co.' with this address. Brother of Joseph Somalvico (2).

SONITERA, Lionel. e1780-1800. 25 Holborn Hill, London

SONOGUINI e1840-60. Llandilo

SORDELLI, G. e1820-40. 23 Baldwins Gardens, Holborn, London

SORDELLI, I. w1800-40. London

SORDELLI, J. e1820-50. London

SORDELLI, L. e1835-55. London

SOWERBY, J. e1830-50. London

SPAHN, F. w1854-69. Clock & watch M. Leighton Buzzard

SPARKES, James. w1855-64. Clock & watch M. Uppingham

SPEAR & CLARKE w1815-17. Math. IM. 27 College Green, Dublin

SPEAR, Richard. w1791-1837. Opt. & math. IM. Dublin
29 Capel St (1791-92) 23 Capel St (1793-1809) 35 College Green (1810) 27 College Green (1812-37)

SPEARS & Co. w1838-64. Opt. & math. IM. Dublin
27 College Green (1838-42) 28 College Green (1843-64)

SPELZINI e1825-45. 8 Brooks Market, Holborn, London

SPELZINI, G. e1810-30

SPELZINI, I. e1810-30

SPELZINI, J. e1810-30. Manchester

SPELZINI, J. e1825-50. 91 Leather Lane, London

SPELZINI, J. e1830-50. 11 Brooks Market, Holborn, London

SPELZINI, John. w1836-59. London
8 Beauchamp St (1836) 11 Beauchamp St (1839-48) 74 Gt Saffron Hill (1856-59)

SPELZINI, Joseph. e1820-40

SPELZINI, J. & Son. e1840-50. 11 Beauchamp St, London

SPELZINO, G. e1800-20. Manchester

SPENCER & BROWNING w1781-84. Opt. & math. IM. 327 Wapping High St, London
A partnership between William Spencer and Samuel Browning.

SPENCER, BROWNING & Co. w1840-73. Opt. math. & phil. IM. London
111 Minories (1840-73) 6 Vine St (1848-73)
A continuation of the firm Spencer, Browning & Rust on the death of Ebenezer Rust, junior.

SPENCER, BROWNING & RUST w1784-1840. Opt. & math. IM. London
327 Wapping High St (1784-97) 66 Wapping (1797-1840)
A partnership between William Spencer, Samuel Browning and Ebenezer Rust who were all apprentices of Richard Rust.

SPENCER, John. w1845-63. Opt. math. & phil. IM. Dublin
3 Aungier St (1845-51) 13 Aungier St (1852-63)

SPENCER, John. w1859-69. Opt. & phil. IM. Glasgow
30 St Enoch Square (1859-64) 39 Union St (1865-69)

SPENCER, John & Son. w1864-88. Opt. math. & phil. IM. Dublin
13 Aungier St (1864-68) 19 Grafton St (1866-83) 23 Nassau St (1884-86)

SPICER, Edward. w1768-72. Math. IM. Plunket St, Dublin

SPICER, Edward & James LYNCH. w1772. Math. IM. Dublin

SPIEGELHALTER, George & Co. w1851-81. Clock & watch M. 6 Mount Place, Whitechapel Rd, London

SPITTALL, James. w1828-48. Clock & watch M & engraver. Whitehaven

SPITTALL, John. w1858-79. Clock & watch M. Whitehaven

SPRINGER, Joshua. w1759-1808. Opt. math. & phil. IM. Bristol
Hadleys Quadrant, St Stephen's Lane (1759-60) 2 Clare St (1775-1808)
Springer succeeded John Wright around 1759 and his trade card shows that he made 'barometers and thermometers of all sorts'. These included stick, wheel and angle types.

SQUIRE, P. e1830-50. 277 Oxford St, London
Chemist to Queen Victoria.

SQUIRRELL, Robert. e1815-45. Stowmarket

SQUIRRELL, William. e1810-30. Clock & watch M. Bildeston

STAIGHT, Thomas. w1829-60. Math. IS. London

STALKER, David. w1855-1900+. Watch, clock & naut. IM. Leith
9 Commercial St (1855-66) 9 & 10 Commercial St (1867-75) 6 Commercial St (1876-1900+)
His trade card included 'barometers, thermometers and patent sympiesometers'. (See Fig. 25.)

STAMPA, C. & Co. w1802-11. e1800-30. Carvers, gilders & looking glass M. London
125 Holborn Hill (1802) 25 Kirby St, Hatton Garden (1803-11)

STAMPA, Dominick. e1800-35. Carver & gilder. Leith Walk and 14 Leith St, Glasgow

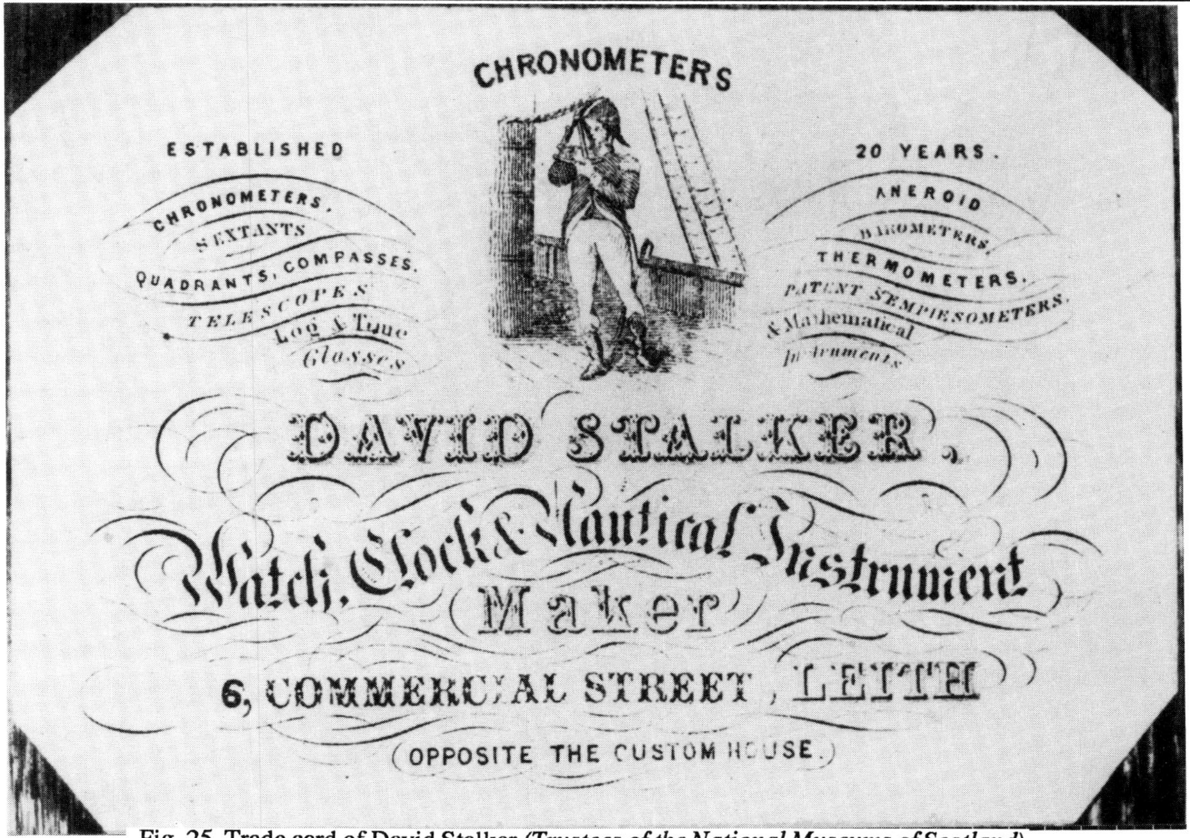

CHRONOMETERS

ESTABLISHED 20 YEARS.

CHRONOMETERS,
SEXTANTS
QUADRANTS, COMPASSES.
TELESCOPES
Log & Time
Glasses

ANEROID
BAROMETERS,
THERMOMETERS,
PATENT SEMPIESOMETERS,
& Mathematical
Instruments

DAVID STALKER,
Watch, Clock & Nautical Instrument
Maker
6, COMMERCIAL STREET, LEITH
(OPPOSITE THE CUSTOM HOUSE.)

Fig. 25 Trade card of David Stalker *(Trustees of the National Museums of Scotland)*

STAMPA, L. e1800-20. London
He made large wheel barometers with a clock above the dial.

STAMPA & Son. w1802-18. Looking glass M. 74 Leather Lane, London

STAMPA, Son & Co. w1802-04. Looking glass M. 74 Leather Lane, London

STAMPA & STEFFENONI w1816. 74 Foster Lane, London

STANILAND, John. w1846-66. Clock & watch M. Malton

STANILAND, Robert. w1840. Clock & watch M. Malton

STANLEY e1830-50. Peterborough

STANLEY, William Ford. w1860-1900+. Math. opt. & phil. IM. London
3 Holborn Bars (1860-64) 3, 4 & 5 Great Turnstile, Holborn (1860-1900+) 13 Railway Approach, London Bridge (1869-91) 7, 8 & 9 Tichborne Court (1872-91)

STATHAM, William Edward. w1858-60. Math. opt. & phil. IM. London
302 Regent St (1858-60) 16 Berners St, Oxford St (1860)

STEBBING, George. w1805-45. Math. IM. Broad St, Portsmouth

STEBBING, George. w1810-45. Opt. & math. IM. 66 High St, Portsmouth

STEBBING, J. R. w1845-57. Opt. IM. Southampton
47 High St (1845) Dock Chambers (1857)

STEBBING, J. R. & H. w1833. Opt. & math. IM. 63 High St, Southampton
Patronised by the Duchess of Kent and Princess Victoria.

STEBBING & WOOD w1851-53. Opt. math. & naut. IM. 47 High St, Southampton
Makers to the Queen and the Royal Yacht Squadron.Some barometers signed 'STEBBING & Co. Opt. to the Queen' e1860-80.

STEDMAN, Christopher. w1750-80. Math. IM. London
At the Globe on London Bridge (1750-60) Globe near the India House, 24 Leadenhall St (1761-80)
The move was forced when the houses on the bridge were pulled down.

STEEL & Son. e1840-60. Duke's Place, Wapping, Liverpool

STEELE, John & Son. w1828-51. Opt. & math. IM. 9 & 10 Duke's Place, Liverpool

STEERS, William. w1837. Clock & watch dealer. Keighley

STEFFANI, D. e1815-35. Eyre St Hill, Hatton Garden, London

de STEFFANI, William. w1826-40. 33 Exmouth St, Spitalfields, London
Barometers also with the address 33 Exmouth St, Wilmington Square, London.

STEFFENONI, Joseph. e1810-30. 74 Leather Lane, Holborn, London

STENSON, John. w1782. Derby
An ivory pendant portable barometer by Daniel Quare has the hood engraved 'Repaired by John Stenson, Derby'.He was a maker and repairer and published a pamphlet in 1782 headed *Observations on the Barometer* which he gave to purchasers.

STEPNEY, William. e1795-1815. Horsham

STERLING e1810-30. London

STERROP, George. c1715-56. Opt. IM. St Paul's Churchyard, London
He succeeded his uncle, Ralph Sterrop, and the family was well-known as instrument-makers.He advertised 'a great choice of barometers, portable or standard'.

STEVENSON, Peter. w1836-1900+. Phil. IM. Edinburgh
9 Lothian St (1836-61) 51 George IV Bridge (1862-70) 5 Forrest Rd (1871-73) 9 Forrest Rd (1874-87) 7 & 9 Forrest Rd (1888-1900+)

STEWARD, Henry. w1823-60. Clock M & jeweller. 6 Low Ousegate, York

STEWARD, James Henry. w1857-1900+. Math. opt. & phil. IM. London
406 Strand (1857-1900+) 67 Strand (1867-68) 63 St Paul's Churchyard (1867-80) 54 Cornhill (1867-92) 66 Strand (1869-88) 456 Strand (1879-88) 457 West Strand (1886-1900+) 7 Gracechurch St (1893-1900+)
Prolific maker of all types of barometers during the second half of the nineteenth century. Advertised as 'maker of the celebrated Lord Bury telescope and maker of the Fitzroy barometers, as in use at all railway termini and principal hotels in London'.

STEWART e1880-1900. Barographs. Limerick

STIER & DILGER w1856-66. Clock & watch M. Bath

STILES, William. w1830-46. Math. & phil. IM. 29 Seward St, Goswell St, London

STILES, William Mason. w1853-66. Math. & phil. IM. 70 Ossulston St, London

STOCKTON, J. e1820-40. London

STOKES, Henry. w1820-33. Hydrometer & phil. IM. London
18 Queen St, Short St, New Court. 110 Hatton Garden. 13 Wingrove Place, Clerkenwell

STOKES, John. w1834-48. Clock & watch M. Knutsford

STOKES & WATSON e1860-80. Manchester

STOLL e1850-70. Dumfries

STONE, John. w1789-42. Clock & watch M. Aylesbury

STONE, John W. w1860-68. Chronometer, opt. & phil. IM. Glasgow
43 West Nile St (1860-62) 35 West Nile St (1863-68)

STOPANI, A. e1815-45. Doncaster
Also 'A. STOPANI & Co.' e1815-25.

STOPANI, A. e1815-50. Sheffield

STOPANI & AMBROSONI e1810-30. Portsmouth

STOPANI, John. w1824-50. Opt. IM. Aberdeen
38 North St (1824-25) 42 Queen St (1827-40) 44 Queen St (1841-43) 68 Broad St (1844-50)

STOPANI, John. e1840-60. Sheffield

STOPANI, N. e1800-20. Doncaster

STOPANI, Nicholas. w1822-25. Orchard St, Sheffield

STOPARD, John. e1750-70. London

STOPFORD, William. e1790-1810
Angle barometers.

STOREY, J. e1810-30. Watch M. Cravel Hill, Henley on Thames

STORR, Batty. b1710-d1793. Clock & watch M. Minster Gates, York

STOTT e1790-1810. Dumfries

STOTT, D. e1845-65. Ashby de la Zouch

STOTT, John. w1876. Clock & watch M. Ashby de la Zouch

STRACHAN, Alexander. w1864-67. Naut. & opt. IM. Aberdeen
50 Regent Quay (1864) 57 Wales St (1867)

STRAIGHT, Thomas. w1839. 26 Bartlett Buildings, Strand, London

STRAUB, C. w1846. Clock & watch M. Norwich

STRAUB & HEBTING w1844-81. Clock & watch M. 77 Blackman St, Borough, London

STREET & Co. e1880-1900+. Newcastle upon Tyne
Aneroid barometers.

STREET, Richard William & Co. w1882-88. Math. opt. & phil. IM. London
39 Commercial Rd (1882-86) 3 Offord Rd (1887-88)

STRICKLAND, J. P. w1866. Clock & watch M. Gravesend

STRICKLAND, William. w1802. e1800-20. Clock M. Tenterden

STRINGA e1840-60. Carmarthen

STRINGA & CAPELLI e1835-55. Newport

STRINGAL, F. e1810-30. Carmarthen

STRINGER, Edwin. w1860-76. Clock & watch M. Stourbridge

STRINGER, F. e1810-30. Brecon

STRIPLING, Thomas. c1820. Clock & watch M. Lichfield

STRIPLING, Thomas & William. w1828-42. Clock & watch M. Lichfield

STROUD, J. e1830-50. Leeds

STROUS, Morris. e1830-50. Farringdon

STURT, F. W. e1860-80. Tunbridge Wells

SUFFELL, Charles. w1844-77. Math. IM. London
132 Long Acre (1844-65) 122 Long Acre (1866-77)

SULLIVAN, John. w1862-73. London
177 Great Dover St (1862-67) 44 Great Dover St (1868-73)

SULLIVAN, Patrick. w1738-43. At ye South back of St Clement's Church near Temple Barr, London
He made stick barometers some of which were used by clockmakers to fit to the doors of their longcase clocks. Christopher Pinchbeck of Cockspur St, London, who called himself 'Senior' clockmaker to the King, used Sullivan's barometers.

SUMERAU, Bartholomew. w1826-42. Looking glass M. 27 Lisle St, London

SUTHERLAND, J. e1820-40. Derby

SUTTER, John. w1811-12. Toddrick's Wynd, Edinburgh

SUTTON, Charles Thomas. w1868-1900+. Opt. math. & phil. IM. 108 Holloway Rd, London

SUTTON, George. w1840-78. Opt. IM. London
14 Bridge Rd, Lambeth (1840-41) 16 Bridge Rd, Lambeth (1843-64) 209 Westminster Bridge Rd (1865-78)

SUTTON, George & Son. w1878-1900+. Opt. IM. 209 Westminster Bridge Rd, London

SUTTON, Robert. w1774-95. Watch M. Stafford

SWAN e1835-55. Carlisle

SWAN, A. e1820-40. Edinburgh

SWAN, Alexander. w1829-36. Glasgow
75 High St (1829) 22 Gallowgate (1830) 112 Gallowgate (1831) 106 Gallowgate (1834-36)

SWEENY, Edward. w1763. Instrument M. Cork
Son of Nathaniel Sweeny.

SWEENY, Edward Nathaniel. w1798. Math & opt. IM. 27 Patrick St, Cork
He advertised that he 'Makes and Sells Barometers and Thermometers, engaged to equal any made in this kingdom'.

SWEENY, Nathaniel. w1702. Instrument M. Cork
Father of Edward Sweeny.

SWEENY, Widow. w1795. Instrument M. Paul St, Cork
Widow of Edward Sweeny.

SWEET e1810-30. London
He made large wheel barometers with a clock above the dial.

SWEET, William and Haydon. e1840-60. London

SWINDON & Sons. e1890-1900. Birmingham

SWYGGETT, Joseph. w1830-49. Opt. math. & phil. IM. 43 Edmund St, King's Cross, London

SYEDS, Agnes. w1817-53. Math. & naut. IM. 379 Rotherhithe Wall, London
John Syeds' widow who carried on his business when he died c1817. The firm was also known as 'Agnes SYEDS & Co.' and 'SYEDS & DAVIS'.

SYEDS, John. w1790-1817. Math. & naut. IM. London
25 Parker's Row, New Rd, Dock Head, Southwark (1790) Fountain, Stairs, Rotherhithe (1805)

SYEDS, John Ramsay. w1855-63. Math. & naut. IM. 379 Rotherhithe, London

SYM, James. w1792-1816. Opt. & math. IM. Glasgow
Ayton Court, Old Venal (1792) Bell St (1799-1801) 2 Bell St (1803-05 & 1808) 16 Bell St (1806) 236 High St (1807, 1809-11 & 1815-16) 266 High St (1812-14)

SYM, James. w1826-46. Opt. & math. IM. 167 High St, Glasgow

SYM, James & Co. w1817-25. Opt. & math. IM. Glasgow
236 High St (1817-24) 82-5 High St (1825)

T

TABEAR, William. w1832-36. 38 Laystall St, London

TABERHAM, Joseph. e1710-30. Waltham Abbey

TABRAR, William. w1832-36. 38 Laystall St, London

TACCHI, A. e1810-40. Bedford

TACCHI, Francis. w1867-68. Phil. IM. 90 Hatton Garden, London

TADEO, John. e1775-1825. Dublin

TAGLIABUE, Angelo. w1832-48. Phil. IM. London
11 Brooke St, Holborn (1832-34) 19 Leather Lane (1835-40) 91 Leather Lane (1841-44) 3 Charles St, Hatton Garden (1845-48)

TAGLIABUE, Angelo & Anthony. w1829-31. Phil. IM. 11 Brooke St, Holborn, London

TAGLIABUE, Anthony. w1832-48. Phil. IM. 31 Brooke St, Holborn, London

TAGLIABUE, Anthony & Co. w1850-51. Phil. IM. 31 Brooke St, Holborn, London

TAGLIABUE, B. C. & Co. e1810-30. 26 Holborn, London

TAGLIABUE, B., GAGGIA & Co. e1810-30. London

TAGLIABUE, C. w1799. 294 High Holborn, London

TAGLIABUE, C. w1820. 68 Hatton Garden, London

TAGLIABUE, Caesar. w1822-46. Opt. IM. London
28 Cross St, Hatton Garden (1822-29) 23 Hatton Garden (1829-46)

TAGLIABUE, Caesar & Co. w1807-14. Opt. IM. 26 High Holborn, London

TAGLIABUE & CASELLA w1838-46. Opt. IM. 23 Hatton Garden, London
A partnership between Caesar Tagliabue and Louis Casella.

TAGLIABUE, Catherine. w1835-38. 11 Brooke St, Holborn, London

TAGLIABUE, C. B. J. & Co. e1810-30. 26 Holborn, London

TAGLIABUE, Charles & Co. w1835-36. 11 Brooke St, Holborn, London

TAGLIABUE & CICERI w1849. Phil. IM. 31 Brooke St, Holborn, London

TAGLIABUE & Co. w1807-14. Opt. IM. 26 High Holborn, London
See Caesar Tagliabue & Co.

TAGLIABUE & Co. e1830-50. Phil. IM. 31 Brooke St, Holborn, London

TAGLIABUE, J. & J. w1817-19. Opt. & phil. IM. 11 Brooke St, Holborn, London
John Tagliabue (1) was one of the partners.

TAGLIABUE, John (1). w1819-52. Phil. IM. 11 Brooke St, Holborn, London

TAGLIABUE, John (2). w1826-38. Phil. IM. London
44 Leather Lane (1826-28) 23 Hatton Garden (1829) 25 Eyre St Hill (1834-38)

TAGLIABUE, John. w1840-46. Phil. IM. 31 Brooke St, Holborn, London

TAGLIABUE, John & Co. w1851-52. 11 Brooke St, Holborn, London

TAGLIABUE, TORRE & Co. w1800-07. Opt. IM. 294 High Holborn, London
Barometers also signed 'TAGLIABUE & TORRE' with this address.

TAGLIABUE & ZAMBRA w1847-50. Phil. IM. 11 Brooke St, Holborn, London
A partnership between John Tagliabue (1) and probably J. C. Zambra.

TAIT, William. w1849-55. Clock & watch M. Nottingham

TANNER, Joseph. w1840-56. Clock & watch M & silversmith. Market Place, Cirencester

TARA, I. e1830-60. Louth

TARA, N. e1810-30. Louth
Barometers also signed 'N. TARRA'.

TARELLI, Anthony. w1827-53. Opt. IM. Newcastle upon Tyne
41 Dean St (1827-44) 42 Dean St (1847-53)

TARELLI, A. & Son. w1853-62. Opt. IM. Newcastle upon Tyne
42 Dean St (1853) 65 Grey St (1855-62)
Barometers also signed 'A. TARELLI & Co.' with this address. A partnership between Anthony Tarelli and a son.

TARELLI, Charles. e1810-30. London

TARELLI, Charles. e1810-35. Banbury

TARELLI, Charles. w1830. e1800-30. Opt. IM. Woodhill, Northampton

TARETH, Charles. e1820-40. Banbury

TARONE, Andrew & Co. w1802-45. Looking glass M. London
7 Greville St (1802-19) 39 Charles St, Hatton Garden (1842-44) 4 Back Hill (1845)

TARONE, Anthony. w1818-46. Mirror M. Dundee
37 Murraygate (1818-29) 32 Murraygate (1834) 12 Castle St (1840) 90 Nethergate (1842) 12 Murraygate (1846)

TARONE, Francis. e1810-30

TARONE, John e1790-1820. 281 Holborn, London

TARONE, John. e1810-30. Glasgow

TARONE, L. e1820-40. Jersey

TARONE, P. e1800-20. Jersey
Barometers with clock above the dial.

TARONE, Peter A. w1809. e1800-30. Tucker St, Bristol

TARONI, A. & G. e1820-40. Hanley

TARONI, F. e1815-35. Clock & watch M. Haverfordwest

TARONI, George. w1840-51. Clock, watch & looking glass M & silversmith. 62 Whitefriargate, Hull

TARONI & LURAGHI w1829-31. 9 City Rd, London

TARONI, P. e1820-40. Jersey

TARRA, N. e1810-30. Louth
Barometers also signed 'N. TARA'.

TARRONI, D. e1850-70. Macclesfield

TARRONI, J. B. w1830. Leeds

TARTS, John. e1750-70. London

TASKER, William. w1813-53. Clock, watch & looking glass M & jeweller. High St, Banbury

TATAMANZA e1810-30. Colchester

TAVO, F. e1805-25. Chester

TAVONE, L. e1810-30. Jersey

TAYLOR e1780-1820. Castle St, Leicester Fields, London

TAYLOR Bros & Co. w1899-1900+. 106 Hatton Garden, London

TAYLOR, C. H. & Co. w1860. 12-13 Buckingham St, Birmingham

TAYLOR, Edmund. w1825-27. Opt. math. & phil. IM. 15 White Horse Yard, Drury Lane, London

TAYLOR, George Rodney. w1827-56. Clock & watch M. Sunderland
He made very unusual wheel barometers with a central dial and carved foliage surround with flowerheads at each end of the case. The indicating hand is manually adjusted by a brass rod and cog mechanism.

TAYLOR, James. w1859-87. Opt. IM. 46 Princes St, Edinburgh

TAYLOR, James Barton. w1845-57. Clock & watch M. Sandgate

TAYLOR, Janet (Mrs). w1845-60. Naut. IM. & navigation teacher. London
1 Fen Court, Fenchurch St. 6 East St, Red Lion Square. The Nautical Academy and Warehouse, 103-104 Minories
In 1833 Mrs Taylor produced a new set of Lunar Tables under the patronage of Queen Charlotte. In 1845 she took over the Nautical Academy which was under the patronage of the Admiralty, Trinity House and the East India Company. She was the sole agent for Dent's chronometers and sold a large number of marine barometers.

TAYLOR, Janet & Co. w1861-75. Math. & naut. IM. London
103-104 Minories (1861-75) 146 Leadenhall St (1861)

TAYLOR, Joseph. w1851-71. Clock & watch M. Pontefract

TAYLOR, Thomas Lee. w1826-41. Clock & watch M. Market Place, Pontefract

TEBBUTT, D. e1835-55. Pollon

TEDEO or TECLEO e1830-50. Dublin

TELAMANZI e1810-30. Colchester

TELAMANZO, P. e1810-30. Macclesfield

TELFORD, W. N. w1865. Clock & watch M. Chester

TERELE, Charles. e1805-25. 60 Gray's Inn Lane, London

TERONI, F. e1810-30

TERONI, J. B. & Co. e1815-35. Stockport

TERRY, Francis. e1790-1800. Clock & watch M. Masham

TERRY, William. c1770-1840. Clock & watch M. Masham

TERZA, A. e1810-30. Nottingham
Barometers also signed 'A. TERZZA'.

TESTE, Joseph. e1810-30. 45 Saffron Hill, London

TESTI, A. w1809. 32 Baldwins Gardens, Leather Lane, London

TESTI, G. & Co. e1810-30. Chester

TESTI, J. e1790-1810. 44 Saffron Hill, London

TESTI, J. e1795-1815. Windmill, Leather Lane, London

TESTI, J. e1810-30. 15 Great Saffron Hill, London

TESTI, J. e1820-40. Chester

TESTI, J. e1820-40. 19 Leather Lane, Holborn, London

TESTI, Joseph. e1815-50. Somerton

TESTI, Joseph. w1822. e1810-30. Looking glass M. 10 Leather Lane, Holborn, London

TESTI, N. e1805-25. 44 Saffron Hill, London

TETTAMANZI, S. e1800-20. Colchester

THATCHER, Henry J. w1875-87. e1860-90. Clock & watch M. Bute St, Cardiff
Sold barometers and sympiesometers.

THEEDAM, E. C. e1875-1900+. Dudley
Also signed 'E. C. THEEDAM Ltd'. Miners' barometers.

THOMAS e1840-60. Newton Abbott

THOMAS, D. w1844. Clock & watch M. Carmarthen

THOMAS, Daniel. w1675-1711. Clock & watch M. Minories, London

THOMAS, John B. w1867-78. e1855-80. Clock & watch M. Southampton

THOMAS, Robert. w1873. Opt. math. & phil. IM. 7a Duke St, Grosvenor Square, London

THOMPSON e1820-45. Yarmouth

THOMPSON e1865-85. Southsea

THOMPSON, J. e1820-40. Wellbeck

THOMPSON, John. w1830. Phil. IM. Nottingham

THOMPSON, John. e1840-60. Opt. math. & phil. IM. Liverpool
Manchester St and 85 Lord St.
Wholesale and retail.

THOMPSON, Joseph Berry. w1827-48. Math. & phil. IM. 36 High St, Wapping, London

THOMPSON, Mark Graystone. w1847-74. Clock & watch M. Tonbridge

THOMS, William. w1848. Phil. IM. 289 Strand, London

THOMSON, Thomas. w1805-09. Glassblower. Cowgate, Edinburgh
Made double barometers similar to those made by Balthazar Knie.

THOMSON'S, Sir W. w1891-93. 10 London St, Fenchurch St, London
John Lilley & Son was Thomson's sole London agent.

THORNBURGH, H. e1800-20

THORNELOE, Charles. w1835-76. Clock & watch M. Lichfield

THORNHILL, W. & Co. e1880-1900+. 144 New Bond St, London
Aneroid barometers.

THURLOW, Edward. w1848-78. Clock & watch M. Hyde, Isle of Wight

TIPPEN, William. w1866-74. Clock & watch M. Charing

TIRA, F. e1790-1810. Louth

TOBIAS, Morris. w1794-1840. Clock & chronometer M. Wapping, London

TOBIAS, Morris & Co. w1802-08. Clock & chronometer M. Wapping, London

TOBIAS, Morris & Levitt. w1817-24. Clock & chronometer M. Wapping and 31 Minories, London

TOCHETTI, Charles. w1825-28. e1825-45. Opt. IM & picture frame M. Aberdeen

TOCHETTI, T. & Co. e1815-35. Aberdeen

TOD, S. e1800-20. Edinburgh

TOGNETTI, James. e1800-30. Plymouth

TOGNIETTI, G. e1810-30. Worcester
Barometers also signed 'G. TOGNIETTI & Co.'.

TOGNIONI & Co. e1810-30. Bristol

TOGNIONI & Co. e1810-30. Plymouth

TOGNOLA, James. e1810-30. Ipswich

TOGNONI & Co. e1815-35. Shepton Mallet

TOGNONI & WANONI e1810-30. Shepton Mallet

TOIA, D. e1825-45. Farringdon

TOMLINSON, John. w1835-61. Clock & watch M. Bull Ring, Horncastle

TOMPION, Thomas. b1638-d1713. Clock M. Dial and Three Crowns, Water Lane, Fleet St, London
The son of a Bedfordshire blacksmith, he became a Master of the Clockmakers' Company in 1704 and is acknowledged as the most famous of English clockmakers. He was not only 'a person justly famous for his excellent skill in making watches and clocks' but also 'not less curious and dexterous in the construction and handworking of other nice mechanick instruments'. Tompion made pillar portable stick barometers similar to those made by Daniel Quare, and it is believed that he made the first wheel instrument which was for Robert Hooke around 1675. Like his clocks, all his barometers are of a very high quality.

TONER, William. w1865-92. Phil. IM. London
3 St Peter's Terrace, Saffron Hill (1865-85) 6 Cyrus St, Clerkenwell (1887-88) 15 Upper Ashby St, Clerkenwell (1889-92)

TOOGOOD, James Thomas. w1878. Clock & watch M. Uckfield

TORADO, Francis. e1790-1810. London

della TORRE e1810-30. Gloucester

TORRE, A. D. e1810-30. London

TORRE, Anthony. w1767-88. Merchant & print S. London
44 Market Lane, Pall Mall (1767-86) 132 Pall Mall (1786-88)
The son of Giovanni Battista Torre. Giovanni owned a shop in Paris which was opened in 1760 and he opened a second shop in Pall Mall in 1767 which was managed by Anthony.

della TORRE, Anthony. w1805-23. Opt. IM & looking glass M. London
12 Leigh St, Red Lion Square (1805-11) 4 Leigh St, Red Lion Square (1815-23)

della TORRE & BARELLI w1826-33. Looking glass & print M. 9 Lamb's Conduit St, London

TORRE & Co. w1805. e1805-30. Opt. IM. 12 Leigh St, Red Lion Square, London

TORRE & Co. e1820-40. 12 Holborn, London

TORRE, Giovanni Battista. w1753-d1780. Print M. 44 Market Lane, Pall Mall, London
He made barometers from 1760 at his shop in Paris and opened a shop in London at 44 Market Lane in 1767; this was managed by his son Anthony.

della TORRE, I. e1830-50. Perth

della TORRE, J. e1820-50. Perth

TORRE, Joseph & Co. w1834-51. Merchants. 9 Lamb's Conduit St, London

della TORRE, Paul. e1800-50. Perth

TORRE, P. D. & Co. e1858-70. 81 Leith St, Edinburgh

della TORRE, S. e1820-40. Perth

TORRELLI, Christopher. w1830. Opt. IM. Wood Hill, Northampton

TORRI, G. e1810-30. London

TORRI & POZZI e1835-55. Wotton Bassett

TORRINI, Emanuel. w1875-81. Clock & watch M. London

TORY & Co. e1835-55. Gloucester

TORY, Joseph & Co. e1820-40. London

TOULMIN, Samuel. w1757-83. Clock & watch M. Strand, London
He made stick and angle barometers.

TOURNIER LES FILS D'EMILE. w1884-89. Math. & phil. IM. London
3-6 Camomile St (1884-86) 4 Ropemaker St, Finsbury (1887-89)

TOVEY, H. e1845-65. Honiton

TOWERS & Co. e1875-95. Widnes

TOWERS, J. W. & Co. Ltd. e1880-1900. Widnes and Manchester

TOWNELEY, Richard. w1660-1705. Amateur instrument M. London
He developed the barometer in conjunction with Sir Jonas Moore and Robert Hooke, including work with barometers and thermometers down coal mines.

TREADGOLD, John George. w1881-82. Opt. & math. IM. 772 Old Kent Rd, London

TREMLETT, Richard. w1852-88. Phil. IM. London
9 Albemarle St, Clerkenwell (1852-58) 7 Guildford Place, Spitalfields (1858-65) 9 Myddelton St (1866-88)

TRESOLDI, A. e1810-30. Westbury

TRESOLDI, G. e1835-55

TRESOLDI, I. e1830-50. 6 Union Buildings, Leather Lane, London

TRESOLDI, J. w1852-60. 6 Union Buildings, Leather Lane, London

TRESOLDI, T. e1815-40. Trowbridge

TRIGERI, G. e1805-25. 28 High Holborn, London

TRIGGS, W. w1862. Clock & watch M. Guildford

TRITSCHLER, Ferdinand H. w1869-79. Clock & watch M. Carlisle

TRITSCHLER, William & Co. w1848-69. Clock & watch M. Carlisle

TROBRIDGE, William James. w1875-83. Clock & watch M. Bath

TROMBETTA, Charles. e1800-20. St Stephens, Norwich

TROMBETTA, Charles. e1805-30. St Georges St, Norwich

TROTTER, Alexander. w1788-1815. Clock & watch M. Jedburgh

TROTTER, John. w1890-1900. Barographs. Glasgow

TROUGHTON, Edward (senior). w1740-60. Math. IM. Surrey St, Strand, London
Troughton divided and engraved instruments for the trade and was assisted by his three nephews John, Joseph and Edward Troughton.

TROUGHTON, Edward (junior). b1753-d1831. Opt. & math. IM. London
Surrey St, Strand. The Orrery, 136 Fleet St (1782)
Apprenticed to his brother John and became his partner in 1770 under the name of J. & E. Troughton. John died in 1804 and Edward continued alone until 1826 when he took William Simms into partnership. Edward was the most famous of the family and was quite a character; he never married, was a man of frugal habits and spent most of his life in his back parlour wearing snuff-stained clothes and a wig, with an ear trumpet in his hand. A reviewer of his work writing in the *Philosophical Magazine* stated 'Mr Troughton stands quite unrivalled in the construction of original astronomical instruments ... he does and always will hold that rank among makers as Sir Isaac Newton does among philosophers.' Troughton made barometers for export as some were engraved with English and French inches. He was a founder member of the Royal Astronomical Society and wrote on astronomical instruments.

TROUGHTON, J. & E. w1770-1900+. Opt. & math. IM. London
Surrey St, Strand. The Orrery, 136 Fleet St (1782-1900+)
A partnership between John and Edward Troughton, the nephews of Edward Troughton (senior). In 1782 the partners took over the business of Benjamin Cole (junior) and, through various mergers and takeovers, are now known as Vickers Instruments Ltd. The partners advertised 'Barometers, Barometer and Thermometer in one frame and Barometer, Thermometer and Hygrometer all in one frame.'

TROUGHTON, J. & J. w1764-70. Opt. & math. IM. Surrey St, Strand, London
A partnership between two brothers, John and Joseph, the nephews of Edward Troughton (senior). Joseph died in 1770 and John then went into partnership with his other brother Edward.

TROUGHTON, John. w1752-84. Opt. & math. IM. London
Surrey St, Strand. The Orrery, 136 Fleet St (1782)
He worked for his uncle Edward Troughton (senior) and was in partnership with a brother Joseph, under the name of J. & J. Troughton, from 1764 to 1770 when Joseph died. He then took his younger brother Edward into partnership and traded as J. & E. Troughton.

TROUGHTON & SIMMS w1826-1900+. Opt. & math. IM. The Orrery, 136 Fleet St, London
A partnership between Edward Troughton (junior) and William Simms. Troughton retired in 1831 but the business continued until, eventually, Cooke, Troughton & Simms Ltd was taken over by Vickers Instruments Ltd. The partnership made a large number and variety of barometers, including stick and wheel domestic types; also Fortin and Gay-Lussac station barometers. They were appointed instrument-makers to the Board of Ordnance, London. The address became 138 Fleet St c1840.

TRUSCOTT, James. w1830-73. Clock M. St Columb, Cornwall

TRUSCOTT, Joseph. w1842-47. e1840-55. Clock & watch M. St Austell

TUCKER, Robert. w1859. e1825-60. Jeweller. 41 North St, Taunton

TULLEY, Henry. w1822-30. e1820-40. Opt. IM. Bath
Kingston Buildings (1822) 3 Pulteney Bridge (1830)

TUNKS, D. w1858. e1840-60. Clock & watch M. Accrington

TUPMAN, George. w1794-1820. Clock & watch M. Charles St, Hanover Square, London

TUPMAN, George & Co. w1875-81. Clock & watch M. Old Bond St, London

TURCHETTI, Peter. e1835-55. Dorchester

TURCONE, G. e1820-40. Manchester

TURELLI, Anthony. w1830-37. 41 Dean St, Newcastle

TURNBULL, B. e1800-50. Cheltenham

TURNBULL & Co. w1894-1900+. Opt. IM. 60 Princes St, Edinburgh

TURNBULL, John Miller. w1865-1900+. Opt. & phil. IM. Edinburgh
14 Nicholson Square (1865-81) 19 South St, David St (1881-84) 6 Rose St (1885-1900)

TURNBULL, Thomas. w1819-40. Clock & watch M. Whitby

TUTHER, John. w1817-25. Opt. IM. London
64 Upper King St, Bloomsbury (1817) 221 High Holborn (1819-25)

TUTTELL, Thomas. w1695-1702. Math. IM. London
Kings Arms and Globe, Charing Cross and Royal Exchange, Cornhill
Apprenticed to Henry Wynne in 1688. He operated from two premises and sold all sorts of instruments including barometers. He was made a member of the Clockmakers' Company in 1695 and 'Mathematical Instrument-maker to the King's most excellent Majesty' in 1700. Sadly, he was drowned whilst on a marine survey in 1702.

TWADDELL, Thomas. w1840-48. Glassblower & hydrometer M. Glasgow
34 Brunswick Place (1840) 36 Glassford St (1841-46) 75 Argyle St (1847-48)

TWADDELL, William. w1792-1839. Glassblower & hydrometer M. Glasgow
Saltmarket (1792-1801) 76 Saltmarket (1803-08) 46 Saltmarket (1809) 11 High St (1810) 450 Gallowgate (1811) 449 Gallowgate (1813-23) 15 Gallowgate (1824-25) 21 Gallowgate (1826-27) 84 Saltmarket (1828-39)

TWADDLE, William. w1855-62. Spirit proof M. Glasgow
10 Melville Lane (1855) 122 Union St (1856-59) 24 Ropework Lane (1860-62)

TYLER, F. (Mrs). w1857-70. Phil. IM. London
21 Charles St, Hatton Garden (1857-58) 23 Charles St, Hatton Garden (1859-70)

TYLER, James. w1844-56. London
5 Charles St, Hatton Garden (1844-55) 21 Charles St, Hatton Garden (1856)

TYLER, James. w1874-1891. 15 Jerusalem Court, Clerkenwell, London

TYLER, John. w1829-36. London
15 Great New St, Fetter Lane (1829-33) 221/2 Kirby St (1836)

TYLER, John. w1892-1900+. 3 Jerusalem Buildings, Jerusalem Court, Clerkenwell, London

TYLER, Robert. w1828-49. Clock & watch M. Melton Mowbray

U

UNDERHILL e1820-40. 2 Corporation St, Manchester

UNDERHILL, T. w1841. e1830-50. Math. IM. 70 Bridge St, Deansgate, Manchester

URE, John. w1821. w1831-33. Opt. & math. IM. Glasgow
40 Stockwell (1821) 136 High St (1831-33)

URE, William. w1812-20. Math. IM. Glasgow
15 Deanside Lane (1812-18) 40 Stockwell (1819-20)

URE, William & Son. w1822-40. Math. IM. Glasgow
40 Stockwell (1822-23) 85 Candleriggs (1824-25) 40 Candleriggs (1826-29) 120 Brunswick St (1830) 120 Brunswick St & 109 Candleriggs (1831-35) 3 Brunswick Court (1837-40)

V

VAGHI, G. e1835-55. Kidderminster

VAGO & Co. e1810-30. London

VAGO, F. e1810-50. Leeds

VAGO, F. e1835-55. Perth

VAGO, P. H. e1820-50. London

VALE, J. w1846-65. Clock & watch M. Bury St Edmunds

VANETTI w1822. Clock & watch M. Brighton

VANINI & MONTINI e1810-30. Peterborough

VANNINI, A. e1840-65. 25 Spring St, Sheffield

VANNINI, Anthony. w1830-50. Looking glass M. 7 Orange St, West St, Sheffield

VANNINI, J. e1835-55. Sheffield

VARCO, Robert. w1873. Silversmith, jeweller & watch M. Fowey

VARGA, J. e1810-30. Chester

VARLEY, Cornelius. b1781-d1873. Opt. & phil. IM. London
Junction Place, Paddington. 228 Tottenham Court Rd. 1 Charles St, Clarendon Square (1811)

VARLEY, Cornelius John. w1855-63. Math. opt. & phil. IM. London
1 Charles St, Clarendon Square (1855-56) 7 York Place, Kentish Town (1857-63)

VARLEY, Cornelius & Samuel Alfred. w1864-68. Math. IM. London
337 Kentish Town Rd and 66 Roman Rd, Barnsbury (1864-68)

VARLEY, Cornelius & Son. w1845-53. Opt. & phil. IM. 1 Charles St, Clarendon Square, London

VASSALLI, G. e1820-45. Scarborough

VASSALLI, Jerome. w1840-58. e1820-60. Clock & watch M & jeweller. 49 Merchants Row, London

VEALE, J. e1840-60. Exmouth

VECCHIO e1810-30. Shaftesbury

del VECCHIO & CETTI w1841-56. Clock & watch M. Shrewsbury

VECCHIO & Co. e1810-30. 22 Union Passage, Bath

del VECCHIO & DOTTI w1840-51. Clock & watch M. New St, Wellington

del VECCHIO & DOTTI w1840-51. Clock & watch M. Shrewsbury

del VECCHIO, G. B. e1835-55. Shrewsbury

VECCHIO, I. e1800-25. Nottingham

VECCHIO, J. e1810-30. Nottingham

del VECCHIO, James. e1810-30. Nottingham

del VECCHIO, James. w1810-38. Print seller and looking glass M. Dublin
26 Westmoreland St (1810-38) 187 & 188 Great Brunswick St (1837-38)

del VECCHIO, James. w1833-38. Looking glass & frame M. Dublin
15 Lower Abbey St (1833-35) 68 Dame St (1836-38)

VEITCH, James. b1771-d1838. Ploughwright & instrument M. Jedburgh
At the age of twelve he started to work for his father making wooden ploughs. He took over the business and by 1808 was making two a week and selling them for £21.16s each. He gave up making ploughs in 1826, when wood was replaced by iron, and concentrated on making telescopes, microscopes, barometers and other philosophical instruments.

VENTOM e1810-30. London

VERGA, I. e1820-40. Bath

VERGA, J. e1805-25. St Ives

VERGA, J. e1815-35. Chester

VERGA, J. e1815-35. London

VERGA, J. e1835-55. Bath

VERGA, J. L. e1820-40

VERGA, John Marie. w1828-34. e1820-45. Carver & gilder. Macclesfield
Market St (1828) Mill St (1834)

VERGA, P. e1810-30. Huntingdon

VERGO, P. e1840-60

VERRIER, James. c1750. Clock M. North Curry, Somerset

He made stick barometers in the style of, and which looked very much like, longcase clocks. He also developed a type of clock movement powered by barometric pressure or temperature change.

VICARINO, Adolphe. w1857-63. Clock & watch M. London

VICARY, John. w1857. e1820-60. Clock & watch M. London

VICARY, Robert. w1869-75. Clock & watch M. London

VICHO, B. e1830-50. Liverpool

VICKERY, J. C. e1875-1900+. Phil. IM. 179, 181 & 183 Regent St, London

VIDEPIED, OKERMANS, POIRCUITTE & Co. w1883-85. Opt. math. & phil. IM. 56 Hatton Garden, London and Paris

VIGLEZZI e1800-20. London

VIMPANI, A. E. w1877. Clock & watch M. Shefford, Beds

VIMPANI, Edmund. w1869. Clock & watch M. London

VIMPANI, H. D. w1867. Clock & watch M. Fareham

VIMPANI, John Dean. w1851-57. Clock & watch M. London

VIMPANI, Richard. w1850-70. Cheltenham

VIMPANI, William. w1878. Fareham

VINCENT, John. w1830. e1825-45. Clock & watch M. Weymouth

VINER & Co. e1830-50. Clock & watch M. 233 Regent St, London

VISMARA, G. B. e1820-50. Bury St Edmunds

VITA e1840-60. Stafford

VITTA, A. e1830-50. Birmingham

VITTORY & Co. e1790-1830. 93 Market St Lane, Manchester

VITTORY & DANNELLI e1800-20. Manchester

VITTORY & LANNETTI e1820-40. 9 Lease Lane, Manchester

VOKES, William. w1856-66. Clock & watch M. Bath

VOLANTERIO, G. e1815-35. Doncaster

VOLANTERIO, Joshua. w1822-41. Opt. IM & looking glass M. Doncaster
Frenchgate (1822) High St (1834) Baxter Gate (1841)

VOLK, M. w1851-62. Clock & watch M. Brighton

VOLONTE, C. e1815-35. Crown Inn, Devizes

VREAM, William. w1710-27. Math. & phil. IM. Two doors from the Royal Oak, Earl St, near Seven Dials, London
At one time employed by Francis Hauksbee the elder, he made instruments for the courses in natural philosophy given at the Academy, Abchurch Lane, London. The instruments included 'all sorts of weather glasses, whether barometers, thermometers, marine barometers, portable thermometers, or hygrometers'.

VULLIAMY, Benjamin. w1781-1820. Clock M. London
Clockmaker to King George III and the son of Justin Vulliamy.

VULLIAMY, Justin. b1712-d1797. Clock & watch M. 68 Pall Mall, London
Born in Switzerland and moved to London around 1730 where he worked for Benjamin Gray. In 1743 Gray took him into partnership and in 1746 he married Gray's daughter. Gray died in 1764 and Vulliamy carried on alone. He was a very fine maker of clocks and watches and also made distinctive wheel barometers in clock-like cases with the influence of the clockmaker's craft in evidence.

WADE e1865-85. Bognor

WADHAM, George. w1856-75. Clock & watch M. Bath

WAES, S. e1850-70. Yarmouth

WAINWRIGHT, J. J. & Co. e1870-90. Cambridge St, Birmingham
Produced a popular arrangement of aneroid barometer, clock and thermometer in a cast iron frame.

WALDEN, J. e1825-46. Jersey

WALDER & MARTEN e1830-50. Littlehampton

WALFORD, John George. w1814-53. Clock & watch M. Banbury

WALKER, Francis. w1810-59. Math. phil. & opt. IM. London
35 Wapping Wall (1810-44) 17 Wapping Wall (1847) 77 Broad St, Ratcliff Cross (1853-59)

WALKER, I. & A. e1840-60. Marine barometers. Liverpool

WALKER, J. & A. w1823-59. Opt. math. & naut. IM. Liverpool and London
33 Pool Lane, Liverpool (1827) 34 Castle St, Liverpool (1847) 47 Bernard St, London

WALKER, J. & E. e1840-60. Marine barometers. Sunderland

WALKER, John. e1890-1900. 1 South Molton St, London

WALKER, Joseph. w1838. Math. & phil. IM. 43 Skinner St, Clerkenwell, London

WALKER, M. & Son. w1885-91. Chronometer & naut. IM. Glasgow
44 & 45 Clyde Place (1885-91) Branches at Cathcart St, Greenock (1886-91) and Bath St, Liverpool (1887-91)

WALLACE e1860-80. Ardrossan

WALLACE, George. w1856-58. Math. opt. & phil. IM. 15½ Buchanan St, Glasgow

WALLACE, Richard. w1856-81. Opt. IM, watch M & jeweller. Limerick
125 George St (1856) 129 George St (1870-81)

WARD, Henry. w1755-1820. Clock & watch M. Blandford

WARD, John. w1843-51. Math. & phil. IM. 79 Bishopsgate Within, London

WARD, William (senior). w1850-61. Clock & watch M. Grimsby

WARD, William (junior). w1861-76. Clock & watch M. Grimsby

WARDALE, John & Co. e1890-1900. London
Aneroid barometers.

WARNER, John. w1684-1722. Math. IM. King's Arms and Globe, Lincoln's Inn Fields, Portugal Row, London
He initially specialised in barometers, and in 1684 helped Col. Windham observe the fall of mercury in the barometer between ground level and the top of the spire of Salisbury Cathedral.He sold barometers identical to those sold by Henry Wynne.

WARWICK, William. w1830. Opt. math. & phil. IM. 16A Sloane Square, Chelsea, London

WASSELL, Charles Frederick. w1869. Clock & watch M. 43 Fenchurch St, London

WATERSON, A. & Co. w1835. Carvers & gilders. 1 & 2 Ronaldson's Buildings, Edinburgh

WATKINS e1815-35. Clare St, Bristol

WATKINS, Francis. w1747-84. Opt. & math. IM. Sir Isaac Newton's Head, 5 Charing Cross, London

The son of Jeremy Watkins of New Church, Radnor, he was apprenticed to Nathaniel Adams in 1737 and started on his own ten years later. An important maker who is best known for his angle barometers which incorporate a 'Perpetual Regulation of Time' which covers a hundred years. In 1763 he took Addison Smith, an apprentice, into partnership under the name of Watkins & Smith; it lasted until 1774 when they split, Watkins continuing at 5 Charing Cross until 1784 when he was succeeded by his two nephews Jeremiah and Walter Watkins.

WATKINS & HILL w1819-57. Opt. math. & phil. IM. 5 Charing Cross, London
This partnership was formed when Jeremiah Watkins took Hill as a partner. They made a large number of stick and wheel barometers; some wheel instruments have a cork float connected to a small toothed brass bar and cogwheel, instead of the standard pulley and glass weights to control the dial indicating hand. The business was taken over by Elliott Bros in 1857 and is now part of the GEC-Elliott Automation Group.

WATKINS, Jeremiah. w1799-1819. Opt. math. & phil. IM. 5 Charing Cross, London
When the partnership in the name of Jeremiah and Walter Watkins ended, Jeremiah continued on his own until he formed the partnership with Hill. He was instrument-maker to the Duke of York, the Duke of Clarence and the East India Company.

WATKINS, Jeremiah & Walter. w1785-98. Opt. math. & phil. IM. 5 Charing Cross, London
Two nephews of Francis Watkins who succeeded to his business in 1785. They advertised 'all sorts of barometers and thermometers' and were instrument-makers to the Duke of Clarence.

WATKINS & SMITH w1763-74. Opt. math. & phil. IM. 5 Charing Cross, London
A partnership between Francis Watkins and Addison Smith, his former apprentice. The firm continued to make angle barometers which incorporated a 'Perpetual Regulation of Time' and advertised 'all sorts of barometers' in English and in French.

WATKINS, William. w1784-1809. Opt. IM. London
22 St James (1784-99) 70 St James (1800-09)
Believed to be a relation of the Francis Watkins family because at least one angle barometer with a perpetual calender signed by William is extant. He also made stick barometers.

WATKINS, William. w1825-30. e1825-40. Opt. & math. IM. 16 St Augustine's Parade, Bristol

WATSON Bros. w1885-94. Opt. math. & phil. IM. London
4 Pall Mall (1885-93) 31 Cockspur St (1894)

WATSON, D. Fraser. e1890-1900. Manchester

WATSON, Thomas William. w1878-84. Math. opt. & phil. IM. 4 Pall Mall, London

WATSON, William & Son. w1873-81. Math. opt. & phil. IM.
313 High Holborn, London

WATSON, William & Sons. w1881-1900+. Opt. math. & phil. IM. London

313 High Holborn (1881-1900+) 9, 10, 11, 16 & 17 Fullwood's Rents, Holborn (1887-1900+)
In 1899 the firm announced that it had been founded in 1837 although the name of W. Watson & Son does not appear in the London directory until 1873. They were wholesalers and retailers, and claimed in 1894 to have 'won 34 gold and other medals at international exhibitions, Paris, Chicago, London, etc.'

WATT, Frederick Samuel. w1890-92. 92 Hatton Garden, London

WATT, James. w1757-71. Math. IM, land surveyor & engineer. Glasgow
In the College (1757-71) Saltmarket (1759-64) Trongate (1764-71)
He is best known for improving the steam engine but he trained as an instrument-maker in Glasgow and London. He was appointed mathematical instrument-maker to the College of Glasgow in 1757 and made stick barometers.

WATT, John. e1840-60. Watch M. Duke St, Huntly, near Aberdeen

WATTLEWORTH e1840-60. Whitehaven

WATTS, Edwin Richard. w1860-98. Math. IM. London
5 Northampton Place, Old Kent Rd (1860-63) 243 Old Kent Rd (1864-73) 123 Camberwell Rd (1874-98)

WATTS, Edwin Richard & Son. w1899-1900+. Math. IM. 123 Camberwell Rd, London

WATTS, William. w1835. e1810-35. Tenbury

WAUTHIER, Jules. w1853-55. 45 Wilmington Square, London

WAYHAM & WATT w1883-89. 92 Hatton Garden, London

WAYHAM, William. w1890. 92 Hatton Garden, London

WEABER & Co. e1835-55. 129 Oxford St, London

WEATHERSTON, John. w1787-1801. Clock & watch M. Woolmarket, Newcastle upon Tyne

WEBB, John. b1760-d1846. Opt. math. & phil. IM. London
408 Oxford St. 192 Tottenham Court Rd. 28 Francis St, Tottenham Rd
His trade card shows that he made, repaired and sold barometers both wholesale and retail. (See Figs 26 and 27.)

WEBB, Joseph Benjamin. w1825-28. Math. phil. & naut. IM. 13 Charles St, City Rd, London

WEBB, R. e1840-60. Brecon

WEBB, R. w1861-66. Clock & watch M. Taunton

WEBB, Richard. w1868-99. Clock M. Brecon

Fig. 26 Trade card of J. Webb *(Science Museum, London)*

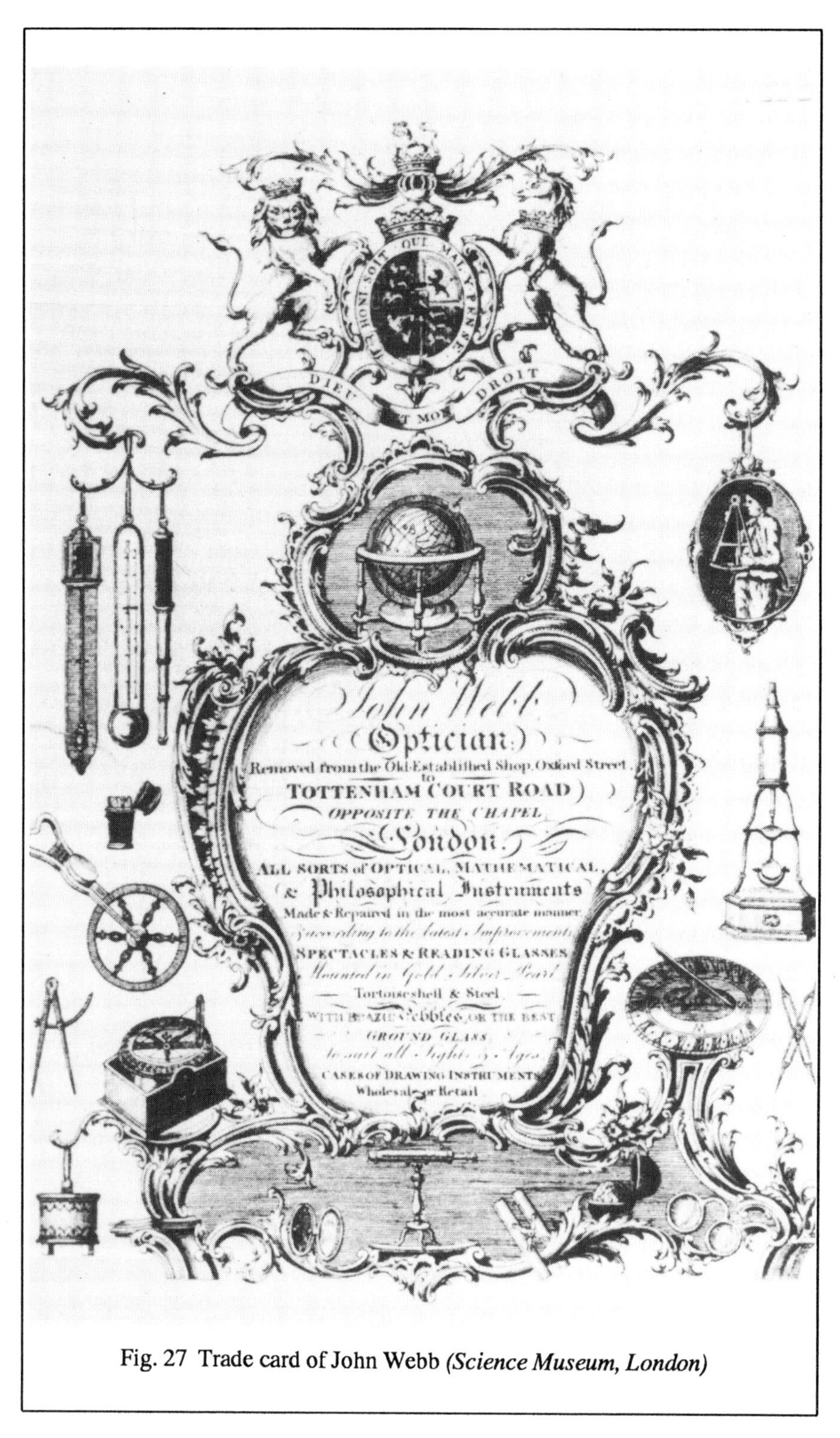

Fig. 27 Trade card of John Webb *(Science Museum, London)*

WEBBER, John. w1832-47. Clock & watch M. Woolwich

WEBBER, William. w1826-55. Clock & watch M. Woolwich

WEBSTER Bros. w1894. Opt. IM. 4 Porchester Rd, London

WEBSTER, Henry. w1843-69. Looking glass M. London
3 Vineyard Walk, Clerkenwell (1843-46) 37 Coppice Row (1847-69)

WEBSTER, James. w1866-76. Clerkenwell, London
148 St John St Rd (1866-67) 89 St John St Rd (1868-76)

WEBSTER, John. w1867-76. e1840-76. London

WEBSTER, R. & Son. e1840-60. Cornhill, London

WECHIO, J. e1820-40. Exeter

WECHIO, J. e1820-40. Shaftesbury

WEEDEN, William John. w1822-32. Opt. math. & phil. IM. 7 Norman St, St Luke's, London

WEHRLE, A. w1851. Clock & watch M. London

WEHRLE, Paul. w1865-75. Clock & watch M. Cambridge

WEICHERT, William. w1865-87. Clock & watch M. Cardiff

WEIR, Silas E. e1800-50. Cookstown

WELBURN, Frederick. w1866. Watch M. Thirsk

WELLER, Frederick William. w1890. 20 Argyle St, London

WELLINGTON, Alexander. w1792-1825. Math. IM. Crown Court, Abinger St, St Anne's, Soho, London
His trade card shows that he was 'successor to the late James Search and mathematical instrument-maker to their Royal Highnesses the Dukes of Gloucester and Cumberland'.

WELLS, John. w1748. Birmingham
Angle barometer signed and dated 1748.

WELLS, Nugent. w1858-99. Clock & watch M. Opt. IM. Newport, Mon.

WELLS, Samuel. w1817-30. Math. & phil. IM. London
3 Clerkenwell Green and 139 Old St, St Luke's

WEST, Charles. w1814-25. Opt. & math. IM. London
5 Cursitor St, Chancery Lane. Serle's Passage, Lincoln's Inn. 33 St James's St

WEST, Francis. w1829-48. Opt. math. & phil. IM. London
17 Rupert St, Drury Lane. 83 Fleet St (1829-48) 41 Strand (1844-48)
His trade card indicated that he was 'successor to Mr Adams and optician to His Majesty'.

WEST, Francis & Co. w1849-60. Opt. math. & phil. IM. London
41 Strand (1849-57) 92 & 93 Fleet St (1949-60)

WEST, Francis Linsell. w1853-84. Math. opt. & phil. IM. London
39 Southampton St, Strand (1853-57) 31 Cockspur St (1858-84)

WEST, Henry Brownlee. e1835-55. Clock M & china merchant. 13 Mary-Port St, Devizes.

WEST, John George & Co. w1860-86. Math. opt. & phil. IM. 92 & 93 Fleet St, London

WESTAWAY, Henry w1845-55. Clock & watch M. Woolwich
A clockmaker who made wheel barometers with a square dial at the top of the case which looked similar to a longcase clock.

WESTERN, William. e1780-1800

WESTLEY, F. e1850-70. 27A Old Bond St, London

WHALEY, William. w1851-56. Clock & watch M. Hartlepool

WHAM, G. w1865. e1845-65. Clock & watch M. Ely

WHEELER, John Jackson. w1864-67. 189 Fulham Rd, London

WHEELER, T. e1880-1900. 217 Coswell St, London

WHEELER, Thomas. w1893-1900+. Phil. IM. 8 Coombs St, City Rd, London

WHEELER, T. S. w1892-93. Phil. IM. 8 Coombs St, City Rd, London
The name was changed to Thomas Wheeler in 1893. Produced aneroid barometers.

WHEELHOUSE & BERCINI w1860-63. Looking glass M. 40 Hatton Garden, London

WHEELHOUSE, Thomas. w1864-69. Looking glass M. 40 Hatton Garden, London

WHIPP, Thomas. w1834-58. Clock & watch M. Rochdale

WHISTON, Thomas. w1856-79. Clock & watch M. Newport, Salop

WHITBREAD & SEELING w1830. Opt. math. & phil. IM. 2 King St, St Luke's, London

WHITCHURCH & Son. e1840-60. Derby

WHITE & BARR w1857-59. Math. opt. & phil. IM. Glasgow
1 Renfield St (1857-59) 60 Gordon St (1857)

WHITE, J. e1830-50. Edinburgh

WHITE, James. w1850-1900+. Opt. math. & phil. IM. Glasgow
24 Renfield St (1850-52) 14 Renfield St (1853-56) 1 Renfield St & 60 Gordon St (1860-63) 95 Buchanan St (1864-68) 78 Union St (1869-75) 241 Sauchiehall St (1876-83) 209 Sauchiehall St (1884-90) 16, 18 & 20 Cambridge St (1884-1900+)
James White traded as 'WHITE & BARR' between 1857 and 1859. He held the appointment of instrument-maker to the University of Glasgow.

WHITEHALL, Edwin. w1848-75. Clock & watch M. Newport, Mon.

WHITEHALL, Robert J. w1880. Clock & watch M. Newport, Mon.

WHITEHOUSE e1840-60. 43 Warwick St, Pimlico, London

WHITEHOUSE, Edmund. w1863-69. Clock & watch M. Coventry St, Haymarket, London

WHITEHOUSE, Nathaniel. w1825-83. Opt. IM. London
3 Cross St, Hatton Garden (1825-37) 1 Castle St, Leicester Square (1838-46) 2 Cranbourn St, Leicester Square (1847-82)
He made combined stick and wheel barometers in one instrument using a single tube.

WHITEHURST, John (1). b1713-d1788. Clock M. Derby and London
22 Irongate, Derby. 4 Bolt Court, Fleet St, London (1776-88)
He started in business as a clockmaker in Derby in 1736 and became well known for his turret clocks; he also invented the 'tell-tale' clock. He was an important and prolific maker of distinctive angle barometers with a 0 to 60 scale rather than inches. In 1775 he moved to London to become 'Stamper of Money Weights' but still continued to make clocks. It is thought that the Derby business was carried on by his brother James until James's son was old enough to run it.

WHITEHURST, John (2). b1761-d1834. Clock M. 22 Irongate, Derby
John was only fourteen when his uncle John Whitehurst (1) moved to London and it is thought that James, his father, took control of the Derby business until his son was old enough to run it. They continued to make the distinctive angle barometers and also made an unusual wheel barometer with the circular dial at the base of a half-round column which contained the mercury tube. John took his son John (3) into partnership in 1810.

WHITEHURST, John (3). b1788-d1855. Clock M. Derby
22 Irongate. 1 Cherry St (1843)
John continued the business after his father's death in 1834 and he made many types of instruments, including barometers.

WHITEHURST & Son. w1810-34. Clock M. 22 Irongate, Derby
A partnership between John Whitehurst (2) and his son John (3). It lasted until the father died in 1834.

WHITFIELD e1880-1900+. 63 Kings Rd, Southsea.

WHITFIELD, George. w1875-99. Clock & watch M. Brecon

WHITFORD, Samuel. w1750-81. Opt. math. & phil. IM. At the Three Spectacles, 27 Ludgate St, near St Paul's, London
His trade card advertised 'Barometers, Diagonal, Standard, or Portable'.

WHITMORE & Son. w1877. Clock & watch M. Northampton
Sold the 'Improved Torricelli Barometer' which is similar to the Royal Polytechnic barometer.

WHITNEY & Co. e1825-45. Shrewsbury

WHYTE & Co. w1875-88. Chronometer & naut. IM. Glasgow
144 Broomielaw (1875-88) 102 & 104 Dale St (1875-80)

WHYTE, James. w1864-73. Chronometer & naut. IM. Glasgow
144 Broomielaw (1864-73) 4 Carrick St (1864-70) 3 James Watt St (1871-73)

WHYTE, THOMSON & Co. w1889-1900+. Chronometer & naut. IM. Glasgow and Govan
142-144 Broomielaw, Glasgow and 123 Harmony Rd, Govan

WHYTOCK e1850-70. Dundee

WIDDOWSON, J. e1890-1900. Aneroid barometers. Nottingham

WIDENHAM, Richard. w1824-32. Chronometer, clock & watch M. 6 East St, Red Lion Square, London

WIGGINS, Frederick. w1873-80. Opt. & naut. IM. 10 King St, Tower Hill, London

WIGGINS, Frederick & Sons. w1881-1900+. Opt. & naut. IM. London
10 King St, Tower Hill (1881-85) 10 Tower Hill (1881-98) 102 & 103 Minories (1891-1900+)

WILKINS, John. w1851-52. Phil. IM. 1 Cropley St, Hoxton, London

WILKINSON, John. w1826-37. Opt. IM & watch M. 54 Briggate, Leeds

WILKINSON, John & Thomas. w1866-71. e1840-71. Clock & watch M. Leeds

WILKINSON, William. c1775-1809. Watch & clock M. Leeds

WILLATS, Benjamin. w1849. Phil. IM. 55 Bartholomew Close, London

WILLATS, Richard. w1850-60. Opt. & phil IM. London
98 Cheapside (1850) 28 Ironmonger Lane (1851-56) 2 Church Lane, Homerton (1857-60)

WILLATS, Thomas. w1844-57. Opt. math. & phil. IM. London
98 Cheapside (1844) 28 Ironmonger Lane (1857)

WILLATS, Thomas & Richard. w1846-53. Opt. math. & phil. IM. London
98 Cheapside (1850) 28 Ironmonger Lane (1851-53)

WILLETT, John Thomas. w1870-71. Math. IM. 614 Old Kent Rd, London

WILLEY, J. e1850-70. Bartlett St, Bath

WILLIAMS e1820-40. Reading

WILLIAMS & HAYDON e1820-40. London

WILLIAMS, Joseph. w1850-90. Clock & watch M & jeweller. 6 Shipquay St, Londonderry

WILLIAMS, Rice. e1730-50. Phil. IM. Somerset House, by the new Church, Strand, London
He made clocks and wheel barometers with cases similar to those of longcase clocks. His trade card shows that he made 'Barometers or Weather Glasses of all sorts, as Wheel, Diagonal, Portable or Marine ... Recommended by the Royal Society'.

WILLIAMS, W. e1840-60. Devonport

WILLIAMS, Walter Gregson. w1876-77. Phil. IM. 109 Kingsland Rd, London

WILLIAMS, William. w1874-87. Clock & watch M. Llanidloes

WILLIAMSON, Robert. e1700-50. Opt. math. & phil. IS. Near the Exchange, Liverpool

WILLIS e1840-60. Basingstoke

WILLMAN & Co. e1830-50. Bangor

WILLSMER, Jesse. w1838. Math. & phil. IM. 2 Gloucester Terrace, London

WILLSON, George. w1810-25. Opt. IM. 44 Kirby St, Hatton Garden, London

WILLSON, Richard. w1835-50. Clock & watch M. Lincoln

WILMOT, George. w1844-46. London
46 Gee St (1844) 14 Willow Grove, Gee St (1845-46)

WILSON, Alexander. c1761-80. Instrument M. Cardiff

WILSON, G. e1810-30. Sermon Lane, Doctors Common, London

WILSON, J. e1835-45. Folkestone

WILSON, J. e1840-60. Appleby

WILSON, J. J. e1860-80. 19 Hudson St, Sunderland
Marine barometers with sympiesometer.

WILSON, John. w1830-41. Clock & watch M & jeweller. Narrow Bridge St, Peterborough

WILSON, John. w1871. e1860-75. Clock & watch M. Bradford

WILSON, Joseph. w1828-62. Clock & watch M. Chichester

WILSON, Joseph T. w1818-55. Clock & watch M & silversmith. Stamford

WILSON, Robert Henry Capel. w1871-93. Phil. IM. Gray's Inn Rd, London
12 Wilson St (1871-93) 37 Gough St (1871-80)
He joined Pastorelli & Rapkin in 1893.

WILSON & SHARP e1890-1900. Barographs. Edinburgh

WILSON & Son. e1835-55. London

WILSON, SON & WALTER e1865-75. Liverpool
Made a very interesting instrument called 'The World's Barometer and Weather Indicator'. It was devised by James Walter, Major, 4th Lancashire Artillery V.

WILSON, W. & Co. e1860-80. 95 Minories, London
Marine barometers with sympiesometer.

WILSON, WARDEN & Co. e1880-1900. London
Aneroid barometers and barographs. Instruments also signed 'WILSON, WARDEN & Co. Ltd'.

WILTON, William. c1800-47. Math. phil. & opt. IM. St Day, Cornwall
Succeeded by E. T. Newton & Son.

WIMBEE, N. e1820-40. Jersey

WINDER, Edward. w1870-78. Clock & watch M. Eastbourne

WING, Tycho. w1731-73. Math. & phil. IM. The Strand, London
He was apprenticed to Thomas Heath and around 1750 became his partner under the name of Heath & Wing. They were together until Heath died in 1773 when Wing sold the business to Thomas Newman and then retired.

WINSER, Albert. w1870-78. Clock & watch M. East Grinstead

WINTER, D. e1835-55. 112 Church St, Bethnal Green, London

WINTER, J. e1820-40. London

WINTER, T. B. e1850-75. Math. naut. opt. & phil. IM. 55 Grey St and 21 Grey St, Newcastle upon Tyne

WINTER, T. B. & Son. e1875-95. Math. naut. opt. & phil. IM. 55 Grey St and 21 Grey St, Newcastle upon Tyne

WINTER, Thomas. w1797-1810. Opt. IM. 6 Brewer St, Golden Square, London

WINTER, Thomas. w1830. Opt. math. & phil. IM. 4 Ebenezer Place, Commercial Rd, Limehouse, London

WINTER, Thomas. w1830-46. Opt. math. & phil. IM. London
9 Wells St, Oxford St and 5 Market St, Oxford St

WINTERHALDER, J. w1844-75. Clock & watch M. 99 Bishopsgate Without, London

WISKER, Elizabeth. w1822-27. Opt. IM. Spurriergate, York
Widow of John Wisker, she carried on the business with the help of her son Matthias.

WISKER, John. w1804-d1822. Opt. IM. Spurriergate, York
Son of Matthew Wisker.

WISKER, J. T. R. e1860-80. Opt. IM. 13 Spurriergate, York

WISKER, Matthew. w1777-1804. Opt. IM. Glass grinder. Spurriergate, York

WISKER, Matthias. w1827-51. Opt. IM. York
Spurriergate (1827-29) 13 Spurriergate (1830-51)
Son of John Wisker.

WITHERSPOON & GAUDIN w1865. Phil. IM. 11 Fox Court, Gray's Inn Rd, London
Aneroid barometers.

WITHERSPOON, James. w1866-80. Phil. IM. 11 Fox Court, Gray's Inn Rd, London
Aneroid barometers.

WITHERSPOON & RUDD w1884-1900+. Math. IM. 11 Fox Court, Gray's Inn Rd, London

WOLF, Ezekiel. w1854. 206 Sherlock St, Birmingham

WOLF, J. J. e1830-50. Southampton

WOLLER, Charles. w1835-68. Clock & watch M. Musical boxes. 63 Edgbaston St, Birmingham

WOLLER & Co. e1830-50. St John's Maddermarket, Norwich

WOLLER, Matthew. w1801-28. Clock & watch M. 51 Edgbaston St, Birmingham
He made stick barometers with printed paper plates and large wheel barometers with

a clock above the dial.

WOLLER & STRAUB c1800. Clock & watch M. Norwich

WOOD, Benjamin. w1810-34. Opt. & math. IM. Liverpool
51 Wapping (1816) 50 Wapping (1822) 21 Bath St (1834)

WOOD, Benjamin J. e1835-55. Opt. & math. IM. 46 Wapping, Liverpool

WOOD, Charles W. w1845-50. Math. & phil. IM. London
170 Bishopsgate Without (1845-47) 167 Bishopsgate Without (1849-50)

WOOD, Edward. w1838. Math. & phil. IM. 15 King St, Clerkenwell, London

WOOD, Edward George. w1855-1900+. Opt. math. & phil. IM. London
117 Cheapside (1855-61) 74 Cheapside (1862-98) 416 Strand (1886-93) 78 Cheapside (1898-99) 1 & 2 Queen St (1899-1900+)

WOOD, George S. w1875-94. Opt. IM. 20 Lord St, Liverpool
He took over the business of Abraham Abraham & Co. at 20 Lord St, Liverpool and added the words 'late Abraham' after his name.

WOOD, Henry & Co. w1842-43. Math. & phil. IM. London
7 Shepperton St, Islington (1842) 1 Long Lane, Smithfield (1843)

WOOD, Henry Joseph. w1867-95. Opt. math. & phil. IM. London
413a Oxford St (1867-73) 429 Oxford St (1874) 355 Oxford St (1875-81) 185 Oxford St (1882-95)

WOODCOCK, Isaiah. e1855-75. London
He patented the use of glazed cardboard for all the wheel barometer dials except, of course, for the mirror.

WOODHEAD, Joseph. w1856-60. 10 Little Warner St, London

WOODRUFF, Charles. w1838-66. Clock & watch M. High St, Margate

WOODS, H. e1860-80. Warrington

WOODS, Robert Carr. e1820-40. Phil. IM. 47 Hatton Garden, London
He described himself as a 'Meteorological Instrument Maker' and was one of the original members of the Meteorological Society. In 1837 he made a large cistern barometer for the Meteorological Society as a standard barometer.

WOODWARD, George. e1825-45. 18 Leather Lane, Holborn, London

WOODWARD, George. w1850-1900+. Globe M. 5 Charles St, Hatton Garden, London

WOODWARD, John Thomas. w1823-56. Opt. IM. London
1 Clements Inn Passage (1823-28) 8 Clements Inn Passage (1830-56)

WOOLLEY, James, Sons & Co. w1891-1900+. Phil. IM. 69 Market St, Manchester

WOOLTERTON, Jerome. w1846-79. Clock & watch M. Saxmundham

WORBOYS, Julius. w1874. Clock & watch M. Ashwell, Baldock

WORSFOLD, Thomas. e1830-50. Clock & watch M. Hampton Wick

WORTHINGTON e1810-30. London

WORTHINGTON & ALLAN w1821-46. Math. IM. 196 Piccadilly, London

WREN, Christopher. b1632-d1723. Math. IM. London
He devised the first recording meteorological instrument in 1663 and foreshadowed the first balance barometer.

WRENCH, Edward. w1835-46. Math. & phil. IM. 6 Gray's Inn Terrace, London

WRIGHT, Alex & Co. c1900. Math. & phil. IM. 1 Westminster Palace Gardens, Artillery Row, Victoria St, London
Catalogue included barometers.

WRIGHT, John. w1753-56. Opt. math. & phil. IM. Sphere and Hadleys Quadrant, near St Stephen's Church, Bristol
An advertisement shows that he sold 'barometers, either standard, diagonal, or portable, with or without thermometers'.

WRIGHT, Thomas. w1707-48. Math. IM. The Orrery and Globe, Fleet St, London
A noted instrument-maker who advertised 'a great choice of instruments ready made ... in silver, brass and ivory ... surveying instruments, sun-dials and weather glasses ... according to the best and latest improvements'. In 1718 he was appointed instrument-maker to the Prince of Wales, who later became George II. He retired in 1748 and was succeeded by Benjamin Cole.

WRIGHT, Thomas. w1830-38. Math. & phil. IM. 28 City Terrace, City Rd, London

WRIGHT, William. w1828. e1828-50. Clock & watch M. Chipping Ongar

WYNN, William. w1810-35. Clock & watch M. Farnham and London
He made an eight day mahogany longcase clock with a barometer in the arch; the mercury tube was suspended from the backboard.

WYNNE, Henry. w1654-1709. Math. IM. Near the Sugar Loaf, Chancery Lane, London
Henry Winn or Wynn, as he was sometimes known, was apprenticed to Ralph Greatorex in 1654; he became a member of the Clockmakers' Company in 1662 and a Master in 1690. He was a renowned instrument-maker and furnished 'any sort of mathematical instruments whether for sea or land' and was particularly noted for his magnetic needles and compasses. He made a pendulum watch, with shagreen case, for the king. Wynne was the first to make and sell barometers, in any number, to the general public from around 1675. In conjunction with John Warner he published a leaflet entitled *Aeroscopium* which advertised the weather glasses sold by the two men. He also issued explanatory leaflets with his instruments.

Y

YARWELL, John. b1648-d1712. Opt. IM . At the Archimedes and Spectacles in St Paul's Churchyard, London. Later at the Archimedes and Three Golden Spectacles. Subsequently the sign was moved to Ludgate St
He became a member of the Spectaclemakers' Company in 1669 and his trade card dated 1697 shows that his stock included 'Magnifying, Multiplying and Weather Glasses'. It is believed that he sold barometers made by John Patrick.

YEAMAN, John. w1752-80. Math. IM. Edinburgh
Bow Head (1773) Back of the Weigh House (1774) Bow Head (1775-80)

YEATES, Andrew. w1840-63. Math. naut. & phil. IM. 12 Brighton Place, New Kent Rd, London (1840-43 and 1850-63)

YEATES, George. w1826-58. Opt. & math. IM. Dublin
70 Camden St (1826-27) 70 Charlemont St (1828-37) 2 Grafton St (1843-58)
The only Irish instrument-maker to exhibit at the Great Exhibition at the Crystal Palace in 1851; his exhibits included two barometers. Instrument-maker to Dublin University.

YEATES, George & Son. w1840-64. Opt. & math. IM. 2 Grafton St, Dublin
Instrument-maker to Dublin University. Successors to George Yeates and succeeded by Yeates & Son.

YEATES, Horatio. w1866-81. Opt. IM. London
221a Regent St (1866) 39 King Square, Goswell St (1867-74) 33 King St, Covent Garden (1875-81)

YEATES, Samuel. w1790-1831. Opt. IM. Dublin
2 Upper Ormond Quay (1790-94) 29 Capel St (1795-1810) 89 Dame St (1811-31) 2 Grafton St (1827-31)

YEATES, Samuel & Son. w1832-39. Opt. IM. Dublin
2 Grafton St (1832-39) 9 Nassau St (1839)

YEATES, Stephen M. w1865-1902. Opt. IM. 2 Grafton St, Dublin
He wrote on the use of the barometer for measuring heights and produced a new table and formula for determining altitudes with the barometer.

YEATES & Son. w1865-1900+. Opt. & math. IM. 2 Grafton St, Dublin
Instrument-makers to the University and Port and Docks' Board. A handbill included 'Wheel, Pediment, and Standard Barometers. Aneroid Barometers. Large Dial Barometers. (Dial 3 feet 6 inches diameter) suitable for Public Buildings'.

YEATES, Thomas. w1828-49. Clock & watch M & jeweller. Penrith
He made stick barometers with the silvered brass register plates headed 'The Great Barometer'.

YEATES, William. w1827-28. Opt. IM & cutler. 18 Capel St, Dublin

YELWARE e1820-40. Taunton

YON, John. w1839-67. Clock & watch M. Southampton

YOULE, William. w1822-66. Opt. math. & phil. IM. London
22 Fieldgate St, Whitechapel (1822-33) 79 Leadenhall St (1834-44) 83 Leadenhall St (1845-66)

Z

ZAGNANI, Francis. w1832-57. Clock & watch M. London

ZAMBRA, Cesare. w1820-22. Saffron Walden
The father of Joseph Warren Zambra, a partner in Negretti & Zambra.

ZAMBRA, G. e1815-35. 51 Spear St, Manchester

ZAMBRA, J. C. e1810-30. Saffron Walden

ZAMBRA, J. C. e1825-50. 23 Brooke St, Holborn, London

ZAMBRA, Joseph Warren. b1822-d1888. London
Born in Saffron Walden, the son of Cesare Zambra, he does not appear to have worked on his own but formed a very successful partnership with Henry Negretti in 1850 in the name of Negretti & Zambra.

ZANETTI & AGNEW w1817-25. Carvers, gilders & looking glass M. 94 Market St, Manchester
A partnership between Vittore Zanetti and his apprentice Thomas Agnew.

ZANETTI, J. e1800-20. 16 St Ann's St, Manchester

ZANETTI, Joseph. w1841. e1820-45. Clock M. 100 King St, Manchester

ZANETTI, Vincent. w1822-26. e1822-45. 5 Wrights Court, Market St, Manchester

ZANETTI, Vincente Vittore. e1810-30. Looking glass & frame M. Manchester
98 Market St Lane and 87 Market St Lane
An advertisement claimed 'barometers, thermometers, of every kind, made and repaired, and warranted good'.

ZANETTI, Vittore. w1810-17. Looking glass & print M. 94 Market St, Manchester
Became Zanetti & Agnew in 1817 when he took his apprentice Thomas Agnew into partnership.

ZANFRINI & GUGERI e1815-50. Blandford

ZAPPA, C . e1805-25. Sheffield

ZEAL, Giles Henry. w1900+. 82 Tuenmill St, London

ZEDEO, J. e1775-1825. Dublin

ZENONE & BUTTI w1823. Carvers & gilders. 5 Carlton St, Edinburgh
A partnership between John Zenone and Louis Joseph Butti which lasted for only a short time.

ZENONE, John. w1825-33. Carver, gilder & looking glass M. Edinburgh
5 Calton St (1825-30) 7 Calton St (1827) 6 Calton St (1830) 9 Calton St (1832-33)

ZENONE, Joseph. w1824-41. Carver, gilder & feather M. Edinburgh
5 Calton St (1824) 8 Calton St (1825-29) 7 Calton St (1830-31) 10 Calton St (1832-41)

ZERBONI, Anthony. w1833-36. Artificial flower M. London
24 Cross St, Hatton Garden. 13 Baldwins Gardens. 106 Hatton Garden

ZERBONI, BATTISTESSA, MOLTENI & GUANZIROLI w1835-6. Looking glass M. London
24 Cross St, Hatton Garden (1835) 13 Baldwins Gardens (1835) 106 Hatton Garden (1836)

ZERBONI & Co. e1830-50. Edinburgh

ZERBONIE, BATTISTESSA & Co. e1820-40. Calton St, Edinburgh

ZIPFEL, Anthony & Co. w1848-51. Clock & watch M. Oldham

ZIPFEL & BEHA w1868. Clock & watch M. Birmingham

ZIPFEL, Bernard. w1836. Clock & watch M. Norwich

ZIPFEL, C. w1846. Clock & watch M. Long Stratton, Norfolk

ZIPFEL, C. w1846. Clock & watch M. Thetford, Norfolk

ZIPFEL, Charles. w1846-75. Clock & watch M. Norwich

ZIPFEL, Charles (junior). w1865-75. Clock & watch M. Norwich

ZIPFEL, George. w1822. e1820-40. Clock & watch M. Little Cockney Lane, Norwich
He made large wheel barometers with a clock above the dial.

ZIPFEL, John. w1830-46. Clock & watch M. Norwich

ZIPFEL, Joseph. w1830-58. Clock & watch M. Norwich

ZIPFEL, Matthew. w1830-65. Clock & watch M. Norwich

ZOTTI, Romualdo. w1863-81. Clock & watch M. London

ZUCCANI, Emilo. w1841-60. Looking glass M. London
41 Brick Lane (1841-45) 32-33 Mansell St (1849) 17 Mansell St (1851-60)

ZURAGHI, Felix. w1832-34. Looking glass M. 9 City Rd, London

Bibliography

Anderson R. G. W., Burnett, J. and Gee, B., *Handlist of Scientific Instrument-Makers' Trade Catalogues 1600-1914* (National Museums of Scotland, Edinburgh, 1990, in association with The Science Museum).

Baillie, G. H., *Watchmakers and Clockmakers of the World*, 3rd edn (N. A. G. Press Ltd, London, 1974).

Banfield, Edwin, *Antique Barometers: an Illustrated Survey* (Baros Books, Trowbridge, 1989).

Banfield, Edwin, *Barometers: Aneroid and Barographs* (Baros Books, Trowbridge, 1985).

Banfield, Edwin, *Barometers: Stick or Cistern Tube* (Baros Books, Trowbridge, 1985).

Banfield, Edwin, *Barometers: Wheel or Banjo* (Baros Books, Trowbridge, 1985).

Bolle, Bert. *Barometers* (Antique Collectors' Club, 1981).

Brown, Joyce, *Mathematical Instrument-Makers in the Grocers' Company 1688-1800* (Science Museum, London, 1979).

Bryden, D. J., *Scottish Scientific Instrument-Makers 1600-1900* (Royal Scottish Museum, Edinburgh, 1972).

Burnett, J. E. and Morrison-Low, A. D., *Vulgar and Mechanick: the Scientific Instrument Trade in Ireland 1650-1921* (National Museums of Scotland and Royal Dublin Society, 1989).

Calvert, H. R., *Scientific Trade Cards in the Science Museum Collection* (Her Majesty's Stationery Office, London, 1971).

Clarke, T. N., Morrison Low, A. D. and Simpson, A. D. C., *Brass and Glass* (National Museums of Scotland, 1989).

Downing, Hayden J., *Scientific Instrument-Makers of Victorian London 1840-1900* (Museum of Victoria, Melbourne, 1988).

Goodison, Nicholas, *English Barometers 1680-1860* (Antique Collectors' Club, 1977).

Loomes, Brian, *Watchmakers and Clockmakers of the World*, Vol. 2 (N. A. G. Press Ltd, London, 1978).

Pearsall, Ronald, *Collecting and Restoring Scientific Instruments* (David & Charles, Newton Abbot, 1974).

Taylor, E. G. R., *The Mathematical Practitioners of Hanoverian England* (Cambridge, 1966).

Taylor, E. G. R., *The Mathematical Practitioners of Tudor and Stuart England* (Cambridge, 1954).